GOOD BLOOD
BAD BLOOD

Science, Nature, and the Myth of the Kallikaks

J. David Smith • Michael L. Wehmeyer

©2012 by American Association on Intellectual and Developmental Disabilities

Published by American Association on Intellectual and Developmental Disabilities (AAIDD)
501 Third Street, NW
Suite 200
Washington, DC 20001-2760

Library of Congress Cataloging-in-Publication Data

Good Blood, Bad Blood. Science, Nature, and the Myth of the Kallikaks / by J. David Smith and Michael L. Wehmeyer.
  p. cm.
  ISBN: 978-1-937604-03-5
1. Eugenics—United States—History. 2. Human reproduction—Government policy--United States. 3. People with mental disabilities—United States—History. I. Smith, J. David. II. Wehmeyer, Michael L. III. The Family that Never Was

HQ755.5.U5S655 2012
363.9'20973—dc23

2012001638

Table of Contents

Preface . . . . *v*

Chapter 1: Vineland, New Jersey 1

Chapter 2: In Search of a Science. 7

Chapter 3: The Kallikak Family 29

Chapter 4: The Rising Tide of American Eugenics
     and Race Science 47

Chapter 5: Intelligence Testing. 59

Chapter 6: Acceptance and Fame. 77

Chapter 7: The Criminal Imbecile 95

Chapter 8: The Rise and Fall of Goddard. 117

Chapter 9: Sterilizing the Unfit, Breeding the Fit 157

Chapter 10: The Kallikaks Revisited. 185

Chapter 11: Emma's Real Story 205

Epilogue 215

Bibliography 217

Index 229

Acknowledgments 247

Preface

John Steinbeck's novel and play *Of Mice and Men* (1937) is an American classic. It is the story of George and Lennie: two alienated drifters, the latter a man with intellectual impairments, the former compelled to watch out for him as they pursue their shared dream of owning a farm and raising rabbits. The book is about friendship and companionship, fairness and unfairness, and life during the Great Depression. But the book is also about power and powerlessness and society's response to and responsibility for people who are among its most vulnerable citizens.

As George struggles to cope with and help Lennie, he sees only two extreme options generated by stigma of that era's prevalent dogma of Social Darwinism—segregate him or eliminate him. In George's eugenic worldview, both animals and "defective" humans were to be dealt with in the same manner. The killing of a fellow migrant worker's old and ill dog, which is perceived to be no longer worth anything to anyone, presages Lennie's death. When George shoots Lennie for what he considers a merciful death, it is with a German Luger, the handgun carried by Nazi officers.[1]

Good Blood, Bad Blood tells the story of the impact of the American eugenics movement—the pseudoscience aimed at improving racial hygiene by better human breeding—through the lens of a notorious eugenic family narrative, *The Kallikak Family*. Its focus is on the life of that book's central character, a woman institutionalized as a child at the turn of the century for allegedly being "feeble-minded." The horrors of the eugenics movement that swept America in the early 20th century—societally sanctioned mass-institutionalization; forced sterilization of tens of thousands of Americans with disabilities and people wrongfully identified as "defective"; the Nazi sterilization and murder of Germany's disabled citizens—are incomprehensible to the modern reader in their full scope and consequences. *Good Blood, Bad Blood* tells the story of the impact of these atrocities on one woman, given the pseudonym Deborah Kallikak, who became the poster child for the cultural fear generated by American eugenicists, who, in turn, provided the Nazi regime with strategies and information to take the eugenic horror to its ultimate and even more horrifying conclusion.

[1] Benson, 1990.

v

The influence of the American eugenics movement on Adolph Hitler began while he was in prison, from April to December of 1924, for his participation in the Beer Hall Putsch. Among the books he read in the course of writing *Mein Kampf* during his internment were New York attorney Madison Grant's *The Passing of the Great Race* (1916) and the two-volume *Grundriss der menschlichen Erblichkeitslehre und Rassen-hygiene* [*Foundation of Human Heredity and Race Hygiene*], published in 1921 by German eugenicists Erwin Baur, Fritz Lenz, and Eugen Fischer. All of these men were frequent correspondents with American eugenicist Charles Davenport[2] and *Foundation of Human Heredity and Race Hygiene* was replete with references to other American eugenicists, including a rendition of the story that is the subject of this book. *The Kallikak Family* was published by psychologist Henry Herbert Goddard in 1912 and was purported to be a natural experiment proving that feeblemindedness and degeneracy were hereditarily transmitted.

It is not surprising, then, that *Mein Kampf* incorporated American eugenic dogma pertaining to sterilization. Medical historian Philip Reilly notes that,

> In *Mein Kampf*, . . . Hitler wrote: "To prevent defective persons from repro-ducing equally defective offspring, is an act dictated by the clearest light of reason. Its carrying out is the most humane act of mankind. It would prevent the unmerited suffering of millions of persons, and, above all would, in the end, result in a steady increase in human welfare."[3]

In July of 1933, Germany passed the *Law for Prevention of Offspring with Hereditary Defects Act*. The act legalized involuntary sterilization for "any person suffering from a hereditary disease . . . if his offspring will suffer from severe hereditary physical or mental damage." Hereditary diseases as defined by the law included feeblemindedness, schizophrenia, blindness, deafness, physical defor-mity, or epilepsy.[4]

As noted, this act owed much to the work of American proponents of eugenics.[5] It was modeled after a proposed sterilization law propagated by Harry H. Laughlin in *Eugenical Sterilization in the United States* (1922), although the German version was more moderate than Laughlin's proposed standard.[6] It was Laughlin's work on sterilization that led the way in exporting the American eugenics movement's message on sterilization to Germany. "The German eugen-icists were especially impressed with Laughlin's work on eugenic sterilization," wrote Reilly. "About 1921 Laughlin, an acknowledged Germanophile, began to write articles about the eugenics movement in Germany for the American

---

[2] Black, 2003, p. 270.
[3] Reilly, 1991, p. 106.
[4] Friedlander, 1995, p. 26.
[5] Sofair and Kaldjian, 2000, p. 312.
[6] Kuhn, 1994, p. 39.

publication *Eugenics News*. During the late 1920s and early 1930s, he also wrote several articles on sterilization for German journals."[7]

Not far behind Laughlin in influence on the Nazi sterilization Act were philanthropist Ezra Gosney and the editor of *American Breeders Magazine,* Paul Popenoe, who established the Human Betterment Foundation in Pasadena, California. Gosney and Popenoe published *Sterilization for Human Betterment* in 1929, a large-scale study of the forced sterilization movement in California. It was translated and published in German in 1930[8] and soon became required reading among the Nazi elite.

As the Nazi government pushed for the passage of the sterilization Act in 1933, the Human Betterment Foundation "mailed an influential pamphlet detailing California's experiences to German racial hygienists and the Nazi administrators responsible for the enforcement of the German law."[9]

"The brochure," noted Stefan Kuhl, "claimed that sterilization served to protect the sterilized person, his or her family, and society at large. It closed by asserting that people were becoming increasingly convinced that a nation that asked its able citizens to risk their lives in times of war was entitled to demand a much smaller sacrifice from its incapable citizens in times of peace." [10]

In 1934, as the forced sterilization of what would become hundreds of thousands of Germans identified as feebleminded began, Adolph Hitler had an aide-de-camp write American eugenicist Leon Whitney to obtain a copy of his book, *The Case for Sterilization.* As he had with Madison Grant, the Führer sent Whitney a letter of thanks. As with Grant's *The Passing of the Great Race,* Whitney's *The Case for Sterilization* recites the Kallikak family story to prove that feeblemindedness was, in Whitney's words, "to a very large extent inherited," and to justify forced sterilization.

The impact of *The Kallikak Family* narrative went beyond just the story's inclusion in texts read by top Nazis, including Hitler. "National Socialists enthusiastically adopted the stories of the Jukes and Kallikaks," wrote Kuhl, "in order to legitimize their own sterilization program. The first German edition of Goddard's book about the Kallikaks was published in 1914. The second edition appeared in November 1933 in a special issue of Friedrich Mann's *Padagogisches Magazin.*"[11]

In other words, *The Kallikak Family* was reprinted in German almost 20 years after its previous and only other German printing, four months after the passage of the *Law for Prevention of Offspring with Hereditary Defects Act,* and only two months prior to the law's implementation.

---

[7] Reilly, 1991, p. 107.
[8] Kuhl, 1994, p. 43.
[9] Kuhl, 1994, p. 43.
[10] Kuhl, 1994, p. 43.
[11] Kuhl, 1994, p. 41.

The law relied on caregivers and medical personnel—mainly physicians, health care workers, and institution superintendents—to "denunciate" people "suffering" from one of the hereditary diseases. Denunciations were sent to hereditary health courts established by the law, consisting of three members: a judge, a physician from the public health services, and a physician knowledgeable about heredity. If the hereditary health court ruled in favor of sterilization, the operation was compulsory, even to the extent of having police use force to ensure compliance.[12]

In the first two years of implementation, 1934–35, 388,400 disabled Germans were turned in by people responsible for their health care or support; all but 20 percent of denunciations came from institution superintendents or physicians. The hereditary health courts were overwhelmed and unable to keep up with the load. Of the nearly 400,000 denunciations, the courts between 1934 and the end of 1936 eventually considered almost 260,000 cases. Of those in 1934, rulings were issued on 67,337 of the cases. The vast majority—62,463 cases—were approved. Even though only a portion of overall denunciations were adjudicated and found in favor of sterilization, the physicians and other medical practitioners conducting the surgeries could not keep up with those cases referred for sterilization. Of the 62,463 people approved for the surgery in 1934, 32,268 people were subject to Hitlerschnitte; Hitler's cut."[13]

More than half of those people forcibly sterilized were classified as "congenitally feebleminded"; 17,070 of them sterilized in 1934 alone. With practice, the system became more efficient and more ruthless. In 1935, 73,174 Germans with disabilities were sterilized; in 1936, 63,547 went under the knife. Some of them did not survive the surgery itself, with 437 deaths reported in the first three years.[14]

In the first three years, more than half of the people forcibly sterilized were identified as feebleminded. That these percentages were likely to have stayed about the same throughout the five years from 1934 to 1939 seems a viable assumption, in large measure because of the flexibility of who might be classified as "feebleminded."

In 1936, as the sterilization campaign became ruthlessly efficient, Harry Hamilton Laughlin was honored for his contributions to German social policy with an honorary doctorate from Heidelberg University.[15] The degree was conferred in appreciation of his services to the science of eugenics and his efforts to purify "the human seed stock."

Data for sterilizations after 1936 are not available, but as Auschwitz survivor and genocide historian Henry Friedlander noted, "it is generally agreed that at least 300,000 persons were sterilized during the years preceding World War II."[16]

[12] Friedlander, 1995, pp. 26–27.
[13] Friedlander, 1995, pp. 28–29.
[14] Friedlander, 1995, pp. 30.
[15] Reilly, 1991, p. 107.
[16] Friedlander, 1995, p. 30.

Preface

In 1939, the abomination that was the forced sterilization of hundreds of thousands of disabled Germans became unspeakably worse; and it began with the children. The Führer ordered subordinates to initiate the systematic murder of infants and children with disabilities. In August of 1939, after months of planning, the German *Reichsministerium des Innern* (Reich Ministry of Interior) issued a decree requiring "midwifes and physicians to report all infants born with specified medical conditions," including idiocy and mongolism, microcephaly, hydrocephalus, and physical deformities.[17]

Informants were also to report children up to age three with these conditions. Report forms were submitted to state and provincial health offices, which then transmitted them to a false governmental agency called the Reich Committee for the Scientific Registration of Severe Hereditary Ailments, or just the Reich Committee. Functionaries there would pass forms on to three "experts"; physicians, who based their decision to kill an infant or child exclusively on information from the form.[18]

To implement the killing program, the Reich Committee established wards at state hospitals and clinics; there were eventually 22 such wards.[19] Once a child was determined to be "defective" and targeted for the killing program, he or she was transferred to a nearby Reich Committee children's ward. If the child was in an institution or a hospital, the transfer was straightforward. There were no parental notification or appeals; just the transfer of the sentenced child. If the child was at home, public health officers were sent to "persuade" the parents to release the child, although the program's real intent was strictly secret.[20]

At each children's ward, the killing of infants and toddlers was left to the participating physicians who used different means to achieve their unholy ends, including starvation. Administering lethal doses of medications such as sedatives or painkillers became the favored method, with these deadly doses given by both physicians and nurses.[21]

"Because many records of the killings have not survived," wrote Friedlander, "it is impossible to calculate the number of children killed in the children's wards during World War II. . . . The best estimate is a total of at least 5,000 murdered children."[22]

From infants and children, the systematic murder of disabled Germans moved to include adults in the summer of 1939. The offices of the adult killing program were located at Villa Number 4 on Tiergarten Strasse in Berlin, which had been confiscated from its previous Jewish owners. The adult killing program

---

[17] Friedlander, 1995, p. 45.
[18] Friedlander, 1995, p. 46.
[19] Friedlander, 1995, p. 46.
[20] Friedlander, 1995, p. 56.
[21] Friedlander, 1995, p. 54.
[22] Friedlander, 1995, p. 61.

soon became known by the address of the headquarters, Tiergarten Strasse 4, or eventually just T4.

On September 21, 1939, the Reich Ministry of Interior issued a decree requiring that all local governments provide a list of institutions for the feebleminded, insane, and epileptics by mid-October. Thereafter, each institution, received a questionnaire requesting information about the facility, including number of patients and information about proximity to transportation networks.[23]

Anyone who has worked in an institution can picture the pathetic scene that unfolded at one German institution or asylum after another: Institution workers packing each person's scant worldly belongings into paper bags; the group led to the front office to wait; a few of the patients in wheelchairs; most compliant, acclimated to years of being told where to go and what to do; some anxious, perhaps rocking back and forth; the group standing, their names ignominiously taped to their backs, their ill-fitting clothes, often not their own, draping off of often undernourished frames.

"On the designated day," chronicled Friedlander, "Gekrat [the T4 transportation entity] arrived to move the patients in large gray buses; the surrendering institution was given a receipt from Gekrat for the patients handed over for transfer. The patients, who usually suspected their fate, often had to be coerced before they entered the notorious vehicles."[24] Their families were told, simply, that their sons, daughters, husbands, and wives had been sent to another institution.

The people were bussed to one of six killing centers established by T4. Grafeneck. Brandenburg. Hartheim. Sonnenstein. Bernburg. Hadamar. Located in previously empty buildings, the centers were renovated to include examination rooms; autopsy rooms; administration, physician, and nursing offices; and a gas chamber and crematorium.[25]

"The gas chamber was constructed to resemble showers," Friedlander described the killing chamber in Brandenburg. "Three by five meters large and 3 meters high, it was paneled with ceramic tiles. Benches for the patients lined the walls. About 10 centimeters above the floor, a pipe with a circumference of about one inch ran along the wall; in this pipe there were small holes through which gas could enter the chamber.... The door to the chamber was constructed like a metal air raid shelter door, with a rectangular window for viewing."[26] Showerheads were added to the room later to convince victims they were heading into a shower room.

The patients arrived at the killing center and were led to an examining room, where they were told to undress. Their clothes and their worldly possessions were labeled and numbered; each person was examined by a physician, a pro-

---

[23] Friedlander 1995, p. 75.
[24] Friedlander, 1995, p. 84.
[25] Friedlander, 1995, p. 87.
[26] Friedlander, 1995, p. 87.

cedure absurdly said to be a "final safeguard against the possible errors made during the medical evaluation process."[27] Each person was assigned a number, which was stamped or taped on his or her body, then was photographed.

In groups and still naked, the condemned were then led into the gas chamber. They were told they were to be bathed, and because they had cognitive disabilities and had done so all their lives, most trusted those in authority and followed obediently. Some of them, though, seemingly knew their fate and had to be sedated or forcibly moved into the killing chamber.

The door was closed and bolted and the gas valve was turned on. Unconsciousness came in five minutes, although those five minutes were not pain free—victims gasped for air, screamed, collapsed, sank into unconsciousness, and eventually died. Their bodies were dragged from the gas chambers, pronounced dead, then taken to the crematorium ovens. "The killing center thus, 'processed' living human beings into ashes in less than 24 hours."[28]

It was the constant smoke billowing from the crematorium chimneys and the smell from that smoke that gave the killing centers away for what they were. The public and clergy had begun to suspect what was really happening and some protested. Hitler ordered the killing program to halt in August of 1941 on the basis of concern about its impact on the Nazi party's image.

During those two years, 70,273 people were "disinfected," as the Nazi's described the murders. The estimates of the number of disabled Germans murdered by their government—but also by the physicians, nurses, public health officials, and others responsible for the health and well-being of these vulnerable people—is estimated to be at 80,000 or more.

And while the horrors of the Nazi atrocities didn't begin with the publication of *The Kallikak Family* in September of 1912, this narrative was, according to Stephen J. Gould, the "primal myth of the eugenics movement"[29] that fueled the fire of the Nazi atrocities. *The Kallikak Family* told the tale of a "degenerate" family from rural New Jersey. Like most books in the eugenic family genre, *The Kallikak Family* described generations of illiterate, poor, and purportedly immoral family members who were chronically unemployed, feebleminded, criminals, and, in general, perceived as threats to "racial hygiene." Unlike other such tales, Goddard's story had a plot twist. The progenitor of this line, an American Revolutionary War soldier called Martin Kallikak, Sr., sired his disreputable ancestral line through a dalliance with an allegedly feebleminded bar maid. Martin Sr., however, righted his moral bearings, married an upstanding Quaker woman, and became the forefather of a second line of descendants that included, as Goddard put it, "respectable citizens, men and women prominent in every phase of life." Goddard's tale contrasting these disparate ancestral lines

---

[27] Friedlander, 1995, p. 94.
[28] Friedlander, 1995, p. 98.
[29] Gould, 1981

reigned as seemingly conclusive proof of the hereditary nature of intelligence, feeblemindedness, criminal behavior, and degeneracy for decades, and was used by American eugenicists to justify their racially and politically charged rhetoric and policies, resulting in the institutionalization and forced sterilization of many of this nation's most vulnerable citizens.

Goddard derived the name Kallikak from the Greek words Kallos (beauty) and Kakos (bad); Goddard's dramatic way of capturing the essence of the story of the Kallikak family, one branch of which was good and the other bad

Kallos. Kakos.

Good blood. Bad blood.

CHAPTER 1

Vineland, New Jersey

> One bright October day, fourteen years ago, there came to the Training
> School at Vineland, a little eight year-old girl.
>
> —Goddard, 1912, p. 1

So began *The Kallikak Family*, psychologist Henry Herbert Goddard's 1912 best-selling pseudoscientific treatise extolling the tale of the supposedly "degenerate" family from rural New Jersey. *The Kallikak Family*, like most books in the eugenic family genre, described generations of illiterate, poor, and purportedly immoral Kallikak family members who were chronically unemployed, feebleminded, criminal, and, in general, perceived as threats to the nation's *racial hygiene*.

The first chapter of *The Kallikak Family* introduced the pseudonymous Deborah Kallikak, an inmate of an institution for the feebleminded—the Vineland Training School—at which Goddard had established a pioneering psychological research laboratory. Deborah's entry into the world had been as ignoble and anonymous as her arrival at the Training School that October day in 1897. She was born in 1889 into the wretchedly poor environs of a late 19th-century almshouse to a single mother who had lost her job as a domestic servant because of her illegitimate pregnancy.[1] Deborah's father, identified as normal but as morally bereft (i.e., financially bankrupt), abandoned the new-born Deborah and her mother to the penury of the almshouse. The possibilities in life for Deborah, her mother, and her three older siblings improved when they were brought to live in the home of a benefactor. Eventually, though, Deborah suffered from the poor decisions of her mother, who entered into a sexual relationship with yet another man that resulted in pregnancy. Unnerved by the promiscuity of Deborah's mother, the benefactor insisted on a marriage between Deborah's mother and this man. Soon thereafter, Deborah's mother and the rest of her family moved out of the benefactor's home; she bore two children with Deborah's stepfather, and moved them to a farmhouse. Deborah's

---

[1] Kellicott, 1911, p. 162.

1

stepfather eventually disappeared and her mother lived openly with the farmer–landlord. The benefactor again arranged for a marriage with the landlord after a divorce between Deborah's stepfather and mother. The farmer consented, with the caveat that the children that were not his would be sent away. This included Deborah.

Thus, Deborah was brought to the gates of the Training School with the suspect explanation that she didn't get along with other children at school—that she might, possibly, be feebleminded. When she entered the Training School, according to school records, she was of average size and weight with no particularly notable physical anomalies. She could wash and dress herself. She was identified as a good listener and imitator, active and excitable, although not particularly affectionate. She was illiterate and could not count—hardly surprising because she had apparently never attended a day of school—but was handy and could use a needle, carry wood, and fill a kettle.

Vineland, New Jersey, was established by 28-year-old Philadelphia attorney and real estate developer Charles Kline Landis in 1861. With $500 gold he borrowed from his mother, Landis purchased 20,000 acres in south New Jersey, situated on the railway line between Millville and Philadelphia. One of Landis's goals was to build a pluralistic community, welcoming people of different faiths and nationalities. He envisioned a community that was truly a melting pot and, to a large degree, his dream reached fruition after his death in 1900. Prominently displayed on early advertisements for Vineland was the note that New Jersey laws were liberal with regard to married women holding property. Women's issues were big in progressive Vineland. Plum Street Hall, for example, was built to host meetings of the Friends of Progress in Vineland, a group organized in 1864 and comprising an interesting mix of agnostics, atheists, Friends (Quakers), and spiritualists who were committed to supporting progressive issues. The list of luminaries who spoke at Plum Street Hall included Frederick Douglass and Susan B. Anthony.

Vineland's progressive nature was manifested in more ways than just rhetoric, speeches, and protest; it was also evident from the largesse of its citizens. In March 1888, the Reverend Olin Garrison, a Methodist clergyman, moved his year-old New Jersey Home for the Education and Care of Feeble-Minded Children from Millville, New Jersey, to Vineland. He was able to do this through the donation of Benjamin Maxham's home and estate and a pledge of $2,000 from the Vineland Board of Trade.

Garrison was tall and thin, with a long face, high forehead, and full, thick brown hair. As a younger man he wore a beard, cut closely; in later years he wore a bushy, walrus mustache. As he aged, the mustache and his still luxuriant hair were of the purest white. He was, by all accounts, a gentle soul and soon became an innovator in the nascent field of caring for feebleminded children. He established the "cottage system" on the Training School campus at a time that larger state-supported institutions for the feebleminded housed their inmates in cavernous, impersonal dormitories. The residents at the Training School lived in these smaller dwellings designed to emulate a homelike atmosphere. Garrison was free to innovate at least partially because he maintained the Training School as a private facility supported by tuition and the generosity of donors who belonged to the Association of the Vineland Training School.

The members of the association were the Vineland elite, over 100 strong, who gave time, talent, and money to the Reverend Garrison's utopian vision, which set the spiritual tone for the Training School: "The Village of Happiness," as its staff fondly called it.

"Always treat the children with kindness and respect; address them in a proper tone of voice; avoid violence and rudeness; restrain your temper under the severest provocations; never scold"[2] commanded Principal Garrison to his expanding staff in 1889.

Garrison was, however, not a healthy man, suffering from an undiagnosed illness that was eventually identified as a cyst. In April of 1900, Garrison passed away following surgery in a Philadelphia hospital, surrounded there by his family and members of the board of directors of his beloved school.[3] He was interred in a tomb in the northwest corner of the Training School's campus.

The final bell of the day sounds, the intensity of its ringing muted as the sound waves travel through the chilled winter air. Children scurry from the school building into the schoolyard, inmates fleeing their daily incarceration. The noise rises to a crescendo: laughter, piercing screams, adult admonitions to "Walk, not run!" and then, within ten minutes, silence, a relieved hush settling on the school campus. It is a scene repeated outside elementary school buildings every school day in every city in the nation.

Had he been among the parents standing outside in the frigid air, shifting from one foot to the next to blunt the impact of the bitter cold and pass the few minutes until their child's exodus, the man for whom this elementary school was named would have smiled. The children's ebullient noises, their half-coated and partially gloved states of dress, and their oblivious disregard of the rebukes for them to walk would have, no doubt, amused Edward Ransom Johnstone. Born December 27, 1870, in Galt, Ontario, "Uncle Ed" became a beloved fixture in Vineland during the 45 years he held the post of superintendent of the Training School following Garrison's death. Opened over half a century after his assumption, the E. R. Johnstone Elementary was a perfect monument to the man who guided the Training School to its international prominence.

---

[2] Johnstone, 1923a, p. 26.
[3] McCaffery, 1965, page 98.

Tall, elfish in features, and with a perennial smile and lit cigar, Johnstone ruled the Training School in the post-Garrison era with a velvet-gloved hand and won the hearts of the parents who trusted their children to his care, including one of his most influential supporters, Nobel laureate Pearl Buck, whose daughter Carol was admitted to the Training School in 1930 at the age of nine.

Buck wrote of Johnstone,

> I knew when I entered his office and shook hands with the quiet, gray-haired man who greeted me with a gentle voice that I had found what I wanted, . . . I told him about my child and what it was that I looked for, and he listened. He was sympathetic, but not with effort. He said diffidently that he did not know whether I would be satisfied with his school, but we might look around. He knew every child and his seeing eyes were noticing everything everywhere. . . . I saw a certain motto, repeated again and again on the walls, on the stationery, hanging above the head's own desk. . . . 'Happiness first and all else follows.'"[4]

An effusive colleague described Johnstone as "generous to a fault, friendly as a puppy, buoyant as the Babe in Toyland; a jovial mixer and good conversationalist; a humorist who knew how to put a jest across; a story teller who could spin stories galore from the inner web or bring Uncle Remus back to life."[5]

Professor Johnstone, as he was called, arrived at the Training School as the assistant superintendent in 1898, a decade after Olin Garrison established the Training School and two years preceding the elder's death. Prior to this, he had been the principal of the educational department at the Indiana School for the Feeble Minded in Ft. Wayne, a job for which he had been recruited by that school's superintendent, his brother-in-law and lifelong mentor, Alexander Johnson.

The staccato sound of footsteps reverberated from the masonry of the two-story Maxham Cottage, the administration building of the New Jersey Training School for Feeble-Minded Boys and Girls. Tendrils of fine white dust kicked up from the crushed limestone walkway and coalesced to form miniature billows in the wake of the impeccably dressed man who walked briskly toward the portico-covered front steps.

Any literal relationship between this building and a cottage was, at best, distant. Referred to as a cottage only because the Training School had adopted the then-new cottage system for institutions, the humbly named structure was christened to honor Maxham, the hotelier and philanthropist who had donated

---

[4] Buck, 1950, pp. 44-45.
[5] Wallin, 1953, p. 48.

his estate, including his home, Scarborough Mansion, and 40 acres of fertile land east of the booming southern New Jersey city of Vineland, for the charitable purpose of housing a school for feebleminded children. Scarborough Mansion was destroyed by fire in December 1896; the Gothic-Renaissance style Maxham Cottage, toward which Henry Herbert Goddard now strode, rose in 1900 from its ashes.

The slate gray, partly cloudy sky belied the balminess of that mid-September Monday morning in 1906, and Goddard had opted to walk from the Vineland Central train station toward the campus. Reaching the grounds of the Training School, Goddard strode past E. B. Moore Cottage, with its single Queen Anne tower, and the square, squat Wilbur Cottage. Circumnavigating the gazebo decorating the front lawn of Maxham, Goddard walked toward the front of the administration building with its imposing three-story twin towers and third floor gabled dormer windows.

The slight and balding Goddard appeared older than his 41 years, his intense and professorial bearing accentuated by a pair of round, rimless glasses. More than three years had passed since he first heard the idea for a psychological research laboratory at the Training School. Earl Barnes, the defrocked first professor of education at Leland Stanford, Jr. University, had spoken to the assembled directors and school association members late in 1903: "Vineland is a garden where unfortunate children are cared for, protected, and loved while they unconsciously whisper to us syllable by syllable the secret of the soul's growth. It may very well be that the most ignorant shall teach us most."[6]

Henry Herbert Goddard arrived at the Training School as the newly appointed director of the first nonuniversity psychological research laboratory in the United States. That it was housed in an institution for the feebleminded portended many things, most of which he could not have imagined as he ascended the wooden steps to the porch and into the dark foyer of Maxham Cottage.

Plum Street Hall, where Vineland's progressives had met to champion causes such as women's suffrage, burned to the ground prior to the August 24, 1920 vote by the state of Tennessee to ratify the Nineteenth Amendment to the U.S. Constitution, becoming the 36th state to do so and ensuring all American women the right to vote. Vineland's reputation as a progressive community valuing diversity and equal rights took a blow earlier than Plum Hall's incineration, however, when Henry Herbert Goddard published *The Kallikak Family* and, in the same year, began a series of investigations at Ellis Island on the intelligence of immigrants that would be used by eugenicists to restrict immigration into the United States.

---

[6] McCaffery, 1965, page 29.

Goddard's instrument of infamy, Deborah Kallikak, was only one of many young women whose primary "sin" had been to be destitute, poorly educated, and attractive at a time when society viewed this combination as a deadly cocktail leading to, as the nation's bellicose then-President Theodore Roosevelt proclaimed, the threat of *race suicide*.

Deborah Kallikak became the poster child for societal fears, the flames of which were fanned by a select group of well-educated, upper-class, White Americans joined by an aspiring professional middle class—funded by the captains of industry—under the banner of the new sciences of genetics and heredity. The name Kallikak would become part of the vernacular; a synonym for backward, inbreeding hillbillies and slum dwellers, even spawning a short-lived eponymous television sitcom, "The Kallikaks," in 1977. The series plot strikingly resembled 1962's successful "The Beverly Hillbillies" (and, ironically, co-starred Bonnie Ebsen, the daughter of Buddy Ebsen, who portrayed The Beverly Hillbillies patriarch, Jed Clampett).

The mythical Deborah Kallikak was destined for infamy. The real Deborah Kallikak was destined only to confinement in institutional warehouses for the remainder of her life. For Deborah, society's punishment was life without parole in an institution. For others like her, it was even worse. Before the era of Goddard's "menace of the feebleminded" ended, somewhere between 40,000 and 50,000 Americans labeled as feebleminded had been involuntarily sterilized.

CHAPTER 2

In Search of a Science

Henry Herbert Goddard was born August 14, 1866, in East Vassalboro, Maine, the fifth child and first son of Henry Clay and Sarah Winslow Goddard. His mother was a descendent of Edward Winslow, a Mayflower pilgrim and, later, Governor of the Plymouth Colony. Goddard's early years were, however, far from privileged. His parents were farmers, and prior to Goddard's birth, reasonably prosperous. By the time he was born this was no longer the case. Goddard biographer Leila Zenderland observed that the Goddard family "demonstrated a striking pattern of downward social mobility."[1] By 1870, Goddard's father had lost the family farm and worked as an agricultural day laborer. Their precipitous decline was attributable to his father's physical incapacity as a result of being gored by a bull, an injury that led to his death in 1875, when Goddard was nine years old.

Sarah Goddard's response to her husband's declining health and death was to cloak herself in the comfort and structure of the Quaker church in which she had been raised. By the time Goddard was six, his mother was frequently a preacher in local churches. Within a year, she was speaking at Friends meetings outside Maine, beginning in Canada. After her husband's death, she spent nine months traveling through Iowa holding church meetings. From Iowa, her visits to Friends meetings expanded throughout North America. In 1884, Sarah remarried and soon departed for Europe, England, and the Middle East.

Because of his mother's increasingly frequent absences and his father's declining health and ultimate demise, Goddard was raised, in essence, by his older, married sister.[2] He received his religious education through Quaker boarding schools and colleges. It was primarily through the charity of the Quaker community and his older sisters that Goddard survived, psychologically and financially, after his father's death.

---

[1] Zenderland, 1998, p. 17
[2] Zenderland, 1998, p. 20.

At age 11, Goddard entered the Quaker Oak Grove Seminary in Vassalboro, Maine. At 17, he enrolled at Haverford College as a scholarship student. He was not a particularly adept student and noted that this financial assistance was more a tribute to his mother's service and recognition of the family's poverty than to his academic record.[3] Plagued by the self-doubts he attributed to his poverty and his insecurity arising from having been, essentially, abandoned by his mother, Goddard dropped out of Haverford to teach in a public school. Although he returned to Haverford a year later and completed his undergraduate training, Goddard was ill equipped, emotionally and financially, to cope on his own. In the autumn of 1887, he moved to Los Angeles to live with a married sister.[4]

By 1889 Goddard had returned to what he knew so well, the relatively cloistered and highly structured life of Haverford. He earned a masters degree there in mathematics. In August 1889, Goddard married Emma Florence Robbins, whom he had met during a year hiatus from Haverford. Emma brought stability to his life that he'd not previously experienced, but nothing to this point portended the influence he was to have. The newlyweds moved to Damascus, Ohio, where both taught at a small Quaker school: Goddard serving as principal and teaching math and moral studies; Emma teaching primary students. Two years later, Goddard returned to his alma mater, Oak Grove, first as a teacher and later as principal. As career trajectories go, Goddard's was hardly meteoric.

In the early 1890s, however, while still working at Oak Grove, Goddard traveled by train the 45 miles from Vassalboro to Lewiston to attend the meeting of the Maine State Teachers Association. There, he heard Clark University President and psychologist Granville Stanley Hall address the association. Hall was the keynote speaker and as he expounded the virtues of his child-study philosophy, Goddard was smitten. Hall's speech set in motion a series of experiences that would change the path of Goddard's career and, ultimately, the lives of Deborah Kallikak and others like her.

Granville Stanley Hall was—with the exception of Hall's own mentor, Harvard psychologist William James—the most important and influential American psychologist in the first 25 years of that discipline's emergence as a distinct field from philosophy and establishment as a credible science. None other than Sigmund Freud called Hall a "king-maker."[5]

Like Goddard, Hall's lineage was old New England stock. He was descended from several Mayflower passengers, including John Alden, a signer of the Mayflower compact, and John Hall, who came to America in 1630 along with Goddard's ancestor, Edward Winthrop. Hall's early training was in the ministry,

[3] Zenderland, 1998, p. 20.
[4] Zenderland, 1998, p. 25.
[5] Rosenzweig, 1992, p. 4.

and he studied at Union Theological Seminary for one year. Although he eventually became disenchanted with the pastorate as a vocation, his psychological theories liberally mixed religion and science. In 1896, the year Goddard entered Clark, Hall suggested that the new psychology, which he was instrumental in founding, reaffirmed the five points of the "new orthodoxy"—God, Christ, sin, regeneration, and the bible (calling it "the greatest book of psychology in the world").[6]

Hall's first academic appointment as a professor of literature and philosophy was at Ohio's Antioch College, a bastion of Unitarian thought in the U.S. West whose first president had been Horace Mann, "the father of American public schools." There he read Wilhelm Wundt's 1874 text *Grundzuge der Physiologischen Psychologie* (Principles of Physiological Psychology). He immediately determined to return to Germany, where he had previously spent six years, and enter Wundt's laboratory. His attempt to resign his position at Antioch was thwarted, however, by insufficient notice, so he stayed in Ohio another year more before embarking for Germany. He was further delayed by a circumstantial meeting while visiting his brother in Cambridge. He met and fell under the spell of William James, whose 1890 masterwork *Principles of Psychology* defined the field and influenced leading theorists in the United States and across the world. Rather than continuing on to Germany, Hall stayed in Cambridge to study with James. In 1878, he was awarded his doctoral degree in psychology, the first such degree awarded in the United States. Hall finally traveled to Germany to apprentice with Wundt, where, shortly before Christmas 1879, Hall, Wundt, and Max Friedman conducted an experiment on "the elements of consciousness" at the University of Leipzig that is viewed by many as the beginning of modern psychology.

On his return to the United States, Hall became Professor of Psychology and Pedagogics at Johns Hopkins University, where he established the first fully operational psychology laboratory in the United States. In April 1888, Boston financier and businessman Jonas Gilman Clark invited Hall to Clark University to become that institution's inaugural president. Under Hall's leadership, Clark University established graduate programs in five departments, including, not surprisingly, a department of psychology that included the even now eclectic mix of neurology, anthropology, and education.

The early days of Clark University's department of psychology were promising. Hall lured some of the most influential scientists of the day to Worcester, including arranging for lectures by Adolph Meyer, the developer of psychobiology and psychiatry's diagnostic procedure now referred to as the *Diagnostic and Statistical Manual*. During his time at Clark, Goddard served as Meyer's teaching assistant in a course titled "Laboratory Histology and Neurology," and

---

[6] Zenderland, 1998, p. 31.

his earliest efforts in his fledgling psychology research laboratory at Vineland emulated his experience in Meyer's lab.

Under the magnetic Hall, who in addition to his duties as president was also professor of psychology, doctoral students began to learn what they needed to know to put the new discipline on the map and to usurp the authority that the field of medicine held over the science of human behavior. In his 1978 text *The Great Psychologists*, Robert Watson wrote of Hall that "His own teaching struck sparks in all directions."[7] He was at his best in his weekly seminar, held at his home, where students and faculty presented papers. Lewis Terman expressed a representative opinion. "For me, Clark University meant briefly three things: freedom to work as I pleased, unlimited library facilities, and Hall's Monday evening seminar."[8] In 1901, psychologist J. E. Wallace Wallin, prior to stints at Vineland and the Skillman Village for Epileptics, served as Hall's assistant, and described his boss as "an omnivorous and rapid reader, endowed with an encyclopedic mind . . . quick at making sweeping generalizations and taking big inductive leaps . . . an indefatigable worker and voluminous writer."[9]

The luster of the new focal point for training in psychology was dimmed somewhat when Hall discovered that the university's namesake and benefactor was not as generous as he had been led to believe. The Goddards had moved their worldly belongings from provincial Vassalboro to Worcester in 1896 so Goddard could study with Hall. But partly because of both the university's financial woes and Hall's bombastic management style, many of the early faculty left prior to Goddard's arrival, including H. H. Donaldson, an internationally prominent neurologist who developed a strain of albino rats (the Wistar Rat) that became the standard for psychological research, and father of U.S. anthropology Franz Boas.[10] Although Goddard came to Clark to soak up the rays from Hall's intellect, it was likely disconcerting to see the distinguished faculty scatter to the far winds. Despite losing many of its brightest stars, however, Clark University and Hall managed to retain their reputations in psychology, as evidenced by Hall's crowning achievement. In celebration of Clark's 20th anniversary in 1909, Hall arranged Freud's only visit to the United States and meeting with William James.

During his prestigious career, Hall pioneered the field of child-study, which as its name implies focused on the detailed study of children with the intent to link psychology with education. He introduced the idea of "adolescence" to the world with his highly influential 1904 two-volume treatise on the subject. He was the first president of the American Psychological Association and founded the *American Journal of Psychology*.

---

[7]Watson, 1978, p. 56.
[8]Watson, 1978, p. 56.
[9]Wallin, 1953.
[10]Cravens, 1978, p. 24.

By the turn of the 20th century, Hall's students held more than half of all psychology doctorates awarded in North America. Those students included a who's who of psychology: Arnold Gesell, the first school psychologist and founder of the influential Yale Institute for Child Development; Lewis Terman, whose revision of the Binet-Simon intelligence test became the gold standard for IQ testing; James McKeen Cattell, the Columbia University psychologist who founded the journals *Psychological Review* and *Science*; John Dewey, who became one of the most (if not the most) significant educational theorists of the 20th century; and, of course, Goddard.

Like other doctoral students under Hall, Goddard embarked on a course of study at Clark that covered psychology and its history, experimental psychology, ethics, neurology, anthropology, and education. If Hall was anything, he was eclectic, publishing on topics ranging from the perception of color to Laura Bridgman, the deaf and blind prodigy who is better known now as the "first Helen Keller"; from a study of dolls to methods of teaching history; and from the psychology of tickling and laughing to an essay on the greatest books of the 19th century. Even Hall's most sympathetic biographers use phrases such as "restless mind" and "caught by the next topic" to describe Hall's frequent shifts in research focus.[11] Given this eclectic program, Hall's mix of the secular and religious, and Goddard's own religious upbringing, it is perhaps not surprising that Goddard's dissertation topic was *The Effects of Mind on Body as Evidenced by Faith Cures*, which was published as a monograph to the *American Journal of Psychology* on his graduation in 1899.

It was at Clark that Goddard was first exposed to the newly proclaimed science of eugenics. Charles Darwin's half-cousin, Francis Galton, had coined the term "eugenics":

> That is, with questions bearing on what is termed in Greek, *eugenes* namely, good in stock, hereditarily endowed with noble qualities. This, and the allied words, *eugeneia*, etc., are equally applicable to men, brutes, and plants. We greatly want a brief word to express the science of improving stock, which is by no means confined to questions of judicious mating, but which, especially in the case of man, takes cognisance of all influences that tend in however remote a degree to give to the more suitable races or strains of blood a better chance of prevailing speedily over the less suitable than they otherwise would have had. The word *eugenics* would sufficiently express the idea; it is at least a neater word and a more generalised one than *viriculture* which I once ventured to use.[12]

Hall held a strongly eugenic perspective. Speaking to attendees at a child welfare conference at Clark in 1910, Hall admonished the gathered to "not inter-

[11]Roback, 1952.
[12]Galton, 1883, page 17.

fere too much with natural selection in the human field," suggesting that if the "rate of increase of the best children diminishes and that of the worst [whom Hall referred to as the three big "d's;" defectives, delinquents, and dependents], increases, the destiny of our land is sealed and our people are doomed to inevitable decay and ultimate extension."[13]

"From the standpoint of eugenic evolution alone considered," opined Hall, "these classes are mostly fit only for extermination in the interests of the progress of the race."[14]

Hall's antipathy toward "defectives, delinquents, and dependents" and his belief in the efficacy of their extermination was an old saw by 1910. Through recorded history even the most enlightened societies have often been less than humane to people with disabilities. In Plato's *Symposium* (360 BCE), Socrates defined love by relating what he learned from Diotima, which included the admonition that "the deformed is always inharmonious with the divine, and the beautiful harmonious." Plato's perfect society, as described in *The Republic* (360 BCE), included the decidedly eugenic suggestion that the "offspring of the inferior, or of the better when they chance to be deformed, will be put away in some mysterious, unknown place, as they should be." Plato's pupil, Aristotle, who parted ways with his teacher on many points, did not, apparently, stray far from the master's viewpoint on disability, as he was a prominent advocate of a law to ban the rearing of "deformed children."

The practices of some ancient societies went beyond putting children with disabilities "away in some mysterious, unknown place." The word "idiot," which was used to refer to people with the most severe intellectual impairments until the mid-1800s, was derived from the Greek words "idatas" and "idios." *Idatas* refers to a private person, and idios means "peculiar." Together, they refer to a person who is different, set aside, peculiar. Spartan and Roman cultures are frequently identified as practicing infanticide for weak or disabled newborns. It is also worth noting that much of *The Republic* deals with ensuring military strength, while Sparta and Rome were known as centers of military might. People with disabilities were, in antiquity, seen as contrary to the societal ideals of beauty and might. They were different, set apart.

Diotima's injunction that what is deformed is always "inharmonious with the divine" points to another factor shaping society's understanding of disability: religion. Across religious traditions and time, disability has been equated with negative aspects of religious belief or performance: the personification of the devil or similar evil entities, faithlessness and disbelief, a test of one's faith, or punishment for sinful behavior on the part of either the parents or the person.

---

[13] Hall, 1910, p. 55.
[14] Hall, 1910, p. 55.

Although they vary, illustrations are available across religious traditions: people are made to see, hear, or walk because their sins are forgiven; people experience disability because of a past life; "cripples" are made to walk because they have faith; disability is a test of the endurance of believers; the faithless are "blind to the truth"; and "epileptics" are cured as demons are cast out.

The teachings of virtually all religious traditions, however, emphasize tolerance and compassion for people who are poor, ill, or disabled. People like Dorothea Dix, Samuel Gridley Howe, or the Reverend Garrison of the Vineland Training School, whose religious beliefs compelled them to act on behalf of their less advantaged brethren, essentially charted the course for services for people with disabilities.

This mix of compassion and condemnation can be seen in the writings of many of the reformers whose efforts resulted in the growth of institutions like the Vineland Training School. Among the most flamboyant of these reformers was Samuel Gridley Howe. A native Bostonian whose paternal grandfather participated in the Boston Tea Party and whose maternal uncle was in charge of fortifying the defenses at the Battle of Bunker Hill, Howe was a romantic soul; a romanticism only youth, social affluence, and an unshaken self-confidence (i.e., arrogance) can breed. On graduation with his medical degree in 1824, Howe joined other idealistic and romantic youth influenced by Lord Byron in the heat of the battle for Greek independence from Turkey. Achieving hero stature for his actions in Greece, Howe returned to Boston seeking his next conquest.

In 1831, Howe accepted the challenge of establishing a school for the blind in Boston and, following a trip to Paris in 1832 to visit European schools, established the New England Asylum for the Blind, later the Perkins Institute for the Blind. His most famous patient was Laura Bridgman.[15] Deaf and blind as the outcome of scarlet fever at an early age, under Howe's tutelage Laura became the first deaf and blind person to learn language.[16]

Samuel Gridley Howe's social activism took him down many paths until his death in 1876. He married fellow antislavery activist Julia Ward, who later penned the *Battle Hymn of the Republic*, and was one of a small band of progressive Bostonians who funded John Brown's bloody crusade against slavery, which brought the country to the brink of civil war.[17] In 1848, Howe established the first public school for the feebleminded in the United States in a wing of the Perkins school. In 1858, he published a report titled *On the Causes of Idiocy*.

"We regarded idiocy as a disease of society, as an outward sign of an inward malady," Howe begins. That malady is the age old culprit, sin. "It appeared to us certain that the existence of so many idiots in every generation *must* be the consequence of some violation of the *natural laws*;—that where there was so much

---

[15] Freeberg, 2001.
[16] Gitter, 2001.
[17] Renehan, 1997.

suffering there must have been sin," continued Howe. It was, however, impious
to attribute to God the glaring imperfection of "so many creatures in the human
shape, but without the light of human reason." Instead, idiocy results, proposed
Howe, from "the chastisements sent by a loving Father to bring back his children to obedience to his beneficent laws."[18]

Howe's pre-Darwinian, pre-Mendelian worldview did not have the vocabu-
lary of evolution and heredity from which to draw. Nevertheless, although feeblemindedness was predominantly seen as attributable to sin in the mid-1800s,
it was a sin very different from the superstition-laden perspectives of earlier
millennia. Indeed, the sins to which Howe attributed idiocy were very similar to
the causes attributed by extreme hereditarians half a century later.

Howe wrote,

[the] moral to be drawn from the prevalent existence of idiocy in society is,
that a very large class of persons ignore the conditions upon which alone
health and reason are given to men, and consequently they sin in various
ways; they disregard the conditions which should be observed in intermarriage; they overlook the hereditary transmission of certain morbid tendencies,
or they pervert the natural appetites of the body into lusts of diverse kinds,
—the natural emotions of the mind into fearful passions—and thus bring
down the awful consequences of their own ignorance and sin upon the heads
of their unoffending children.[19]

Conditions of intermarriage, hereditary transmission of morbid tendencies,
perversions of the natural appetites of the body . . . all become major platforms
for future eugenicists.

Howe concluded,

Idiocy is an insult to the majesty of Heaven. If such parent erred in ignorance;
if he had always obeyed the laws of life and morality, as far as he knew them,
still must his suffering be grievous; but if he sinned against the clear light of
God's law; if he secretly defiled the temple of his soul, ran riot in lust, fed the
fire of passion until it burnt out the very core of his body, and then planted a
spark from the smouldering ashes to shoot up into unhallowed flames in the
bosom of his child, how horrible must be his sensations when he looks upon
that child, consuming, morally, every day before his eyes! Talk about the dread
of a material hell in the far-off future! The fear of that can be nothing to the
fear of plunging one's own child in the hell of passion *here*.[20]

---

[18] Howe, 1858, p. 2.
[19] Howe, 1858, p. 5.
[20] Howe, 1858, p. 10.

❧ ❧ ❧

When Goddard left the cloistered surrounds of Clark, the scientific land-scape in the United States was changing rapidly and dramatically. The mid-1800 theological doctrines concerning the progress of mankind espoused by reform-ers like Howe and that served as just cause for acting on behalf of the poor and downtrodden had been, by the turn of the 20th century, replaced by a different cultural ethos, the need for social control. The primary ingredients mixed into this cultural cauldron were the problems of immigration, racial inequality and segregation, and social competency. The cauldron was stirred by a generation of scientists in the fields of biology and genetics, psychology, anthropology, and sociology, buoyed by the "triumph of evolution" in American science.[21]

Writing in *The Causes of Idiocy* in 1858, Samuel Gridley Howe noted that the "sin" in which many persons engaged that resulted in the "societal disease" of idiocy was that "they overlook the hereditary transmission of certain morbid ten-dencies" and, thus, "bring down the awful consequences of their own ignorance and sin upon the heads of their unoffending children."[22] Howe's identification of the "sin" resulting in idiocy as "overlooking hereditary transmissions" seems a far cry from earlier attributions of the causes of disability, ranging from the wrath of God to demon possession. Both, to varying degrees however, evidence a belief that individual human characteristics, such as feeblemindedness, are inherited.[23]

That belief was the core tenet of the new biology that emerged in the late 1800s, but it was not new to that period. The French scientist Jean-Baptiste Lamarck is frequently identified as having advanced the first modern theory of evolution in his book *Philosophie Zoologique* (1809), although in reality his approach was more philosophical than scientific and he offered no new ideas with regard to heredity and evolution. Nevertheless, Lamarck is linked in per-petuity with the idea that organisms could pass on, through heredity, acquired characteristics.

The most frequently cited events in the history of evolution are the July 1858 delivery of Alfred Russell Wallace and Charles Darwin's papers on natural selec-tion, and Darwin's November 1859 publication of *The Origin of Species*. The con-cept of "survival of the fittest," so critical to Darwin's *Origin*, was, regrettably, also to become the linchpin of subsequent arguments for eugenic sterilization and institutionalization of the feebleminded.

English clergyman, historian, and political economics professor Thomas Robert Malthus (1766–1834) introduced the idea of survival of the fittest in his influential *Essay on the Principle of Population*, published first in 1798. England's Industrial Revolution, from 1750 to 1830, transformed the country from an

---

[21] Cravens, 1978.
[22] Howe, 1858, p. 7.
[23] Carlson, 2001, pp. 109-110.

agrarian economy with a largely rural population to an urban society engaged increasingly in manufacturing. In 1750, the population of England was four million, with 700,000 people living in its most populous city, London. In 1851, when England hosted the first World's Fair exhibition celebrating science and industry—the focal point of which was the Crystal Palace—its population was 21 million, with nearly 2.5 million of them in London, along with nearly equal numbers of livestock and other domestic animals. The mass migration from the rural regions to the urban core created a glut in the labor market, driving down wages and resulting in a growing class of poor. Malthus's *Essay* was composed in response to previous writers, most noticeably Thomas Godwin (Mary Shelley's father), who expressed the belief that capitalism was exploitative and who forwarded an alternative view of society in which those who earned more than what they needed would distribute the surplus to the needy.

Malthus began his rebuttal with two statements of "fact" and one hypothesis. The first fact was that food is necessary to the existence of man. The second was "the passion between the sexes is necessary, and will remain nearly in its present state." The hypothesis, since shown to be unsubstantiated, was that unchecked populations increase in a geometric ratio, whereas subsistence increases only in an arithmetic ratio. Malthus concluded that, given the limits on food production and, presumably, the limitless capacity of human beings to procreate, that "the power of population is indefinitely greater than the power in the earth to produce subsistence for man." Furthermore, as per Malthus, society's efforts to address the growing blight of poverty and want was detrimental to the natural order.

"The poor-laws of England tend to depress the general condition of the poor in these two ways," wrote Malthus. "This first obvious tendency is to increase population without increasing the food for its support. Secondly, the quantity of provisions consumed in workhouses upon a part of the society, that cannot in general be considered the most valuable part, diminishes the shares that would otherwise belong to more worthy members; and thus in the same manner forces more to become dependent."

Malthus's basic premise was that the "surplus" population was, in essence, a drain on the economic stability of a nation and that any efforts to curtail the two "natural checks" on population growth, called positive checks and preventive checks, would result in greater harm, not only to the poor but also to the "fit." Positive checks were those, such as famine, plague, and war, which increased the death rate. Preventive checks were those that reduced the birth rate, such as birth control and "moral restraint." Only when these checks were in place could population's power be kept from outstripping the power of sustenance, according to Malthus.

One of the dangers of Malthus's ideas is that they have a certain amount of plausibility among the public, even today. Concerns about overpopulation and the lack of sustenance and nourishment are found in discourse and in fiction.

For example, one of the setting events for Arthur C. Clarke's classic *2001: A Space Odyssey* involved a "political situation,"

> As long as he could remember, it had been not a "situation" so much as a permanent crisis . . .
>
> Though birth control was cheap, reliable, and endorsed by all the main religions, it had come too late; the population of the world was now six billion. Laws had even been passed in some authoritarian societies limiting families to two children, but their enforcement had proved impracticable. As a result, food was short in every country; even the United States had meatless days, and wide-spread famine was predicted within fifteen years, despite heroic efforts to farm the sea and to develop synthetic foods.[24]

Malthus's ideas were not offered with the intent to contribute to theories of evolution, per se, but were instead intended to propose actions pertaining to social control, justified in its negative impact on some members of society by the benefit to others or the whole. Although treatment of people who were deemed as feebleminded was driven by expressions of social justice and religious obligation for much of the 19th century, as illustrated by the actions of social activists like Samuel Gridley Howe, the seeds of the American eugenic movement were sewn by Malthus. Themes of population control mixed with racial prejudice would lead to images of "race suicide"; themes of social control and social hygiene became the solution to perceived societal problems of the fecundity of the poor and ignorant; Malthusian ideas of social control were mingled with scientific theories of evolution, and the line between science and prejudice blurred with the emergence of social Darwinism and eugenics.

It is, unfortunately, not a significant leap from the feebleminded as a manifestation of sin, to the feebleminded as surplus population, to the feebleminded as menaces to society. Goddard's contribution to this crescendo was merely the final step toward social control.

In 1838, Darwin read Malthus's *Essay* and, directly or indirectly, the espousal of "survival of the fittest" provided one piece of the puzzle for Darwin's theory of natural selection. Darwin's evolutionary theories were not intended by him to be applied as a model for social control, although Darwin himself believed that people who were feebleminded were evolutionary mistakes.

Victorian-era philosopher Herbert Spencer is primarily associated with the movement applying evolutionary theory to explain social phenomena that was eventually called "social Darwinism," although as Elof Axel Carlson, author

---

[24]Clarke, 1968, p. 43.

of *The Unfit: A History of a Bad Idea*, observed, it really should be called social Spencerism. Spencer both popularized the term *evolution* and coined the term "survival of the fittest" in his own writings about evolution, most of which appeared several years before Darwin's publication of *Origin*.

Spencer proposed that laws of evolution as applied to species could also be applied to societies and governments. "This law of organic progress is the law of all progress," Spencer wrote in *Progress: It's Law and Cause* (1857). "Whether it be in the development of the Earth, in the development of Life upon its surface, the development of Society, of Government . . . this same evolution of the simple into the complex, through a process of continuous differentiation, holds throughout." Spencer, and his American disciple William Graham Sumner, proposed an economic doctrine that applied principles of natural selection to the social order. In this worldview, however, "the survival of the fittest" referred not to the processes creating new species, but instead to the process of culling degenerate members of a society out of that society.[25]

Like Malthus, social Darwinists objected to many charitable efforts on the part of governments, referring to them as "tampering" with the natural order of societies.[26] Moreover, Spencer viewed the elimination of degenerate members of society as part of the progress toward improving humanity. Subsequent expostulations of the theory of eugenics were grounded in the basic philosophy of social Darwinism that was combined with newly emerging understandings of mechanisms of genetics. In the United States, propelled by social Darwinists like Sumner, the tycoons of industry latched onto the notions of the "survival of the fittest" as scientific justification for their largely monopolistic practices, arguing that the weeding out of the unfit was better for the economy and society as a whole.

When his groundbreaking paper on evolution was read before the Linnean Society on July 1, 1858, Charles Darwin was not in attendance. Instead, he was home dealing with the death of his youngest son and namesake, Charles Waring Darwin, who had expired from scarlet fever on June 28, six months shy of his second birthday. Charles Waring was never a healthy child, and Darwin and his wife, Emma, were concerned about the progress of his development. It became increasingly evident that the youngest Darwin was feebleminded.

"The poor little baby was born without its full share of intelligence," opined Darwin's daughter, Henrietta.[27]

"He was small for his age and backward in walking and talking," memorialized Darwin at his son's funeral.[28]

---

[25] Carlson, 2001, p. 127.
[26] Trent, 1994, p. 135.
[27] Litchfield, 1915, p. 162.
[28] Darwin, 1858, p. 521.

Darwin biographer John Bowlby, one of the most important child psychologists of the 20th century in his own right, concludes that Charles Waring had Down syndrome. Whether this was indeed the cause of young Darwin's backwardness or not, it is one of life's ironies that Darwin's theories would be transmuted by Spencer and others, including Galton and another of Darwin's sons, Leonard, a major figure in the movement's adoption, with the result that people like his youngest son were subjected to eugenicist's solutions for social control.

In 1899, sheepskin in hand from Clark, Henry Herbert Goddard accepted a position as professor of psychology at the State Normal School, a teacher training college in West Chester, Pennsylvania. There, he immediately and not surprisingly began a campaign to include the practices pertaining to child-study he had learned at Clark into the educational system in Pennsylvania, not only for its pedagogic value, but also to demonstrate the utility of psychology for the field of education.

The child-study movement had been established by Hall as a means to just that end. In 1891, Hall had published a study titled *The Contents of Children's Minds on Entering School* in which he had employed kindergarten teachers to collect detailed information about their students using procedures that included questionnaires and direct observation, data from which Hall extrapolated and hypothesized about the minds of children.

This method—having teachers gather prodigious amounts of data about the minutia of child behavior through direct observation, longhand records, and questionnaires so that the psychologist might translate these data into insights about the child and, ultimately, educational practices—became the modus operandi for researchers in the movement.[29] Child-study societies were established in state after state, deputizing teachers to go forth, observe, and record. In 1894, the National Education Association established a child-study department. Hall, speaking at the department's dedication, evangelized that child-study " . . . realized what was in the mind of Jesus Christ when he said that the little child should lead them."[30]

And observe and record they did. Earl Barnes, whose original idea it was to found a psychological laboratory at Vineland, was Goddard's accomplice in child-study evangelism in Pennsylvania and a major contributor to the child-study literature during his tenure at Leland Stanford Jr. University. Barnes had been appointed the first professor of education at Stanford in 1891, arriving there from Indiana University along with IU President David Starr Jordan when the latter, who become one of the most visible spokespersons in the American eugenics movement, was appointed Stanford's inaugural president. When, in

[29] Pulliam and Van Patten, 1995, p. 135.
[30] Zenderland, 1998, p. 49.

1897, Barnes was asked by Jordan to resign his appointment at Stanford because he'd had an extramarital affair,[31] he and his apparently understanding wife, herself a Stanford history professor, traveled to Europe to lecture. While in London the next year, Barnes's wife died of heart disease and he returned to the United States,[32] eventually settling in Philadelphia, where he made his living as a freelance writer and lecturer, often speaking, ironically given his Stanford debacle, to women's groups as an early male champion of the emerging feminist movement.

While at Stanford, Barnes published numerous studies employing the child-study method that illustrate the sheer volume of information child-study advocates collected. In conducting a study of children's interests in 1892, for example, Barnes partnered with the Monterey county school district to collect information from children about what was most attractive to them.

"On the day after receiving this circular letter, provide all the children in your room with paper and pencil, at the composition or spelling hour," Job Wood, Monterey school superintendent, instructed teachers, "[and instruct them to write] what is a knife, bread, doll, water, armchair, hat, garden, piece of sugar, thread, horse, table, mamma, potatoes, bottle, flower, snail, mouth, lamp, bird, dog, carriage, pencil, earthworm, shoes, finger, clock, house, wolf, omnibus, balloon, village, box, handkerchief."[33]

With further instructions to give no other directions that might suggest to children what they might think on hearing the words, Wood instructed teachers to gather up and return the papers to his office. More than 2,000 of Monterey's compliant children served as subjects for this study, with a total of 37,136 statements analyzed by Barnes.

"It is possible," Barnes concluded in the study, "when we have made sufficiently extended studies in a sufficient number of directions . . . to build educational activities on definite laws, which will rest on as scientific a basis as our treatment of typhoid fever with such children now does."[34]

Barnes's study of children's interests was not unique in its scope. In a subsequent study of children's religious life and feeling, he collected the compositions of 1,091 children on God, death, heaven, hell, angels, ghosts, witches, prayer, and religious ceremonies.[35] A long-term collaboration between Barnes and Oakland schools resulted in child-study data on introspection, memory, visualizing power, association, physical conditions, children's fears, fear in school work, color sense, children's play, children's perceptions of their rights, and development of historical sense. Each of those studies had 4,000 or more student participants and literally tens of thousands of student responses. As child-study departments of

---

[31] Earl Barnes papers http://www.oac.cdlib.org/findaid/ark:/13030/tf82900674/.
[32] Mary Sheldon Barnes papers http://asteria.fivecolleges.edu/findaids/sophiasmith/mnsss2.html
[33] Barnes, 1893, p. 5.
[34] Barnes, 1893, p. 8.
[35] Barnes, 1897.

educational agencies grew and more disciples joined the cause, psychologists like Barnes and Hall had a readymade cadre of teachers willing to generate reams and reams of data.

Hall placed his child-study efforts in the context of what a colleague at Clark referred to as Hall's genetic philosophy of psychology, the principles of which applied Darwinian natural selection and evolution to the development of mental processes. The "chief end" of the application of this philosophy to education was "to carry on the race toward perfection, by bringing the youth of each succeeding generation to a higher degree of development than the one which has preceded."[36] Many of Hall's contemporaries, including other psychologists, were critical of methods employed in the child-study movement, noting that the data was collected by practitioners not trained in psychological methods and that virtually any conclusion could be substantiated by selectively using information in the voluminous data set. Nevertheless, modern educational historians identify Hall's child-study method as a precursor to the modern disciplines of child and developmental psychology, as well as the study of exceptional children.

The linkages between child-study and eugenics are less frequently documented, but one can follow the path. Hall's genetic psychology, from which child-study emerged, had a clear eugenic intent: to improve the quality of the race. Although the movement's methods were criticized, child-study constituted one of the first systematic attempts to measure the mental life of children. Previous studies of children's mental life focused on observations of a small number of children, often a single child, such as Darwin's observations of his oldest son William's development, published in the journal *Mind* in 1872. The capacity to easily measure the mental ability of large numbers of children was critical to the growth of psychology as a viable discipline. Hall's students, including Goddard, Terman, and Cattell, were the pioneers in the next stage of this effort, the measurement of intelligence, which, in turn, became a primary tool in the eugenic arsenal. Even relatively innocuous child-study efforts, such as the studies conducted by Barnes, provide evidence of the movement from child-study to intelligence testing; the litany of words that students in Monterey responded to in 1892 were not randomly generated by Barnes, but were instead culled from publications by Alfred Binet, the French scientist who is identified as the father of intelligence testing.

By November 1900, a child-study department had been established in the Pennsylvania Teachers Association, primarily because of Goddard's evangelistic efforts across the state. He was, however, a prophet without honor in his own country. The principal at West Chester did not share his enthusiasm for child-study and consistently told Goddard that psychology was of no practical value to teachers.[37]

---

[36] Partridge, 1912, p. 23.
[37] Zenderland, 1978, p. 45.

❧ ❧ ❧

The late winter storms had delayed trains in and out of Philadelphia's Broad Street Train Station, and Goddard arrived late for the 1900 meeting of the New Jersey Association for the Study of Childhood and Youth in Trenton. As he entered the meeting room, attempting not to disrupt the ongoing discussion, his attention fell on a young man at the podium whose presentation on child-study had elicited questions from the obviously appreciative audience.

"I had not heard anything so fascinating since I left the tutelage of Stanley Hall,"[38] said Goddard of the ensuing discussion.

Goddard turned to the man seated next to him. "Who is that young man?" he asked.

"The Superintendent of the Training School for the Feebleminded, in South Jersey," responded the man. "I think his name is Johnson."

Later that day, Goddard introduced himself to E. R. Johnstone, and the two immediately recognized one another as kindred souls. Goddard spoke of his excitement that his efforts in Pennsylvania to form a child-study department at the state teachers association were about to pay off, and of his frustration in getting his own principal to recognize the importance of the efforts. Johnstone spoke of his fascination with the idea that it was possible to study children as a means of understanding their behavior.

Before the day had ended, Johnstone had invited Goddard to visit the Training School, an invitation Goddard accepted later that year. On December 7, 1901, Goddard and Johnstone ran into one another again at another child-study meeting, this one in Newark.

"Like the lover who goes to church hoping he will see his enamorata, I went to Newark hoping to see Johnstone," gushed Goddard.

Both Goddard and Earl Barnes presented papers at the meeting. At lunch, Johnstone joined Goddard and Barnes, among others, in a lively discussion of the papers.

"So profitable was this discussion," noted Johnstone, "that when the three of us returned to Philadelphia on the same train, one member of the party spoke of how valuable it would be for meetings entirely informal to be held from time to time for the discussion of questions relating to education."

"On that train was born another of Johnstone's big ideas, the Feeble-Minded Club," noted Goddard.

Johnstone offered the hospitality of the Training School and lunch provisions, and the three identified a select few who would be invited. Within a few weeks, the plans were set and the first meeting of the Feeble-Minded Club was held, with attendees that included Goddard, Johnstone, Barnes, and Maurice Fels.

---

[38]This and subsequent quotes pertaining to the Goddard and Johnstone meeting from Doll, 1932.

Fels was Philadelphia Soap magnate Samuel Fel's younger brother, a self-styled educational reformer who, like Johnstone, would eventually have a Vineland school named after him.[39] The group met twice annually, all but one time at Vineland. Members included a mix of public school, university, government, and public welfare officials, most of whom joined Johnstone in smoking a cigar, leading the waitresses, almost all of whom were Training School inmates, to dub the gathering the Smokers Club.

Meeting with his cronies in the Feeble-Minded Club was one of the few activities Goddard enjoyed during this time. In 1903, Goddard sought respite from the unremitting drudgery of West Chester by taking a sabbatical to study in Europe. While in Zurich, he studied with Ernst Meumann, the founder of "experimental pedagogy" and a student of Wundt. The focus of experimental pedagogy was to investigate the development of children and differences in their aptitude, and to apply this, analytically, to schoolwork.

Meanwhile, momentum built for the establishment of the Research Laboratory. At the semiannual meetings of the Feeble-Minded Club, practitioners, politicians, and professors discussed the importance of research to understanding feeblemindedness and its consequences. Barnes's human-laboratory-and-garden speech at the annual meeting of the Training School Association in June of 1903 planted the seed in the minds of many. In 1904, Johnstone and Alice Morrison, who taught at Vineland for more than 50 years, began a summer school for public schoolteachers, bringing them to the institution to spend the summer learning how to work with feebleminded children. This was, in essence, the first teacher preparation program for special educators in the nation, and created yet another use for research . . . to identify effective practices.

"Members of the Feeble-Minded Club discussed many questions raised by the teachers and also by ourselves," Johnstone confessed, referring to teachers involved in the summer school program at Vineland, "which we did not seem to be able to answer, and it really seemed that the time was ripe for the establishment here of a psychological laboratory."[40]

Goddard arrived at the Research Laboratory at The Vineland Training School with a religious-like fervor focused on establishing psychology as a legitimate science. Vineland was an anomaly among institutions for the feebleminded. Johnstone was the only superintendent among his brethren administrators without a medical degree. In fact, when hired as assistant superintendent, Johnstone displaced a medical doctor who had, previously, served as second officer for the

---

[39] Rosen, 2000, p. 78.
[40] Doll, 1932, p. 8.

Training School. The Research Laboratory and Vineland's educational focus was a challenge to the status of physicians in the field of feeblemindedness.

"No well-informed man claims that chronic, congenital imbecility in any of its forms or degrees is curable," noted Training School founder Garrison in his report to the Training School Board of Directors the year Deborah was admitted. Garrison lamented,

> therefore, as Hervey B. Wilbur, M.D., a most able pioneer in our work, so well said, "Concerning the treatment of the feeble-minded I would suggest that the experienced educator should be called in rather than the physician. The developing of the mind and the disciplining of the individual is more the province of the teacher than of the physician." It has been a great misfortune to the work in America that this advice has not been more closely followed.[41]

The vitriolic nature of the struggle between psychology and medicine at the start of the 20th century was exemplified in an episode relayed by J. E. Wallace Wallin, an early American psychologist and pioneer in the field of special education in the United States.

Wallin spent the summer of 1910 substituting for Goddard in the Vineland summer school program while Goddard traveled to Europe. On Goddard's return, Wallin accepted a position with the New Jersey Village for Epileptics, located across the state in Skillman, north of Trenton in the more industrialized section of New Jersey, to establish what eventually became the New Jersey State Psychological Services. The differences between Vineland and Skillman, however, were more than just geographic. The superintendent at Skillman, David Weeks, was a physician who treated Wallin as if he were little more than an hourly worker. From sweeping the laboratory floor to doing all his own correspondence, Wallin was provided little or no support. Because he was not an M.D., he could not enter any of the inmate's cottages, even to perform the psychological testing for which he was hired, without explicit permission from the superintendent himself. Weeks even required Wallin to submit all his scientific papers to be vetted prior to their presentation at conferences. Finally, Wallin could tolerate the situation no longer. Demanding an audience with Weeks, Wallin proffered his immediate resignation.

Weeks seemed taken aback with Wallin's decision, further indication of Wallin's status in the institution. According to Weeks's perspective, Wallin was being treated just as a psychologist should; that is, just as any other worker. He was puzzled that Wallin should feel otherwise and, responding negatively to Wallin's offer, inquired as to Wallin's motivation.

---

[41] Garrison, 1897, pp. 23-34.

"You have made various unfounded accusations which I repudiate in toto and have cast aspersions upon my profession," responded the always loquacious Wallin, who titled one of his autobiographical pieces *Vagrant Reminiscences of an Oligophrenist* (i.e., someone whose work is of or pertains to intellectual disability).

It is my inescapable duty, which I shall not shirk, of stating my position without hedging, quibbling, or circumlocution. I came here as a professional man and not as an attendant. I will not remain in the position for one minute no matter what the inducements may be if my status is that of an attendant. I am as much a professional worker as you are or any member of your medical staff. In point of fact, my college and university training is more extensive than that of any other member of your staff and your attempt to belittle my rank in the eyes of your physicians was worse than ludicrous and asinine: it is downright unprofessional and unethical. Your attempt to debase the status of a psychologist to the rank of a menial employee is abhorrent and would be condemned by every psychologist who has the doctorate from a reputable university.[42]

Every psychologist would condemn the way in which Wallin was treated, perhaps, but *not* every physician. Nor does Wallin's incensed reply compare Weeks's behavior with that of his peers in the medical field, for there were no such differences worth comparing. Weeks viewed psychologists as did others in his profession; as little more than menial workers. Wallin, like Goddard, was a soldier in the crusade to defend his profession. It was not his own indignities he objected to, but the indignities heaped on his profession.

When he arrived at Vineland the morning of September 17, 1906, Goddard's new psychological laboratory was situated in a small, second-story room of a workshop on the campus. Sparsely furnished—one desk, a few chairs, and a few empty shelves— Goddard must have wondered momentarily if he'd made a mistake. Such misgivings were, however, only transitory—there was too much work to do.

Despite his Pennsylvania forays into child-study and its scattershot survey and questionnaire methods, Goddard's newly established laboratory was influenced more by the psychology of Wundt than it was Hall's child-study methodology. Wundt unmercifully criticized any practical application of psychology. His experimental approach focused on measuring seemingly inconsequential aspects of human behavior and physiology.[43] When Wundt's student Ernst

---

[42] Wallin, 1953, p. 47.
[43] Hunt, 1994, p. 139.

Meumann, with whom Goddard studied in Zurich, applied principles of psychology to education, Wundt disavowed him completely.[44] Wundt's laboratory contained all makes and models of paraphernalia to measure physiological, sensory, and motor phenomenon.

Emulating Wundt, Goddard gathered about him what he could to launch studies collecting anthropometric data; that is, measurements of all aspects of the human body, such as standing and sitting height, right and left grip strength, and weight,[45] used for comparative purposes. His laboratory had ergographs, dynamometers, spirometers, automatographs, and chronoscopes.[46]

By early 1907, Goddard was ready to begin data collection.

Other events during the year, however, did not bode well for the people whom Goddard sought to understand. After years of sterilizing people with intellectual disability illegally, Indiana became the first state in the nation to legalize the procedure with "all confirmed criminals, idiots, rapists and imbeciles." Meanwhile, under pressure from eugenicists and the general public, the U.S. Immigration Offices added imbeciles and feeble-minded persons to its exclusion list.

Not surprisingly, perhaps, Goddard's earliest research in his newly established psychological laboratory did not stray far from either his Clark training or his evangelical mission to legitimize psychology.

"I shall never forget the impression made upon me," wrote Goddard in 1907, "when Dr. Adolf Meyer took us into his laboratory at Worcester and taking a brain from a jar said, 'this is the brain of the patient you saw last spring. You recall the symptoms. We shall now examine this and probably shall find such and such conditions.' His prediction was verified at every point!

"We have begun work at Vineland along these lines."[47]

Not the literal line of work of dissecting brains, but the work of designing treatment based on science. Instead of collecting anthropometric data as an indicator of intelligence, Goddard's first efforts at the Vineland laboratory were launched seeking that coin of the realm of a *real* science: facts.

"Psychology needs the defective . . . and our institutions cannot better serve humanity than by devoting themselves to observing and recording such facts as can lead to advance in the general knowledge of the mind."[48]

Thus, off in search of such facts went Goddard. He used his ergograph, dynamometer, spirometer, automatograph, chronoscope and other tools of anthropometry to the collection of facts about the feebleminded inmates of the Vineland Training School. Not that this was easy. Unfortunately for Goddard, many of the inmates of the Vineland Training School were not willing or able

---

[44] Hunt, 1994, p. 134.
[45] Doll, 1916.
[46] Zenderland, 1998.
[47] Goddard, 1907a, pp. 29-30.
[48] Goddard, 1907a, p. 19.

volunteers. They rocked and reeled, swayed sideways and back and forth, fidg-
eted, darted out of the testing area, recoiled when hooked to machines, hollered,
bucked, hit out, and generally made it difficult, if not impossible, to collect reliable data. Even when compliant, many of the inmates could not talk or compre-
hend the instructions required to complete the test.

"He would not try to hold it still," complained Goddard, referring to one
inmate's attempts on the automatograph. "I explained and illustrated, held his
hand, and threatened him when he moved, but to no use, he could not be made
to do it."[49]

Never try to teach a pig to sing, the saying goes, it will only frustrate you and
annoy the pig. Goddard's efforts were, for the most part, simply frustrating him
and annoying the inmates.

Notably, however, at this juncture Goddard was attacking the "problem of the
feeble-minded" with a belief in the capacity of education and, apparently, the
plasticity of human intelligence.

"It comes about, then, that the great problem before us in our institutions
is the problem of education," said Goddard, speaking at the annual meeting
of the American Association for the Study of the Feeble-Minded held at the
Massachusetts School for the Feeble-Minded in Waverly, Massachusetts, during the summer of 1907.

> The outcome of a year's work with these children, living with them, convers-
> ing with them and their attendants, watching them at their work and play
> (and I put more confidence in what is learned in this way than in laboratory
> machinery), is the conviction that mind is the same in them as in us, within
> the limits of their experience. The differences we find are due to difference in
> environment and the way in which they have reacted to it, rather than to dif-
> ferences in the nature of the being reacted.
>
> The problem of the feeble-minded is a psychological and educational
> problem. We must devise educational methods based on sound psychology.[50]

That Goddard's belief in the power of education trumped, at least initially, his
eugenically oriented training under Hall is not particularly surprising given how
he'd spent the past few years of his career. He'd invested years at West Chester
attempting to prove that psychology could benefit teaching and learning, hardly
a viable stance if all psychology was to show was that intelligence was ineluctab-
bly determined by heredity.

In addition, during his first summer at Vineland Goddard had joined the staff
of the Vineland Summer School. The summer school, established in 1904 by
Johnstone and Alice Morrison, brought educators into the institution to spend

---

[49] Goddard, 1907b, p. 8.
[50] Goddard, 1907a, pp. 22-23.

the summer learning how to work with feebleminded students, thus constituting the first teacher preparation program for special educators in the nation.
Students, all women, paid $25 for their lodging and tuition, and were given a
six-week crash course in the education of feebleminded children.[51]

As New Year's Day of 1908 approached and Goddard began his second full
year at Vineland, his frustrations extended beyond the uncooperative nature
of the experimental subjects he was studying to include a familiar problem in
anthropometry. His hard-earned data—every inch, pound, second, and kilogram
painstakingly collected, coded, and collated—was proving to have no relationship whatsoever with indicators of capacity, in this case staff reports of capacity
or a simple puzzle-based test of capacity.

As Goddard sat at his desk, contemplating these discouraging findings, he
stared absently at the verse framed and mounted above his desk. Excerpted from
John Greenleaf Whittier's poem "The Prayer of Agassiz," the ode memorialized an event in the life of Louis Agassiz, a Swiss-born naturalist and scientist
who did much to popularize science in the United States but who, ironically
given Goddard's association with the eugenics movement, was a lifelong critic
of Darwinian evolution. Whittier, a 19th-century Quaker, abolitionist, and poet,
was once popular enough to have several states declare a holiday marking his
birthday and most Quaker school children of Goddard's era read and memo-
rized his work.

> We are groping here to find
> What the hieroglyphics mean
> What the Thought which underlies
> Nature's masking and disguise,
> What it is that hides beneath
> Blight and bloom and birth and death.[52]

Perhaps it was Goddard's recollection from his Quaker school days of the
poem's opening lines—"On the isle of Penikese, Ringed about by sapphire seas,
Fanned by breezes salt and cool"—that brought to mind the idea that his "grop-
ing for the meaning of the hieroglyphics" might be refreshed by travel across the
Atlantic, but as he later lamented, "After two years my work was so poor, I had
accomplished so little, that I went abroad to see if I could not get some ideas."[53]

His trip to Europe was to prove more fruitful than he could ever have imagined.

---

[51] Fleming, 1965, p. 95.
[52] Bjorkman, 1911, p. 333.
[53] Zenderland, 1998, p. 91.

CHAPTER 3

The Kallikak Family

Following the 1877 publication of Richard Dugdale's study of the Juke family, the first eugenic family narrative to gain wide attention and popularity, eugenicists pumped out a stream of family eugenic stories; pseudoscientific genealogies chronicling the lives of society's supposedly least capable families: the Smoky Pilgrims, The Pineys, the Dacks, the Happy Hickories, the Nams, and, most notoriously, the Kallikaks. These eugenic family sagas influenced the public's understanding of what constituted "degeneracy" for nearly half a century, and provided the fodder for subsequent, more lethal, experimentation with human life.

These tales dramatically illustrate that what is considered "degenerate," "atypical," or "aberrant" is, by and large, defined by society. In the context of the early 20th century, with the explosion of interest in biology brought about by the rediscovery of Mendel's laws of heredity, the burgeoning efforts of psychologists to measure intelligence, and the applications of Darwinian principles of natural selection to social issues such as immigration and human welfare, it is not surprising that many of the people who came to be defined as degenerate were just different. The Latin roots of the word degenerate are, in this context, instructive. The noun "degenerate" has its etymological roots in the Latin word *degenerare*, which means, "to depart from one's own kind." Degenerare is, in turn, a compilation of "de" (Latin: apart, away, down, or out) and "genus" (race).

Degenerate. Apart from our race. Different from us.

In a social context in which hereditarian and biological explanations of human behavior held sway over environmental explanations, being poor, uneducated, from rural areas, immigrants, and, in many cases, female, become equated with degeneracy and, subsequently, with crime and a panoply of other social ills.

Although not published until September of 1912, the story of the Kallikak family was already known and being used to justify a eugenic agenda. Psychologist J. E. Wallace Wallin, while filling in for Goddard at Vineland during the summer of 1910, recalled the first time he met Deborah and noted that she was known as Deborah even then. Goddard himself had alluded to a particularly compelling family story, surely the Kallikak story, in letters to eugenicist Charles B. Davenport in 1910.

Deborah's sad saga appears publicly first, however, in *The Social Direction of Human Evolution: An Outline of the Science of Eugenics*, published in April of 1911, more than a year before the publication of *The Kallikak Family*. *Social Direction* was authored by William Kellicott, professor of biology at Goucher College in Baltimore. Unlike Goddard, Kellicott's version focused primarily on Deborah's mother, whom Goddard and the fieldworker who assisted Goddard, Elizabeth Kite, named Martha Kallikak.

"Goddard has recently published several family histories showing feeble-mindedness," began Kellicott, attributing the story in a footnote to simply "data from Goddard." "One of the most significant of these," he continued, "significant both socially and eugenically—is summarized here. Here we have a feeble-minded woman who has had three husbands (including one who was not her husband) and the result has been nothing but feeble-minded children."[1]

This woman was a handsome girl, apparently having inherited some refinement from her mother, although her father was a feeble-minded, alcoholic brute. Somewhere about the age of seventeen or eighteen she went out to do housework in a family in one of the towns of this State [New Jersey]. She soon became the mother of an illegitimate child. It was born in an almshouse to which she fled after she had been discharged from the home where she had been at work. After this, charitably disposed people tried to do what they could for her, giving her a home for herself and her child in return for the work which she could do. However, she soon appeared in the same condition. An effort was then made to discover the father of this second child, and when he was found to be a drunken, feeble-minded epileptic living in the neighborhood, in order to save the legitimacy of the child, her friends [*sic*] saw to it that a marriage ceremony took place. Later another feeble-minded child was born to them. Then the whole family secured a home with an unmarried farmer in the neighborhood. They lived there together until another child was forthcoming which the husband refused to own. When, finally, the farmer acknowledged this child to be his, the same good friends [*sic*] interfered, went into the court and procured a divorce from the husband, and had the woman married to the father of the expected fourth child. This proved to be feeble-minded, and they have had four other feeble-minded children, making eight in all, born of this woman.[2]

---

[1] Kellicott, 1911, p. 162.
[2] Kellicott, 1911, pp. 162–163.

Almost remarkably, given the notoriety of Goddard and *The Kallikak Family*, Kellicott's brief story provides more detail about Deborah's pre-Vineland life than exists in Goddard's book. Goddard wasn't interested in Deborah's life, he was interested in the tale that he could weave from Martin Kallikak's alleged dalliance.

In the February 3, 1912, edition of *Harper's Weekly*, "The State and the Fool," by freelance contributor Robert Slosse, first exposed the Kallikak story to a non-academic audience. Known for the editorial cartoons of Thomas Nash and its woodblock illustrations of current events, the popular news magazine heavily influenced American public opinion. The article begins,

> In rural New Jersey not long ago, a girl of seventeen came to do the home-work of a worthy family. Her father was a drunken brute. Her mother was tuberculous, but had a degree of refinement. The girl had apparently inherited this refinement. She was also pretty. It was not long before the worthy family discharged her for good and sufficient cause, and she fled to the almshouse, where she gave birth to an illegitimate child.[3]

The story repeated much the same as Kellicott's text, but before a much broader audience. Like Kellicott's, it also focused on the story of Deborah's mother.

> Good Samaritans subsequently gave her and her child a home in exchange for more housework. It soon became evident that her offense against society had been repeated [referring to the second out-of-wedlock pregnancy]. Her new employers were just people in the fear of God and instead of casting her off they searched diligently and found the father of this second child. He proved to be a drunken epileptic of the neighborhood. Nevertheless, to free the child from the handicap of illegitimacy, the good people insisted that the pair should be married forthwith. They were, and in this wedlock, a third child was born. Then this family of five obtained a home with an unmarried farmer in exchange for such work as they could do about his place.
>
> The benefactors of this young wife were beginning to feel that they had done very well by her when her fourth child was born. Her husband refused to acknowledge it. Again, the good people interested themselves, and they managed to wring from the farmer the confession that the child was his. He was evidently fond of the mother, and her epileptic husband was strongly minded to put her away. The disagreeable situation seemed in a way providential to her good friends, as it enabled them to divorce the young woman from an undesirable husband and to remarry her to one who, though also somewhat feeble-minded, was both willing and able to support her and her progeny.

---

[3] Sloss, 1912, p. 17.

Perhaps the reader feels that this sordid tale might better not have come to light.[4]

Sloss obviously didn't share this sentiment for discretion. His justification for doing so was the moral lesson of the "problem that demands the immediate attention of society," suggesting that had the lessons imparted through the Jukes been heeded, the good folks of New Jersey might have "avoided the mistake of marrying her to two feeble-minded husbands."[5]

Goddard himself gets only a brief mention in the article's closing paragraph, credited with doing research that "estimates that sixty-five percent of those with a feeble-minded heredity prove ineducable," Deborah gets more visibility. Not in print, because like Kellicott, Sloss does not mention Deborah by name, but in a picture. In the far right column there is a black and white photo of Deborah, one that eventually appeared in *The Kallikak Family*, with Deborah in an elegant white dress standing in a garden, gazing down to her right at a palm plant, two large bows in her hair. In *Harper's Weekly*, she is identified as "a girl aged twenty-two with the mentality of a child of nine years." The same photo in *The Kallikak Family* identifies it as Deborah at 15, and the error probably occurred because she would have been 22 when the book was published in 1912.

Finally, in June of 1912, the Vineland Training School hosted the 36th Annual Meeting of the American Association for the Study of the Feebleminded. The first day's activities, commencing at 10:30 A.M. on June 4, took place in Garrison Hall. Virtually all of the Vineland professional staff presented at the meeting. On the second day of the meeting, the assembled dignitaries met across the street at the State Institution for the Care and Training of Feeble-Minded Women (Deborah's future home), and heard from Goddard on the mental improvement of institutional cases and Elizabeth Kite on fieldwork.

"There seems to be an occasional criticism of the field-workers which Dr. Goddard has sent out," began Kite, "that they think that everybody they see is feeble-minded."[6]

After stating a few of the principles used in gathering information in the field, Kite fielded questions.

"In the matter of determining mental intelligence," asked A. C. Rogers, the Faribault, Minnesota, superintendent, "I would like to ask [Miss Kite] what concrete standard she uses for making this evaluation. Isn't it after all really a question largely as to whether they have been able to make a decent living and to maintain themselves on a social and economic equality . . . ?"

"I intended to speak of this before," Kite responded. "The knowledge of the children here at Vineland is our standard. I am constantly holding up the individ-

---

[4] Sloss, 1912, p. 17.

[5] Sloss, 1912, p. 17.

[6] Kite, 1913, p. 145.

ual whom I am judging for comparison with the children or child we have here from the same family, otherwise it would be impossible in many cases to decide."

"I would like to ask Miss Kite how she manages to ascertain the exact mental condition of ancestors or collaterals," queried Fernald. "I should think it would be very difficult after the lapse of a generation to even approximate the facts."

Kite responded:

Of course, there are really but very few cases where we have endeavored to study the mentality of a person who has been dead seventy-five years," replied Kite, "but still there are a few such cases . . . For instance, take the one case now quite well known (the "Kallikak" case), the revolutionary soldier whose child was the great-great-grandfather of one of our cases here. He himself died in 1860, his mother died in 1842. Now the information about his mother—I grant it is involved and her mental condition must be in a measure assumed for there is little direct proof for putting her down as feeble-minded because I can get no one who remembers her, though I found several people who remember that their mothers recognized something about her different from other women and they talked about her a great deal. Now that alone would not have so much value if it were not considered in connection with known members of the family—this particular family, where there are so many dead members marked as defective, who have made such a profound impression on the whole neighborhood where they lived.[7]

Kite never really answered Fernald's question, going on for a bit about her own dogged pursuit of family members and the environmental and social circumstances that led her to the seemingly, at least as she told it, inescapable conclusion of feeblemindedness. It is evident, however, from her presentation and from the audience's questions, that Deborah's story was well-known. The book's publication in September made "Deborah's Story" known around the world.

The impact of *The Kallikak Family* was significant. Following its publication, Goddard received literally hundreds of letters from around the country, most of which asked the good doctor to estimate whether a particular union within the writer's family might result in feeblemindedness. One Quaker correspondent was so grateful to Goddard that he sent him a donation.

"I cannot think of accepting thy check," Goddard replied, reverting momentarily back into the Quaker phrasing of his upbringing, "for such unsatisfactory advice on this, but if satisfactory to thee, I will turn it over to the institution that it may help on the cause."[8]

---

[7] Kite, 1913, p. 154.
[8] McCaffrey, 1965, p. 243.

It is difficult to locate a biology or psychology text in the years immediately following the publication of the Kallikak book that does not cite the study as conclusive evidence of the hereditary nature of feeblemindedness and, by extension, of human intelligence. Eugenicists cited Goddard's study to justify their hereditarian stance as early as 1911, a year before the book even appeared in print. In 1914, the biology text *A Civic Biology Presented in Problems* by George William Hunter was published, which John Thomas Scopes (of the famous 1925 Scopes Trial) used to teach evolution to students at Rhea County Central High School in Dayton, Tennessee. Hunter's text included a presentation of eugenic thought as scientific fact and an overview of the Kallikak story. In 1927, *The Callicac Family* [sic] was entered into the record as evidence in *Buck v. Bell*, the case that resulted in the Supreme Court decision establishing the constitutionality of involuntary sterilization of "mentally defective" people.[9] In 1933, *The Kallikak Family* was reprinted in German, the same year Nazi Germany passed the "Law for Prevention of Offspring with Hereditary Defects Act." The act was based on the model sterilization law drawn up by American eugenicist Harry H. Laughlin, a star witness in *Buck v. Bell*, and it legalized involuntary sterilization of Germans with disabilities.

The story of Deborah's lineage was a national best seller and it is evident that Goddard intended *The Kallikak Family* as a moral tale written for the masses.

"It is true that we have made rather dogmatic statements and have drawn conclusions that do not seem scientifically warranted from the data," Goddard admits. "We have done this because it seems necessary to make these statements and conclusions for the benefit of the lay reader, and it was impossible to present in this book all of the data that would substantiate them. The present study of the Kallikak family is a genuine story of real people. The name is, of course, fictitious, as are all of the names throughout the story. The results here presented come after two years of constant work, investigating the conditions of this family."[10]

Goddard emulated the founder of the eugenics movement, Sir Francis Galton, in naming his "degenerate" family. Galton coined the term "eugenics" from the Greek roots meaning "good in birth." Similarly, Kallikak was derived from the Greek words *Kallos* (beauty) and *Kakos* (bad); Goddard's dramatic way of portraying the essence of the story of the Kallikak family, one branch of which was good and the other bad.

The Kallikak Family is dedicated to Samuel Fels, benefactor of the Research Laboratory at Vineland. Goddard, in the preface to the book, expressed the purpose of the laboratory: "As soon as possible after the beginning of this work,

---

[9] Lombardo, 2008.
[10] Goddard, 1912, p. xi.

a definite start was made toward determining the cause of feeblemindedness. After some preliminary work, it was concluded that the only way to get the information needed was by sending trained workers to the homes of the children, to learn by careful and wise questioning the facts that could be obtained."[11]

The story itself is simple and, given its significant influence at the time, obviously compelling. It begins with Deborah's admission to Vineland.

"One bright October day, fourteen years ago, there came to the Training School at Vineland, a little eight-year-old girl. She had been born in an almshouse. Her mother had afterwards married, not the father of this child, but the prospective father of another child, and later had divorced him and married another man, who was also the father of some of her children.

"On the plea that the child did not get along well at school and might possibly be feeble-minded, she gained admission to the Training School, there to begin a career which has been interesting and valuable to the Institution, and which has led to an investigation that cannot fail to prove of great social import."[12]

Having failed to prove anything of *great social import* using the tightly controlled, laboratory-based experiments taught to him at Clark University, Goddard had abandoned this approach to pursue answers to questions of the causes of feeblemindedness through the more promising field of eugenics. To do so, Goddard needed data from the field.

"The Vineland Training School has for two years employed field workers. These are women highly trained, of broad human experience, and interested in social problems. As a result of weeks of residence at the Training School, they become acquainted with the condition of the feeble-minded. They study all the grades, note their peculiarities, and acquaint themselves with the methods of testing and recognizing them. They then go out with an introduction from the Superintendent to the homes of the children and there ask that all the facts which are available may be furnished, in order that we can know more about the child and be better able to care for him and more wisely train him." [13]

So out they went into the slums, the hollows, and the barrens; a cadre of female fieldworkers, many well educated but unable to break the barrier of gender to secure professional jobs with decent wages. Among them was Elizabeth S. Kite, who had recently returned to Philadelphia from the University of London. She was fluent in French and English. She translated, during her tenure at Vineland, the works of Alfred Binet (developer of the first intelligence test) for Goddard, and, after Vineland, the letters between George Washington and Pierre L'Enfant, the engineer who designed Washington, D.C. In 1909, however, Elizabeth Kite was simply one of several fieldworkers at Vineland.

---

[11] Goddard, 1912, p. viii.

[12] Goddard, 1912, pp. 1–2.

[13] Goddard, 1912, p. 13.

To Goddard and his fieldworkers, there appeared to be an almost inexhaustible supply of what they believed to be degenerate families to inform their studies.

"The surprise and horror of it all was that no matter where we traced them, whether in the prosperous rural district, in the city slums to which some had drifted, or in the more remote mountain regions, or whether it was a question of the second or the sixth generation, an appalling amount of defectiveness was everywhere found."[14]

One family, however, stood out even in this sea of so-called degeneracy.

"In the course of the work of tracing various members of the family, our field worker (Kite) occasionally found herself in the midst of a good family of the same name, which apparently was in no way related to the girl whose ancestry we were investigating. In such cases, there was nothing to be done but to beat a retreat and start again in another direction. However, these cases became so frequent that there gradually grew the conviction that ours must be a degenerate offshoot from an older family of better stock."[15]

"Definite work was undertaken in order to locate the point at which the separation took place." Goddard explained. "Over and over, the investigation was laid aside in sheer despair of ever being able to find absolute proofs or to establish missing links in the testimony. Then some freshly discovered facts, that came after quite unexpectedly, would throw new light on the situation, and the work would be resumed."[16]

"The great-great-grandfather of Deborah was Martin Kallikak. That we knew. We had also traced the good family, before alluded to, back to an ancestor belonging to an older generation than this Martin Kallikak, but bearing the same name. He was the father of a large family. His eldest son was named Frederick, but there was no son by the name of Martin. Consequently, no connection could be made. Many months later, a granddaughter of Martin revealed in a burst of confidence the situation. She told us (and this was afterwards fully verified) that Martin had a *half brother* Frederick,—and that Martin never had an own brother 'because,' as she now naïvely expressed it, 'you see, his mother had him before she was married.' Deeper scrutiny into the life of Martin Kallikak Sr., which was made possible through well-preserved family records, enabled us to complete the story."[17]

And so the simple, deceivingly elegant natural experiment unfolds in Goddard's narrative.

"When Martin Sr., of the good family, was a boy of fifteen, his father died, leaving him without parental care or oversight. Just before attaining his major-

---

[14] Goddard, 1912, p. 16.
[15] Goddard, 1912, p. 16.
[16] Goddard, 1912, pp. 16–17.
[17] Goddard, 1912, p. 17.

ity, the young man joined one of the numerous military companies that were formed to protect the country at the beginning of the Revolution. At one of the taverns frequented by the militia he met a feeble-minded girl by whom he became the father of a feeble-minded son. This child was given, by its mother, the name of the father in full, and thus has been handed down to posterity the father's name and the mother's mental capacity. This illegitimate boy was Martin Kallikak Jr., the great-great-grandfather of our Deborah, and from him have come four hundred and eighty descendants. One hundred and forty-three of these, we have conclusive proof, were or are feeble-minded, while only forty-six have been found normal. The rest are unknown or doubtful."[18]

"These people" Goddard continues, "have married into other families, generally of about the same type, so that we now have on record and charted eleven hundred and forty-six individuals. Of this large group, we have discovered that two hundred and sixty-two were feeble-minded, while one hundred and ninety-seven are considered normal, the remaining five hundred and eighty-one being still undetermined."[19]

"This is the ghastly story of the descendants of Martin Kallikak Sr., from the nameless feeble-minded girl. . . . Although Martin himself paid no further attention to the girl nor her child," Goddard lectures, "society has had to pay the heavy price of all the evil he engendered."[20]

If the Kallikak story had ended here, it would be just another of the now nearly forgotten eugenic family fables and would have had little to say about heredity that could not be explained by poverty. But here the tale takes a twist that, Goddard realized, distinguished it from anything published up to that time and that would turn just another eugenic family story into the primal myth of the American eugenic movement.

Deborah's story concludes, "Martin Sr., on leaving the Revolutionary Army, straightened up and married a respectable girl of good family, and through that union has come another line of descendants of radically different character. These now number four hundred and ninety-six in direct descent. All of them are normal people. Three men only have been found among them who were somewhat degenerate, but they were not defective. Two of these were alcoholic, and the other sexually loose." [21]

"All of the legitimate children of Martin Sr. married into the best families in their state, the descendants of colonial governors, signers of the Declaration

---

[18] Goddard, 1912, p. 18.

[19] Goddard, 1912, pp. 18–19.

[20] Goddard, 1912, p. 29.

[21] Goddard, 1912, p. 29.

of Independence, soldiers and even the founders of a great university. Indeed, in this family and its collateral branches, we find nothing but good representative citizenship. There are doctors, lawyers, judges, educators, traders, landholders, in short, respectable citizens, men and women prominent in every phase of social life. They have scattered over the United States and are prominent in their communities wherever they have gone. Half a dozen towns in New Jersey are named from the families into which Martin's descendants have married. There have been no feeble-minded among them; no illegitimate children; no immoral women; only one man was sexually loose. There has been no epilepsy, no criminals, no keepers of houses of prostitution. Only fifteen children have died in infancy. There has been one 'insane,' a case of religious mania, perhaps inherited, but not from the Kallikak side. The appetite for strong drink has been present here and there in this family from the beginning. It was in Martin Sr., and was cultivated at a time when such practices were common everywhere. But while the other branch of the family has had twenty-four victims of habitual drunkenness, this side scores only two." [22]

Good seed. Bad seed.

Kallos. Kakos.

By the time *The Kallikak Family* was published, the school that the Rev. Olin Garrison had founded in his home a quarter of a century earlier had grown considerably. The original Maxham Cottage, which had been destroyed by fire in December of 1896, one year before Deborah Kallikak's arrival at the institution gates, was replaced by the twin towered administration building, built in 1900, that had greeted Henry Goddard on his arrival. This second iteration of Maxham Cottage became the iconic image most closely associated with the Vineland Training School and was featured in dozens of different postcards sent by the seemingly proud residents of Vineland to their aunts, uncles, cousins, and acquaintances.

Garrison organized the Training School around a cottage plan. "Instead of a huge central building and adjacent equally imposing structures that presented an impressive façade of importance, there would be clusters of cottages and a small administration building," explained Kathrine McCaffery, writing about The Training School in 1965. Garrison urged adoption of this system "since the homelike atmosphere was essential for the children's growth." [23]

The importance of the cottage plan to Vineland's "happiness first, all else follows" philosophy was noted by contemporary observers. "The children— some 400 in number—are housed in large family groups, classified according to mental grade, in ten attractive little cottages furnished in as homelike and

---

[22] Goddard, 1912, p. 30.

[23] McCaffery, 1965, p. 70.

"un-institutional" a manner as the most exacting could ask," wrote Frances Bjorkman in 1911. "Each of these is presided over by a 'house-mother' selected not only for her experience, but for her love for and sympathetic understanding of the particular class of children with which she has to deal, so that in the home life as well as in the strictly educational activities, the children are subjected to only those influences that the Vineland people recognized as most favorable to the development of mind and soul."[24]

There were, however, other less charitable reasons that, by 1910, had compelled most institutions to adopt the cottage plan. Early institutions were often built using the Kirkbride plan, named after Thomas Kirkbride, a founder of what is now the *American Psychiatric Association*. Kirkbride was superintendent of the institution for the insane in Pennsylvania and in 1854 published *On the Construction, Organization and General Arrangements of Hospitals for the Insane*, which soon became the standard handbook for institution construction.

Kirkbride wrote:

for an institution it is believed that the best, most convenient, and most economical form will be found to be a centre building with wings on each side, so arranged as to give ample accomodations for the resident officers and their families, and for the classification and comfort of the patients, and all employed in their care. In the centre building should be the kitchens, sculleries, main store rooms, a reception room for patients, a general business office, superintendent's office, medical office and library, visiting rooms for friends of patients, a public parlor and managers' room, a lecture room or chapel, and apartments for the superintending physician's family,—in case that officer resides in the building,—and for other officers of the institution.

The wings should be so arranged as to have at least eight distinct classes of patients on each side; each class should occupy a separate ward, and each ward should have in it a parlor, or possibly an alcove as a substitute, a dining room with a dumb waiter connected with it, and a speaking tube or telephone leading to the kitchen or some other central part of the basement story, a corridor, single lodging rooms for patients, an associated dormitory for not less than four beds, communicating with an attendant's chamber, one or two rooms of sufficient size for a patient with a special attendant, a clothes room, a bath room, a wash and sink room, and two or more water closets.

There should also be provided for each sex in its appropriate wing, at least one ward for patients who are too ill to remain in their own chambers, a railroad for the distribution of food, etc., two work rooms, a museum and reading

---

[24] Bjorkman, 1911, p. 330.

room, a school room, a series of drying closets, at least one on each story, or, better, one for each ward, and various other fixtures . . .[25]

While Kirkbride buildings were often architecturally magisterial, there were problems inherent with these large complexes, particularly once the populations of institutions exceeded their original design capacity by three and fourfold. For one, diseases spread rapidly among the inmates housed together on wards. Martin Barr's Pennsylvania Training School, which never adopted the cottage system, had ten percent of its inmate population die in the flu pandemic of 1918. It wasn't only the flu, however—whooping cough, scarlet fever, smallpox, measles—being in a hospital for the feebleminded could be bad for your health.

Separate cottages made it possible to contain a disease outbreak and to quarantine the sick inmates. In addition, the cottage system protected against the massive loss of life potentially associated with conflagrations that were still all too common in that era, as illustrated by the destruction by fire of the original Maxham Hall at Vineland in 1899.

The cottage system had administrative benefits as well. Primarily, the smaller units made it easier to segregate inmates by condition or level of impairment. Cottages for "low grade boys," "high grade girls," "moral imbeciles," young children, "epileptics," "mongoloid idiots," and every other configuration proliferated. As Historian James Trent noted, "high" and "low" grades were determined mainly by an inmate's capacity to perform the myriad types of complex work activities that comprised the running of an institution, and by 1910 much of the routine experienced by Deborah and her fellow inmates involved compulsory labor to meet the demands of the increasingly underfunded and overcrowded institutions.

"The most common inmate activity, apart from work on the farm, was the care of custodial cases and small children," observed Trent. "Inmate work at the institution was assigned on the basis of both sex and ability. Predictably, males labored on the farm; worked the heavy machinery in the laundry, print shop, or boiler room; and tended to the institution's assortment of animals. Females performed domestic chores, did the sewing and mending and the constantly needed hand laundry."[26]

Inmate work was justified and framed by superintendents as rehabilitation for the inmate. The truth, however, is that like an addict needing his fix, once the institutional system was hooked on free, inmate labor, it became a hard habit to break. Superintendents relied on the more capable inmates to perform the unskilled labor required to run the institution: mopping floors, preparing meals, laundering clothes, watching younger or more disabled inmates. The larger the institution became, the more this unpaid labor became necessary. Like a vicious

---

[25] Kirkbride, 1880, pp. 54–55.
[26] Trent, 1994, p. 103–104.

cycle, the availability of more skilled inmates to watch their less skilled counterparts enabled superintendents to meet the increasing demand from the public
to take in more severely disabled inmates, thus increasing the demand for the
skilled "high grade" laborer. These inmates, then, became too valuable for the
superintendents to release and were retained at the institution, independent of
any rehabilitation goal. Few left the institution through rehabilitation: not the
skilled and certainly not the unskilled.

No type of labor went unused. Trent noted that "when Martin Barr published his highly respected *Mental Defectives* in 1904, he thanked three 'boys'
for their help in the preparation of his book. One inmate had taken photographs for the book, another had done translations, and the third had typed the
entire manuscript."[27]

Deborah performed a wide array of tasks during her years at Vineland, including serving as a teacher's aide for the kindergarten class. She also worked in the
school dining room and was a helper in the woodcarving class. In fact, Deborah's
capacities earned her the *privilege* of working for the Johnstone family.

"In her teens, Deborah's abilities as a domestic were such that she was freed from
the usual institutional chores and designated to serve in the home of the superintendent—a privilege which set her apart from the other girls," observed Edgar
Doll, Jr., son of Goddard's assistant who, like Deborah's charges in the Johnstone
family, grew up in Vineland. "In this role she was proudest of her responsibilities in
tending to the superintendent's oldest son as a baby. She often referred to him as
'my baby,' and years later boasted justifiably of her skill in starching and ironing the
frilly garments with which infants were clad in those days. She would also relate
with relish how the chores were interspersed with slyly sliding down banisters,
with building snowmen, and even with hiding a dirty diaper under the porch so
one of the boys of the family wouldn't be punished. On occasion she accompanied
the family to their summer home at the shore."[28]

Compulsory work was only one aspect of the daily routines of inmates like
Deborah. Social historian Wolf Wolfensberger identified three trends in institutionalization—isolation, enlargement, and economization—which by 1910
dictated many aspects of these daily routines.[29]

Institutions were initially built to isolate inmates from society, "in order
to spare him the stresses he [*sic*] was believed incapable of bearing," noted
Wolfensberger, "and to provide him with protection from the persecution and
ridicule of the nondevient." Wolfensberger cited two early examples of this.
Issac Kerlin, Barr's predecessor who had been appointed superintendent of the
Pennsylvania School for Idiotic and Feeble-minded Children in 1864, noted in

---

[27] Trent, 1994, p. 103.

[28] Doll, 1983, p. 31.

[29] Wolfensberger, 1975, p. 29.

1884 that the "grounds of the institution should be hedged or fenced to keep off improper intrusion but be freely used by the inmates for walking, exercise and work." Hervey Wilbur, who in 1848 opened the first private school for the feebleminded in the United States, wrote in 1879 that institution grounds be "fenced for the privacy of the inmates." Kerlin referred to institutions as "cities of refuge" for the feebleminded.[30]

By 1910, the causal direction for isolation had changed from protecting the inmate from society to protecting society from the inmate. The fences, hedges, and other barriers kept inmates in, not the public out. Even so, some inmates had more freedom than others. "Higher grade" males "had free range of the institution grounds"[31] wrote Alfred Wilmarth, who after a stint at the institution in Elwyn, Pennsylvania, became superintendent of the Wisconsin Home for the Feeble-Minded. However, because of fears about females becoming pregnant, women, "higher grade" or not, did not share the same privilege and even within the institution grounds were curtailed in their freedom to move about.[32]

The pressures applied by growing public demands for segregation, the burgeoning size of the institutional population, and the demand for economizing increasingly eroded any sense of individualization. The feebleminded were lumped together as a class of people causing social problems, and they were treated as such. In many institutions, although not Vineland, inmates wore uniforms.

Deborah's presence at the Vineland Training School was fundamental to Goddard's saga of the Kallikak Family—fundamental in the sense, of course, that she was the starting point for his and Kite's odyssey back through the Kallikak generations and because she was the only member of the family who was actually evaluated with an intelligence test. The identification of all the other living family members, and earlier generations of the family, as feebleminded was done by brief and informal observations at best; and by rumor, reputation, and unreliable recollections in most cases. To Goddard, Deborah served as his most compelling evidence of the continuing and inevitable influence of hereditary as the primary cause of feeblemindedness. Accordingly, he described Deborah's deficits and vulnerabilities in detail.

In the accounts of Deborah's life from other people, however, repeated references are made to her seeming normality and, in many areas of her life, her exceptional abilities. Visitors and new employees often expressed disbelief when told she was feebleminded. Throughout the institutional reports, her performance on tests of academic or abstract abilities was held to be of greater importance than the obvious strengths she demonstrated in her daily life. And, if one looks closely, there were a myriad of such strengths.

---

[30] Wolfensberger, 1975, p. 29.

[31] Trent, 1994, p. 102.

[32] Trent, 1994, p. 102.

Wallin provided an example of the first impression left by Deborah. "I want to take the deepest plunge first," said Wallin to Superintendent Johnstone during his first week at Vineland during the summer of 1910. "I want to visit the cottage for the lowest grades first."

"Go to that cottage over there," replied Johnstone.

"At the door," continued Wallin, recounting the episode more than 40 years later, "I was met by an attractive girl of about 21 who showed me about the building and who answered my questions very politely. I thanked her as I left, thinking she was an attendant.

"A couple of days later I saw the same girl teaching or assisting in teaching a kindergarten class and also in the band playing an instrument.

"Later, I became curious and discovered to my surprise that she was the girl who became internationally famous as Deborah Kallikak in 1912. In fact, she was known by that name in 1910."[33]

Institution reports document that by the age of 10, Deborah could read, write, and count to some degree. By the age of 11, Deborah was identified as a budding musician, able to memorize music quickly and playing the scales of C and F on a cornet. Reports from 1904 indicated that the 15-year-old Deborah had become skillful with a sewing machine and made some of her own clothing. Her artistic talent continued to bud. "Drawing, painting, coloring, and any kind of hand work she does quite nicely,"[34] noted a report form that year.

"This year she had made a carved book rest with mission ends and is now working on a shirtwaist box with mortise and tenon joints and lap joints. The top will be paneled." By 1909, records indicated that Deborah "made the suit which she had embroidered earlier in the year, using the machine in making it."[35] She also was teaching other inmates how to upholster and do woodcarving.

But, life was not all work and worry. Vineland's creed was, of course, "happiness first, all else follows." This and the fact that when one confines a large group of people to an institution for every hour of every day there are many hours to fill, led, in an era before television, to many of those hours being filled with arts and entertainments. "Entertainments, plays concerts, jollifications of all kinds are going on constantly," observed Bjorkman. Once a week, there were contests at Vineland in which "every child, down to the dullest, is given a chance to show off what he can do in the line in which he is most proficient, be it only scrubbing floors or washing dishes—and just as much applause is given to those who do scrub floors and wash dishes."[36]

[33] Wallin, 1943, p. 52.

[34] Goddard, 1912, p. 6.

[35] Goddard, 1912, p. 6.

[36] Bjorkman, 1911, p. 329.

Music was also a pervasive part of the institutional scene. Superintendents established bands and orchestras and performed regularly, often for the public. During Wallin's stint at Vineland, he accompanied many of the inmates on a field trip to the sister institution in Elwyn. While there, "an excellent band concert was presented by the inmates, one of whom had one of the largest hydrocephalic heads I have ever seen."[37] Deborah played cornet in the Vineland band and reveled in the opportunity to entertain and to be seen.

Holidays were also a focal point for inmates. "Christmas eve every child hangs up its stocking and wakes to find it bulging with its own peculiar wants—and there is always a tree, and a Santa Claus, and more presents on Christmas Day," wrote Bjorkman in 1911. "Every holiday, down to the most insignificant, is celebrated with its own appropriate exercises."[38]

Boat rides. Picnics. Musicals. Field trips. Orchestral performances. Plays. Holiday festivities. Vineland even had a zoo. "On the institution grounds there is a little Zoo containing wolves, foxes, ferrets, rabbits, squirrels, guinea-pigs, and many different kinds of birds," observed Bjorkman. "There is a fountain with gold fish in it, a merry-go-round, many swings. There are tennis courts, an athletic field, school gardens, a band-stand."[39]

In 1910, when Wallin met Deborah, she was 21 years old and had lived at Vineland two-thirds of her young life, a life that was settling into the routines of an institution for the feebleminded.

In 1911, the year before *The Kallikak Family* was published, 22-year-old Deborah Kallikak was described in institutional records as a skillful and hard worker who lacked confidence in herself. She continued to excel in woodworking and dressmaking. Academic subjects were still a problem, but the records indicate that across the years of her confinement at the Training School, she made considerable progress in multiple areas of her life, particularly in nonacademic learning and in social skills.

Still, Goddard would write, referring to Deborah only one year later, that "[h]ere is a child who has been most carefully guarded. She has been persistently trained since she was eight years old, and yet nothing has been accomplished in the direction of higher intelligence or general education."[40]

The photographs of Deborah in *The Kallikak Family* seem to tell a story different from the description of deficit and defect in that book's narrative. These black and white photos portray an attractive young woman with a sculptural face; its length emphasized by her dark hair, pulled behind her into a ponytail or braid but still full and luxuriant as if it was fighting against the restraint intro-

---

[37] Wallin, 1953, p. 53.

[38] Bjorkman, 1911, p. 329.

[39] Bjorkman, 1911, p. 330.

[40] Goddard, 1912, pp. 11–12.

duced by the braid or the ever-present bow spreading out behind her head like gossamer wings. Her nose was broader across its bridge than might be considered pretty by some standards, but that only emphasized her dark, captivating eyes. In pictures where Deborah is not looking at the camera, the result is an almost coquettish effect, as if she's shy or contemplative, but mainly mysterious and somewhat exotic. Deborah in a maid's uniform gazing at a table she has set or looking toward the horizon while sitting in the back of a wagon filled to the brimming with much younger children she is supervising provide other glimpses of her personality. When her gaze meets the camera, however, her Jellicle eyes and slight smile suggest that she knows that you don't know everything about her.

Her gaze was not the only thing to suggest this knowledge. "Hers was a body which moved with full knowledge of the impact of its movements on the opposite sex" once noted an acquaintance.[41]

And that, for Goddard, was the real problem. "Today if this young woman were to leave the institution, she would at once become a prey to the designs of evil men or evil women and would lead a life that would be vicious, immoral, or criminal, though because of her mentality she herself would not be responsible. There is nothing that she might not be led into, because she has no power of control, and all her instincts and appetites are in the direction that would lead to vice."[42]

In the full-page photograph of Deborah opposite the title page of *The Kallikak Family*, Deborah sits, posed in a straight-back chair in front of a vertically striped screen shielding filing cabinets in Goddard's psychology laboratory, an American shorthaired cat perched in her lap and an open book held in her hands before her. With her feet crossed demurely in front of her, barely visible below the expanse of her petticoat and skirt, it is not the book that Deborah is looking at, it is you; and one cannot escape thinking that it is you who is the open book.

In another photo, a hay wagon packed with children and straw lurched along the chalk path away from Maxham. Four matrons, bedecked in bonnets to fend off the threatening afternoon sun, perched along the rails, their wards clustered in the middle. One child sucks her thumb, clutching a white comfort rag. All are dressed in white linen, as if they were nobility out for a Sunday excursion. There is not a sign of excitement or anticipation in the group, save one girl, perhaps 13 years old, leaning across to whisper something to her friend. In the back corner of the wagon, Deborah sits, staring down behind the cart, hands clutched, hair braided. She is not looking at anything in particular and perhaps, as is her wont, she is simply being coquettish for the camera. One is left, though, with a sense

---

[41] Doll, 1983, p. 32.

[42] Goddard, 1912, pp. 11–12.

that there is a wistfulness, a longing for something in her gaze. A longing for freedom, perhaps?

Nobel laureate Pearl Buck, whose daughter Carol would be admitted to the Vineland Training School 20 years later, captured it best when writing about her experiences in China. "None who have always been free can understand the terrible fascinating power of the hope of freedom to those who are not free."[43]

Perhaps that's what is in Deborah's eyes, a terrible, fascinating hope for freedom; unspoken, probably even unrealized

---

[43] Buck, 1943, p. 21.

CHAPTER 4

The Rising Tide of American Eugenics and Race Science

In early March of 1909, a letter from Charles Davenport was delivered to Edward Johnstone at the Vineland Training School. The brief note was incorrectly addressed to Mr. E. R. Johnston, thus capturing the original spelling of the Superintendent's surname.

> Dear Sir,
>
> Have you at your institution heredity data concerning feeble mindedness? If you have published any such data in your reports, I should be glad to receive such."
>
> Sincerely, C.B. Davenport[1]

Johnstone forwarded the note to Goddard.

"Our data are meagre and so unreliable that we have not considered it worth while to make any tabulated study of these records,"[2] Goddard responded, apologetically, on March 15. He was referring to information routinely gathered from parents at the time their son or daughter was admitted to the Training School. Unreliable might be a too-gentle indictment of the information contained in the Vineland inmates' files. The parents' attributions of the causes of their son's or daughter's impairment reflected the general ignorance and stereotypes of the era: a mix of the religious explanations espoused by Howe in the mid-1800s; rural superstitions and old wives tales; and the scientific, or prescientific, explanations promulgated by the social scientists of the late 19th and early 20th cen-

---

[1] Davenport, 1909a.
[2] Zenderland, 1998, p. 153.

turies. Leila Zenderland noted, for example, that in a report derived from similar parent-as-informant records from the 1880s, parents had attributed their child's impairment "not only to diseases but also to snakebite, lightening, overeating, loss of property, homesickness, and frozen feet."[3]

Goddard intended, he promised in his reply to Davenport, to send a post-admission survey to families and parents and to write to "parties who know the family in question and are not too intimate to tell the truth about them."[4] His early efforts at this were "yielding fruit slowly," Goddard intimated, citing a promising case of a Vineland child born in an almshouse to an unwed mother who had since remarried several times.

Deborah's story, unfolding for Goddard as early as March of 1909.

Davenport responded promptly, expressing his enthusiasm for Goddard's reply and requesting the opportunity to visit the Training School campus, which he did in April. Perhaps because of Goddard's effusive response, Davenport, who was director of the Eugenics Research Office and among the most prominent eugenicists in the country, saw in him a potential ally. Perhaps, more simply, he visited because Vineland was nearby. In either case, these initial communications begat more and more frequent letters and visits.

"In answering it," Zenderland observed, referring to Goddard's response to Davenport's initial query, "Goddard began a correspondence that would alter the rest of his career . . ."[5]

On May 5, 1909, Goddard wrote Davenport asking for a clear explanation of Mendel's laws. Replying on May 7, Davenport suggested that Goddard read *Mendelism*, by Reginald Crundall Punnett.

Punnett was a Cambridge University–trained zoologist who, along with William Bateson, is credited with establishing the field of genetics. Bateson and Punnett were the cofounders of the *Journal of Genetics* and Punnett replaced Bateson when the latter left Cambridge, becoming the first Arthur Balfour Professor of Genetics at Cambridge. Punnett is best remembered today as the creator of the eponymously named Punnett Square, which has become the standard for determining how traits will be passed on to the offspring of two parents.

Punnett's most important book was titled simply *Mendelism* and appeared in Britain in May 1905. An American edition was not available, however, until April 1909 and it was to that edition that Davenport referred Goddard. "As fascinating as a novel and as instructive as true science"[6] Goddard exclaimed about *Mendelism* in a review he later published in the *Training School Bulletin*. The

---

[3] Zenderland, 1998, p. 153.
[4] Zenderland, 1998, p. 154.
[5] Zenderland, 1998, p. 153.
[6] Goddard, 1911c, p. 80.

book convinced Goddard, Zenderland noted, "that Mendelian biology would ultimately supply new answers to long-standing questions about the causes of inherited conditions, among them mental deficiency."[7]

July 4 fell on a Sunday in 1909 and Henry and Emma Goddard celebrated the holiday in Vineland. The following Monday morning, Goddard boarded the train at the Vineland Central station bound for Philadelphia's Broad Street Station, traveling to Worcester's Union Depot where he disembarked and headed to his alma mater to participate in yet another G. Stanley Hall extravaganza, this time a Conference for Research and Child Welfare. Goddard revisited his earlier work, co-chairing a panel on child study on Tuesday evening, while Johnstone presented *Welfare of the Feebleminded* on Thursday afternoon, arguing that "the stream of degeneracy must be checked" and recommending either sterilization or permanent custodial care."[8]

Johnstone's was not the only reference to eugenics at the conference. In June 1909, Hall had written Davenport requesting "any publications in the form of reports, by-laws, constitution, membership, history or anything else pertaining to eugenics or the Carnegie Bureau of Evolution"[9] to display at the conference. On Thursday night, John Franklin Bobbitt, a recent Clark Ph.D. graduate in psychology who would subsequently become a leader in the social efficiency movement, presented a keynote address on *Practical Eugenics*.

After the conference, Hall wrote Davenport once more to see if Davenport might refer someone to take an appointment at Clark in the area of genetics and eugenics, particularly someone who "knows his Weismann, Mendel, etc."[10] Davenport responded to Hall's query in early September, indicating he didn't know anyone who would come at the salary Hall had mentioned, other than some women working as fieldworkers.

Goddard, meanwhile, was quickly becoming integrated into the growing, intermingled web of associations that provided the foundation for the American eugenics movement. By the end of 1909, he had been appointed secretary to a subcommittee on feeblemindedness of the American Breeders Association's Committee on Eugenics, which Davenport had founded in 1906 to "investigate and report on heredity in the human race," as well as "to emphasize the value of superior blood and the menace to society of inferior blood."[11] The subcommittee, chaired by Faribault Minnesota superintendent A. C. Rogers, included H. H. Donaldson from the Wister Institute and Massachusetts superintendent Walter Fernald.

---

[7] Zenderland, 1998, p. 156.
[8] Johnstone, 1909, pp. 127–128.
[9] Hall, 1909a.
[10] Hall, 1909b.
[11] Haller, 1982, p. 62.

Goddard had followed through, as well, on his earlier promise to Davenport that he was going to create a post-admission survey with which to gather data from families of the Vineland inmates and, more importantly, had received a small donation allowing him to hire two fieldworkers. One was Elizabeth Kite, who began work on November 8, 1909.[12] In December 1909, Goddard presented some of the findings from his initial efforts in family studies at the American Breeders Association annual meeting in Boston.

"The [new after-admission] blank was sent to all parents and physicians, with a little note urging them for the sake of the child to tell all they possibly could about the child's relatives, their condition, any diseases they had had, any habits, such as alcoholism, any insanity or the like which had occurred in the family.

"It was expected that this would only be preliminary to more detailed and careful work later. We were, however, greatly surprised," reported Goddard somewhat incredulously, "at the amount of information received, which has since been proved to be generally very accurate. Upon the basis of this information, we prepared charts of the children, which were truly remarkable in what they revealed as to the etiology of feeble-mindedness."[13]

It is important to consider what was not discussed by Goddard. First, there was no detailed description of any of the items that composed what was, in essence, the questionnaire he was using to gather data. In the age of polls and surveys, we are quite aware that how questions are asked, what questions are not asked, how items' answers are structured, and a myriad of other survey or questionnaire design issues impact responses. Further, Goddard's implications to the contrary, parents and family members may very well have deemed it important to answer in a way that would be considered desirable by an authority figure, particularly in the circumstance of an unfamiliar and educated fieldworker showing up at their door. Some of them may have believed that answering fraudulently was justified if being truthful would negatively impact their child's chances of remaining at Vineland.

Goddard certainly knew that the reliability of the information he was receiving was not a function of the amount of information received, yet having no other way to verify his statement that the data was "generally very accurate," he followed that path.

"The relation between the superintendent at Vineland and the parents of the children is so intimate and friendly that we have had complete cooperation from the start," Goddard observed. "The response has been full, free, and hearty. Parents do all in their power to help us get the facts. There is very rarely anything like an attempt to conceal the facts that they know."[14]

Therein lies the rub, of course, and Goddard knew that as well. It is likely most of these respondents knew very few facts.

---

[12] Goddard, 1914a, p. 25.
[13] Goddard, 1910b, p. 165.
[14] Goddard, 1910b, p. 165.

"Of course," admitted Goddard, "many of these parents are ignorant, often feeble-minded, and cannot tell all that we should like to know."

All . . . or even some?

"Nevertheless, by adroit questioning and cross-reference, we have been able to get what we believe to be very accurate data in a very large percentage of our cases."[15]

Adroit questioning by professionals could get the facts from otherwise unreliable respondents. This was Goddard's belief from the start, even at this early stage of his eugenic research. By all indicators, he believed this. He wanted to place psychology ahead of medicine in the field of feeblemindedness; studies in heredity provided a means to achieve this. He wanted to believe the data because he could, from that data, tell compelling stories about the hereditary nature of feeblemindedness. In the end, with Deborah Kallikak and innumerable others, it appears the data were anything but accurate.

In early 1910, Davenport offered Goddard the opportunity to publish his Boston presentation in an issue of *American Breeders Magazine*. "My dear Dr. Davenport," Goddard modestly wrote in reply, "you know there was not much to my Boston dinner report except a showing of some charts. Would the Association want to reproduce some of those charts? Or would a verbal account of the families be desirable? If charts, how many? I will be glad to get up something, but you see I do not know just what is suitable."[16]

Goddard concluded his letter to Davenport.

"Perhaps the situation may be better understood if I say to you that our field worker, for example, has written up two very striking stories in regard to the family histories that she has worked out. These are entirely impersonal and would never reach the families that are described, nevertheless, so strong has been our feeling that someone else to whom we might later go for information might read these and feel that perhaps that was the purpose for which we were getting information, and so their mouths would be closed in regard to their own family."[17]

One of these striking stories is almost certainly the tale of Deborah Kallikak's poverty and abandonment.

Even more prestigiously, though, this same article was reprinted by Davenport as the first in a new monograph series published by the Eugenics Record Office (ERO). In fact, the first two monographs in the *Eugenics Record Office Bulletin* series were Vineland products and both essentially detailed the charting methods that would be used to create the eugenic family studies over the next two decades, including *The Kallikak Family*.

The charts were, fundamentally, family trees depicting the genealogy and, to a lesser degree, the hereditary nature, of inmates' families. The actual charting process was described in this second bulletin as having been adopted by a com-

---

[15] Goddard, 1910b, p. 165–166.
[16] Goddard, 1910c.
[17] Goddard, 1910c.

mittee of the American Association for the Study of the Feeble-Minded during its annual meeting in Lincoln Illinois in 1910, the committee was comprised of Johnstone, Goddard, Rogers, and David Weeks (director of the New Jersey State Village for Epileptics in Skillman), among others.

> The system is a rectangular one, the symbols for the individuals of a fraternity (full brothers and sisters) being on the same horizontal line, with each later generation placed below the next earlier. Male individuals are indicated by squares, females by circles, suspended by vertical lines from the horizontal line. Members of one fraternity are connected by the same horizontal line. The rank of birth in the fraternity is indicated by a serial number placed immediately above the fraternity line. The fraternity line is connected by a vertical line to a line joining the symbols of father and mother (the mating line). The mating line may be a short horizontal one or oblique, passing from one consort to the other as emergencies of space decide. Dotted mating lines are used for illegal unions. In the case of illegitimate children, the descent line is dotted.[18]

In addition to the square for males and circle for females, the charts coded enough deficits and diseases to warm Davenport's cold heart; an ABCs of defectology, as it were: A is for Alcoholic, B is for Blind, C is for Criminalistic, D is for Deaf, E is for Epileptic, F is for Feeble-minded, G is for Gonorrheal, I is for Insane, M is for Migrainous, N is for Neurotic, P is for Parylitic, S is for Syphalitic, Sx is for Sexually immoral, T is for Tubercular, and V is for Vagrant.

Goddard used this charting method, beginning with his report to the American Breeders Association in which he indicated he had completed 80 such charts (although only 18 appear in the article). It continued through *The Kallikak Family* and into his magnum opus of family charting, *Feeblemindedness; Its Causes and Consequences*, published in 1914, which included 344 such charts on 327 case studies. If for nothing else, one has to admire Goddard's work ethic. Without the support of modern word processing and drawing software, preparing these charts was a momentous task.

"My Dear Dr. Davenport," Goddard penned on March 15, 1910 on the train on the way to give a presentation on eugenics to the Michigan Schoolmasters Club. "I left at home to be forwarded to you the summary of 15 families that we have worked up. I have been wretchedly delayed in getting this ready. The fact is I have no one in my office who can make up these charts in anything but the crudest form."[19]

That Goddard was traveling to Michigan to present to the Michigan Schoolmasters Club—an organization cofounded by John Dewey whose mem-

---

[18]Davenport, Laughlin, Weeks, Johnstone, & Goddard, 1911, p. 1.
[19]Goddard, 1910d.

bership consisted of university and college presidents, school superintendents, and high school principals and teachers—as early as one year after Davenport's initial query speaks volumes to the degree to which Goddard had transformed his evangelic zeal from child study to eugenics.

On November 12, 1909, Davenport delivered an invited lecture to the American Academy of Medicine at Yale University. Those remarks were published in 1910 as *Eugenics: The Science of Human Improvement by Better Breeding* and in this speech and text, his belief in the single gene transmission of feeble-mindedness is clearly spelled out.

"That imbecility is due to the absence of some definite simple factor is indicated by the simplicity of its method of inheritance," Davenport explained to the physicians assembled in New Haven that evening. "Two imbecile parents, whether related or not, have only imbecile offspring. Barr gives us such data. There is, so far as I am aware, no case on record where two imbecile parents have produced a normal child. So definite and certain is the result of the marriage of two imbeciles, and so disastrous is reproduction by any imbecile under any conditions [*sic*] that it is a disgrace of the first magnitude that thousands of children are annually born in this country of imbecile parents to replace and probably more than replace the deaths in the army of about 150,000 mental defectives which this country supports. The country owes it to itself as a matter of self-preservation that every imbecile of reproductive age should be held in such restraint that reproduction is out of the question. If this proves to be impracticable then sterilization is necessary—where the life of the state is threatened extreme measures may and must be taken."[20]

"My dear Dr. Davenport, the little booklet on Eugenics is fine," effused Goddard in his March 15 letter to Davenport. "Can I get a dozen copies? Have you any objections to our reprinting parts of it in our paper?"[21]

Davenport's "fine little booklet" became Goddard's Eugenics bible and before 1910 ended, Goddard had cemented his role as Davenport's confidant and colleague.

"If you can bring Mrs. Davenport and spend the night with us, it will be very delightful," fawned Goddard in a letter to Davenport on June 17, 1910. "I shall be here until the second or third of July, and will be delighted to see you at any time."[22]

Later that month, Davenport again communicated with Goddard. "I have a matter of importance for the new work," he began. "Mrs. Harriman has been very busy with the settlement of the estate, with her daughter's wedding and

[20] Davenport, 1910b, pp. 14–15.
[21] Goddard, 1910d.
[22] Goddard, 1910e.

lately with illness in her family so that she has not got to the point of making definitely any large appropriations. Nevertheless it is quite certain that some support is coming from this direction."[23]

"She wishes however," Davenport continued, "to make a beginning without delay and would like to see some workers trained for field work next Autumn. She is willing to pay something toward the expenses of a few students who will spend six weeks here this summer and then will be available for work in connection with the different laboratories in the Autumn. Of the ten students I propose to send three to you at Vineland for continuation and extension of the field work in the State. Could you make use of them to advantage?"[24]

Harriman had also pledged to pay some living expenses and salary for field-workers.

"What I should like to have you do," Davenport concluded, "if you would consent to this general arrangement, would be to name three persons who would like to go into the field work in the future and who would come to Cold Spring Harbor for six weeks, beginning about July 6th on a scholarship of $75. Their training would not be special but would deal with general principles of heredity with a special reference to Mendelism and the methods of field work."[25]

"My dear Dr. Davenport," Goddard apologetically replied on Independence Day, 1910. "Your three letters have all been received. I have not answered because I have been busy trying to get hold of the people to send to you. We appreciate the offer very much indeed, and hope we may be able to send you somebody. We certainly shall be glad to accept the services of the three that you propose to send to us for field work in the fall. I am sorry that I cannot give you at once the names of three persons who will come and take the course. I am hoping that we can send two but am not sure even of that. I am sorry that I am going away and shall not be here to attend to the details of this matter, but Prof. Johnstone is intensely interested in it and will do all that he can to further the matter."[26]

Goddard was scrambling to meet Davenport's aggressive turnaround time to identify potential fieldworkers while preparing for a third excursion to Europe, this time departing July 9 and returning toward the end of August. Before leaving for Europe, Goddard hired fieldworkers to be trained using some seed money from Mary Harriman, but this was only one way in which Goddard was integrating his work with that of Davenport and the ERO. Goddard was an author on the first two ERO publications. By 1911, Harry Hamilton Laughlin, Davenport's second in command at the ERO, was secretary of the American Breeders Association's "Committee to Study and Report on the Best Practical

[23] Davenport, 1910c.
[24] Davenport, 1910c.
[25] Davenport, 1910c.
[26] Goddard, 1910f.

Means of Cutting off the Defective Germ Plasm in the American Population," a committee to which Henry Goddard served as advisor.

With Goddard's incorporation into Davenport's master plan, his publications become increasingly eugenically focused. In 1911, he published articles titled "Elimination of Feeble-Mindedness," "Feeble-Mindedness and Criminality," and "The Menace of the Feeble Minded," as well as the aforementioned *ERO Bulletin 1*, "Heredity of Feeble-Mindedness."

"What can be done to prevent this stream of bad protoplasm from coming into the world and keeping us busy with social problems?" Goddard asked rhetorically in "The Menace of the Feeble Minded." "We can, if we will, prevent the birth of feeble minded children by, *first* preventing the marriage of feeble minded people, *second* by putting in institutions where they may be kept for life, all persons who are capable of begetting or bearing children and who would be likely to give birth to feeble minded children. *Thirdly*, we can sterilize these persons who would become the parents of feeble minded children."[27]

In *The Kallikak Family*, Goddard juxtaposed the decidedly environmental approach taken in the Jukes family story against his own hereditary findings in the Kallikak research. "The reader will recall the famous story of the Jukes family published by Richard L. Dugdale in 1877, a startling array of criminals, paupers, and diseased persons, more or less related to each other and extending over seven generations,"[28] Goddard reminded readers. "Fortunately for the cause of science," he gloated, "the Kallikak family, in the persons of Martin Kallikak Jr. and his descendants, are not open to this argument. They were feeble-minded, and no amount of education or good environment can change a feeble-minded individual into a normal one, any more than it can change a red-haired stock into a black-haired stock. The striking fact of the enormous proportion of feeble-minded individuals in the descendants of Martin Kallikak Jr. and the total absence of such in the descendants of his half brothers and sisters is conclusive on this point. Clearly it was not environment that has made that good family. They made their environment; and their own good blood, with the good blood in the families into which they married."[29]

The tale to which Goddard refers was *The Jukes: A Study in Crime, Pauperism, Disease, and Heredity*, the original eugenic family story. Elisha Harris, a physician who was the corresponding secretary of the Prison Association of New York first identified the pseudonymous Jukes. Harris identified the reoccurrence of several family names in some of the New York county prisons, particularly Ulster County, and traced the common lineage of these miscreants back six

---

[27] Goddard, 1911e, p. 8.
[28] Goddard, 1912, p. 51.
[29] Goddard, 1912, p. 54.

generations to a woman he called "Margaret, mother of criminals."[30] Dugdale, also a member of the executive board of the association, devoted more time to further investigate this errant family, and began collecting information on the Jukes in 1874. Dugdale eventually studied the records of 709 people, 540 of whom were of "Juke blood" and an additional 169 who married into the Juke family. Of the 709 people he studied, 180 had been in the poorhouse or received similar charity, 140 were identified as criminals, 50 were prostitutes, and 40 of these had venereal disease. Dugdale estimated that the financial cost to society for supporting the Jukes over a 75-year period was $1.3 million. Adjusted for inflation, that would total over $21 million today.

Unlike Goddard, Dugdale did not just wink at the role of environment in human behavior and then expound on the role of heredity as fully explanatory. Instead, Dugdale's solutions to the problem of the Jukes were, largely, environmental: employment, better wages, affordable housing.[31]

The consanguinity of all those degenerate Jukes was, unfortunately, simply too tempting for eugenicists, and they pounced on the story as supporting their hereditarian perspective almost as soon as it was published. Speaking in 1877, for example, Francis Galton, the founder of eugenics, argued that the "criminal nature tends to be inherited," and advanced the case of the Jukes as evidence thereof.

Had the public that was so willing to believe eugenicist's spin on the Jukes story bothered to look at Dugdale's original, they would have noted that the so-called "Jukes family" consisted of not one, but 42 different families. Indeed, Dugdale emphasized that only 540 of the 790 Jukes were even related in any way by blood.[32] One has to wonder if the case for the hereditary nature of pauperism and crime putatively illustrated by the Jukes would have been as convincing to the public had they recognized this. Perhaps so, given the societal and cultural context of the turn of the 20th century.

Goddard, however, knew that was a problem and he qualified his statement referring to the Jukes as representing "persons, more or less related to each other and extending over seven generations."

More or less, indeed.

Mainly less.

On January 17, 1911, Sir Francis Galton succumbed to respiratory problems at a rented house in Surrey, England. By the time of Galton's death, observed Mark Haller, the idea that germinated when he read his half-cousin's master-work *Origins of the Species* in December of 1859 had become a worldwide move-

---

[30] Carlson, 2001, page 162.
[31] Carlson, 2001, page 171.
[32] Rafter, 1988.

ment.[33] In his native country of England, the Eugenics Education Society was well established. In the United States, the ERO was launched. And in Germany, the Gesellschaft für Rassen Hygiene had been founded in Munich by biologist and social Darwinist Alfred Ploetz, author of *Grundlinien einer Rassenhygiene* (Racial Hygiene Basics).

Immediately following Galton's death, planning began for an international meeting on eugenics to honor the founder. That international community came together at the First International Congress on Eugenics, held July 24–30, 1912, in the Great Hall at the University of London. The president of the congress was Major Leonard Darwin, Charles and Emma Darwin's fourth son and eighth child, who assumed the presidency of the British Eugenics Society on the death of his half-cousin, once removed and held that post until 1928. Vice-presidents to the congress included Alexander Graham Bell; the Right Honorable Sir Winston Churchill, First Lord of the Admiralty; Charles Davenport; Professor M. Von Gruger, president of the Gesellschaft für Rassen Hygiene; David Starr Jordan, president of Stanford University; Col. Sir David Burnett, the Lord Mayor of London; the Lord Bishop of Oxford; Charles Eliot, president emeritus of Harvard University; Alfred Ploetz; August Weismann; and Bleecker von Wagenen, a prominent New York attorney, eugenicist, and donor to the Vineland Training School Research Department representing the Board of Trustees for the Vineland Training School. The American Consultative Committee for the congress, with Jordan as chair and Davenport as secretary, included Bell, William Castle, Adolph Meyers, Vernon Kellogg (a Stanford University biologist), and William Tower. Members of the general committee of the congress included J. Langdon Down, who first described the condition of Down syndrome, and Havelock Ellis, the British progressive thinker and sexologist. It was an impressive gathering of the scientific and political elite.

The congress kicked off with the Inaugural Banquet, held in the Hotel Cecil on the evening of July 24, where for 7 shillings and 6 pence, conference attendees could dine in elegance among the notables. The Hotel Cecil was the largest hotel in London at the time, with more than 800 rooms and lavish ballroom and banquet facilities, and the distinguished guests were welcomed and feted by the Lord Mayor of London himself. The presentation of papers began the next day, with readers allowed 25 minutes to present the major points of their paper and 20 minutes allotted for discussion. Congress attendees all wore a button badge depicting the likeness of Francis Galton, with one's status (organizing committee, reader, executive committee) designated by the color of the ribbon attached to the badge. Each day culminated with a reception hosted by dignitaries, including, on Friday, a reception at the home of the U.S. Ambassador to Britain Whitelaw Reid, a William McKinley protégé.

---

[33] Haller, 1963.

The papers for the congress were divided into four sections: Biology and Eugenics, Practical Eugenics, Sociology and Eugenics, and Medicine and Eugenics. As befitting the man whose image was pinned to the lapel of attendees, the speakers were a who's who of biology, sociology, and eugenics. Weeks, coauthor—with Goddard, Johnston, Davenport, and Laughlin—of the *Eugenic Records Office Bulletin 2*, spoke on the inheritance of epilepsy; Punnett read a paper on eugenics and genetics, and William Bateson led the discussion that followed; Davenport spoke on marriage laws and customs; Van Wagenen presented the preliminary report from the American Breeders Association's *Committee to Study and Report on the Best Practical Means of Cutting off the Defective Germ Plasm in the American Population* (for which Laughlin was secretary and Goddard a member); and Kellogg spoke on eugenics and militarism.

Even wider ranging were the exhibits displayed for the congress. Davenport exhibited charts on the defective classes in the American Breeders Association section; Charles Darwin's sons William and Leonard exhibited photographs of their venerated father and Down house, where *Origins* had been written, as well as two letters written by Darwin on "Worms and Their Habits"; several exhibits highlighted Alfred Plotz's nature and aims of race hygiene; and family histories abounded documenting the putative hereditary nature of virtually every human social and biological trait, characteristic, or vice. There were hosts of displays emphasizing Neo-Malthusian notions of population explosion, fecundity of the unfit, and heredity; exhibits on mixed-race marriages; and an exhibit by British educational psychologist Cyril Burt, whose later discredited studies of twins formed the foundation for arguments pertaining to the purely hereditary nature of intelligence, focused on mental testing.

Goddard was present at the congress in spirit, if not in flesh. The congress program proudly noted that "the American Eugenics Record Office is sending an important exhibit, as are also the State Epileptic Colony of New Jersey, and Dr. Goddard, of Vineland."

The First International Congress on Eugenics marked a turning point in the eugenics movement. It was, in many ways, the zenith of the positive eugenics movement. There would be two more international congresses, both organized by Laughlin and each increasingly more focused on Davenport and Laughlin's negative eugenic agenda. Both were increasingly less well attended and, when so, only by ERO devotees. Galton's era had ended. The American eugenicists, led by Davenport and Laughlin, took control of the eugenic message.

Two months later, Goddard published *The Kallikak Family*. Bolstered by the public's anxieties about race suicide, crime, and poverty, and social work's emphasis on social and moral hygiene, the American eugenics movement embraced an increasingly strident and negative eugenic stance.

CHAPTER 5

Intelligence Testing

At the same time that Goddard was increasing his visibility in the American eugenics movement, he was also building a reputation as one of the preeminent mental testers in the country. In the spring of 1908, disillusioned and disheartened by his lack of success applying anthropometric techniques to the study of feebleminded, Goddard had embarked on a two month, 3,000 mile journey across seven European countries to visit institutions, special classes, and other psychologists. While in Paris,[1] Goddard tried to meet with French psychologist Alfred Binet, who in 1905 had published the first version of a measure of children's intelligence. He was unsuccessful and met instead with one of Binet's rivals, Pierre Janet, who convinced Goddard that Binet's lab was largely a myth with nothing going on.

In Belgium, Goddard's fortunes turned when he met with Ovide Decroly. In 1901, Decroly had established an institute—part special education school, part psychological laboratory—within his home in Brussels. The methods he developed, which emphasized educating children in normal environments, were soon applied to children without disabilities and by 1907 his pedagogy had reformed school practice throughout Belgium.[2] Decroly gave Goddard copies of several papers Binet and his doctoral student, Theodore Simon, had published in the *L'Anee Psychologique* during 1905.

At the end of 1908, Goddard published a short article on the 1905 Binet test in the Vineland publication *The Training School Bulletin*. By that time, however, Binet and Simon had published a revision of their original scale. The 1908 Binet-Simon Scale revision was more than just a sequel to the original. As Binet biographer Theta Wolf observed, even the titles of the articles reporting the two versions illustrate the transformation between the 1905 and 1908 versions. The original was described as providing new methods for the diagnosis of the intel-

---

[1] Fancher, 1985, p. 106.
[2] Dubreucq, 2001, p. 249.

lectual level of the abnormal, the second version referred to a scale to measure the development of intelligence among children. "Thus," noted Wolf, "a method of assessing the lack of intelligence was transformed into a method of assessing the intelligence of all children."[3]

The new version, translated into English from the original French for Goddard by Elizabeth Kite, retained unaltered only 14 of the original items from the 1905 version. Another nine items were dropped completely, seven were modified, and 33 new items were added. The scale was now normed by age range, allowing for the determination of mental levels. Age III (mental age levels were always denoted in Roman numerals) tasks involved having children point to their nose, eye, and mouth; repeat the phrases "It rains" and "I am hungry," and state their surname. Age IV tasks asked if children knew their sex; could name a key, knife, or penny; and could repeat the numerals 7, 4, and 8. Age V tasks included having children compare different weights, copy a square, and count four pennies. Items in the Age VI section involved differentiating between morning and afternoon; defining fork, table, chair, horse, and mamma; showing right hand and left ear; and the always-questionable activity of choosing the prettier face among pairs offered. The faces were all female and all white. The supposedly less attractive faces were those of women who were obviously overweight or who had a hooked or large nose.

At Age VII, children were to count 13 pennies, fill in missing information in pictures, copy a diamond and a written phrase, and identify four common pieces of money. Age VIII items included comparing butterfly with fly, wood with glass, and paper with cardboard in 20 seconds; counting backward from 20 to 1 in 20 seconds; naming four colors; counting the value of stamps in 15 seconds; and repeating the numeral string 4, 7, 3, 9, and 5. Age IX items involved making change, knowing the date, naming the days of the week, and arranging weights by order of size. At Age X, children had to name the months of the year within 15 seconds, know money denominations up to $10, draw a design from memory after having been shown it for 10 seconds, and identify what one should do if one missed a train, was accidentally struck by a playmate, was detained and might be late to school, and the rather ambiguous "before taking part in an important affair." By Age XI, children were to identify the "nonsense" in three of five scenarios.

"I am going to read you some sentences in which there is some nonsense," the test administrator was instructed to say to the child. "Listen very carefully and tell me what the nonsense is."

"An unfortunate bicycle rider has had his head broken and is dead from the fall. They have taken him to the hospital and they do not believe that he will recover. What is the nonsense?"

---

[3] Wolf, 1973, p. 190.

"Yesterday they found on the fortifications the body of an unfortunate young girl cut into eighteen pieces. They believe that she killed herself. What is the nonsense?"

"Yesterday there was an accident on the railroad. But, it was not very bad. There were only forty-eight killed. What is the nonsense?"

And, finally:

"Someone said: If in a moment of despair I should commit suicide, I should not choose Friday. For Friday is an unlucky day, and that would bring me bad luck. What is the nonsense?"

When queried about the relative ghoulishness of these stories, Binet claimed that French children laughed at the scenarios. Perhaps the frivolity was lost in translation.

The remainder of the Age XI items involved giving 60 words in three minutes; rhyming all correct words with day, spring, and mill; and defining the terms "charity," "justice," and "goodness" (a series of words that seem incongruous when juxtaposed with the morbid nonsense task). At age XII, the final age level for the scale, the items involved repeating seven numeral strings; rhyming words; repeating one or more sentences with 26 syllables; distinguishing the difference between the word pairs "pleasure–honor," "evolution–revolution," and "event–advent"; and, so as not to lose the morbid thread, a task having children complete two sentences.

"I am going to read you a sentence," the examiner was to say, "but will stop just before coming to the end. Listen carefully and see if you can finish it as it should be":

A person out walking in the woods suddenly stopped, much frightened, and ran to the nearest police to report that he had seen hanging from the limb of a tree . . . a what?

And,

My neighbor has been having strange visitors. He has received one after the other a doctor, a lawyer, and a minister. What has happened at my neighbor's?[4]

The basal age for the test was the uppermost age at which the child answered all items or all of the items but one correctly. From this basal age forward, the child was given one mental age year credit for every five additional tests passed.

Apparently stimulated enough by the readings Decroly had given him, Goddard sought out information on Binet and Simon's 1908 revision. He was at first skeptical.

---

[4] Kuhlmann, 1911, pp. 77-87.

"The writer," said Goddard, referring to himself, "quickly realized that he was in no position to pass judgment upon this instrument. Here was a psychologist of world-wide reputation who offered this plan and claimed that it had at least some value. It was not good sense to throw it aside because one reading of it was not convincing."[5]

Perhaps too, though, Goddard felt little enthusiasm for returning to the drudgery of anthropometric or child-study data collection. Whatever the reason, Goddard translated the 1911 article, publishing a portion of it in *The Training School Bulletin*, and began trying it out with the inmates at Vineland. Unlike the anthropometric data, the Binet-Simon data did correlate positively with teacher estimates of their charges' mental capacities.

Goddard recounted at a meeting of the American Association for the Study of the Feeble-Minded, referring to a list of mental ages determined by his translation of the Binet-Simon Scale for each Vineland inmate, "At our executive meeting, composed of the heads of all the departments of the institution, these lists were read one at a time, and the members present were asked to express their opinion as to whether the children given in any one list seemed to them to be all of about the same mental capacity."[6]

After repeating this process with teachers at Vineland, Goddard found himself "very surprised and encouraged." Encouraged enough that in the fall of 1909 he began a wider study. Falling back on his child-study expertise, Goddard developed a survey "containing a rather long, and as it seemed to us at the time, a rather exhaustive list of questions in regard to the children"[7]; the children being every feebleminded child in Vineland. The results with 400 of the Vineland inmates were equally promising. Goddard was hooked, and soon became the most prominent advocate of the Binet-Simon Scale in the United States. Binet and Simon published a third version of the scale in 1911, and Goddard translated and standardized this version with 2,000 schoolchildren in the city of Vineland.

To collect his data from the "2,000" schoolchildren of Vineland, Goddard trained five of his laboratory assistants to conduct the Binet-Simon Scale tests. At the elementary grade schools, they were set up with a table and a few chairs situated in the hall or a waiting area, where they administered the 1911 version of the scale to up to 30 children a day. Testing at the middle and high school levels was conducted in groups in the children's classrooms. Goddard was contradictory in his description of these examiners' training, at one point describing them as "all expert in the use of these tests, having been trained in the laboratory,"[8] and then in almost the next breath describing the examiners as

[5] Zenderland, 1998, p. 97.
[6] Goddard, 1911a, p. 18.
[7] Goddard, 1911a, p. 20.
[8] Goddard, 1911b, p. 232.

"all more or less trained."[9] Goddard summarized his study as providing evidence of "two things: first, that the Binet Scale was wonderfully accurate; and second, that a child cannot learn the things that are beyond his grade of intelligence."[10]

It is worth pausing at this point to comment on the relative lack of sophistication for this research when compared to standards for psychological practice and research today, although not necessarily with the standards of the day. With the exception of creating a graph to depict the distribution of the match between the children's mental age (MA) and chronological age (CA), data—in the form of either frequencies or percentages of MA scores or frequencies of students' MA at, below, or above their CA—were not subjected to any statistical tests of normality, goodness of fit, or distribution. The only indicator of interrater reliability (e.g., the degree to which each examiner's scores were similar, on the whole, with other examiners' scores) was a comparison of the distribution of each woman's cases—referring, one would infer, to the distribution of MA scores. Even though one examiner's results were, apparently, marred by the incorrect administration of one test item, there does not appear to be any evidence that the scores of children with whom that administrator erred were discarded. Further, a test essentially developed and normed to be individually administered was then administered in a group-testing format for some of the study participants.

Then there is Goddard's reliability when reporting even simple mathematically calculated outcomes. Throughout his articles, Leila Zenderland has observed, Goddard incorrectly summed columns, misreported numbers and percent of subjects, and generally committed a great many basic arithmetic mistakes. His claim of 2,000 children tested must also be taken with a grain of salt, not because of mathematical error, unless one assumes that Goddard erred in rounding up by 500 children. In fact, his tables report data for only 1,547 children and Zenderland noted that if you do the math yourself, adding up the frequencies in the tables stating the total of 1,547, you only get 1,536 children.[11] In part, this is because Goddard found that, despite his acclamation that the Binet-Simon scale was *wonderfully accurate*—repeated twice in the paper along with the equally laudatory claim that the test was *wonderfully valuable*—it was, in fact, of no value beyond sixth-grade students. "The seventh, eighth, and ninth grades being practically able to pass the twelve year Binet tests and the thirteen year tests being found too difficult, none of the Binet tests were given to those grades," he admitted.[12] Not a particularly encouraging finding, but one that did not diminish Goddard's enthusiasm.

Goddard made the most out of his finding that the graph of the distribution of the discrepancy between the children's MA and CA, ranging from an MA

---

9 Goddard, 1911b, p. 233.
10 Goddard, 1911b, p. 233.
11 Zenderland, 1998, p.125.
12 Goddard, 1911b, p. 251.

of seven years below CA to four years above CA, approximated the by-now-familiar bell curve, with the largest frequency being children whose MA and CA matched, although the distribution at the lower end of the scale (e.g., MA lower than CA) was skewed.

"To a person familiar with statistical methods the foregoing curve of itself amounts to practically a mathematical demonstration of the accuracy of the tests," Goddard proclaimed.[13]

"The significance of these figures obtained from the general results is very great," Goddard then continued. "There is every reason to believe, and statisticians confirm this, that any group of two thousand children may be taken as a fair sample of conditions to be found in any number of children in any country. Consequently, whatever proportions or percentage are found here may be taken to be very closely the standard to be found elsewhere."[14]

Except, of course, that he drew his sample entirely from a single New Jersey public school system that may or may not have been representative of school systems in New Jersey, let alone in California or France. Or that he used research assistants who, despite his claims to expertise, had at least questionable reliability. Or that he only reported data from elementary-age students.

Goddard then overlaid his findings with regard to the MA–CA discrepancy onto a two-tiered classification system. The first involved students whose MA scores were two or three years lower than their CA. They constituted 15 percent of his sample, Goddard noted, and labeled these children as "merely backward . . . that is to say, they are not permanently arrested in their development."[15]

"They need help and with help they may be advanced to come up to the normal, or if always slow, nevertheless they can learn enough to be useful and respected citizens, but they must have special help. The Special Class for the slow child is needed for these."[16]

Children with MAs four or more years below their CA were, claimed Goddard based on his experience, "so far back that they can never catch up, or in other words, they are where they are because there is a serious difficulty which can never be overcome—they are feebleminded."

These children, which Goddard determined constituted 3 percent of the sample, were a threat to the progress of the "normal child," and should be segregated and provided a specially trained teacher, although ultimately they need to go to an institution for the feebleminded "where they will be cared for and prevented from contaminating society."[17] Of course, the latter 3 percent were not children with obvious or severe levels of cognitive impairment; such children were simply

---

[13] Goddard, 1911b, p. 236.
[14] Goddard, 1911b, p. 236.
[15] Goddard, 1911b, p. 236.
[16] Goddard, 1911b, p. 237.
[17] Goddard, 1911b, p. 237.

not allowed in the public school system in 1910, and resided in family homes or institutions for "idiots" and "imbeciles." No, these were the Deborah's of the world; apparently normal but, as revealed by the wonder of Binet-Simon Scale testing, actually degenerates.

Goddard used the findings from this large sample to create his own revision to the Binet-Simon Scale, which he announced at the NEA meeting in San Francisco in July of 1911.[18] By 1927, it was estimated that more than 30,000 copies of the Goddard revision of the Binet-Simon Scale had been distributed by the Training School.

In the same year he published his study of the use of the Binet-Simon Scale with 2,000—give or take 500—schoolchildren, Goddard was asked by Harvard Professor of Education Paul Hanus to participate in the New York City School Survey of 1911–1912.

Zenderland observed,

> Such an entrée was indeed another coup, "both for applied psychology and for Goddard personally, for it meant that within three short years, Goddard had taken Binet's tests from an institutional school of under 400, to a public school district of under 2,000, to the nation's largest school system—a system with more than three-quarters of a million students. Goddard had thus gained the opportunity to demonstrate the relevance of psychological testing to public schooling on a scale far surpassing anything yet attempted by his contemporaries.[19]

The New York City School Survey was a progeny of the political infighting that continues to beleaguer large urban school districts today. William Maxwell, the New York City Schools superintendent had run afoul of the New York City Schools Board of Education. In early summer of 1911, the board established a Committee on School Inquiry under its Board of Estimate and Apportionment and commissioned a comprehensive study of virtually all aspects of the New York school system, including teacher hiring needs, school and class size, school facilities, standards, and the system's administrative structure. Maxwell immediately recognized the study for what it was—an end run by the board of education to curtail spending and restrict his power.

To head the study, the Committee on School Inquiry appointed Hanus. Like Goddard in psychology, Hanus was a pioneer in efforts to get his field, education, recognized as a legitimate science. In 1891, Hanus had been the first professor of education at Harvard and, by 1911, was an established expert. He

---

[18] Goddard, 1911g.
[19] Zenderland, 1998, p. 131.

began his appointment as Director of Educational Aspects of School Inquiry on June 1, 1911, and was soon embroiled in the political machinations that dogged the study. From interfering bureaucrats and on-again–off-again funding, to selective leaks and releases of the study documents, Hanus struggled for the first six months to plan the study and obtain adequate funding. Although the initial charge detailed a 12-month review, by November of 1911 the infighting and budget woes signaled the death of the inquiry as of the end of 1911. On December 27, however, Hanus received a letter authorizing him to proceed with all diligence.

During the planning phase, Hanus identified a handful of distinguished experts to serve as consultants to the study. These included Edward Elliott, Professor of Education Administration at the University of Wisconsin and later president of Purdue University; Frank M. McMurry, Professor of Elementary Education at Teachers' College, Columbia University, and coauthor of the *Tarr and McMurry Common School Geographies,* an early geography text; Frank W. Ballou, Professor of Education at the University of Cincinnati, and later superintendent of the Washington, D.C., school system; Frank V. Thompson, Assistant Superintendent of Schools in Boston, and an expert on educating immigrant children; Stuart A. Courtis, author of the Courtis Tests in Arithmetic; and Goddard.

"The aims of the inquiry are constructive throughout," observed Hanus. "We have aimed to deal judicially with the achievements, merits, and defects of the school system. But since our chief purpose was constructive criticism we have given most attention to such defects as we have been able to point out."

As such, it is hardly surprising that when the report, published in 1913 as a series of 10 volumes in what was titled the *School Efficiency Series,* was released, it was greeted less than enthusiastically by Maxwell and others. Elizabeth Farrell, an early reformer who implemented the first large-scale effort to educate students who were feebleminded (and who came to New York because of Maxwell's championing), was incensed by the aspects of the report pertaining to ungraded (special education) classes, and authored by Goddard.

Goddard's report, titled *School Training of Defective Children,* was predictable in its tone and recommendations.

"The best way of detecting these children is to employ individuals who have lived for a year or more in institutions among children known to be feedbleminded," Goddard wrote self-servingly and consistent with the methods employed in the Kallikak study. "Through familiarity with the feeble-minded and study of them, a person becomes expert in recognizing them."

"Another method, perhaps equally good," continued Goddard almost inevitably, "is the use of the Binet-Simon Measuring Scale of Intelligence."[20]

---

[20] Goddard, 1914b, p. xvii.

Goddard personally visited 125 of the 131 ungraded classes in the district. Consistent with Hanus's marching orders to engage in constructive criticism, Goddard was critical of any attempts to teach academic content; of the materials used in the ungraded classrooms; of the way the rooms were set up; even of the type of tables used.

He had equally specific recommendations for Kindergarten chairs and tables ("may be supplied with rubber tips on the legs if desired"); bathroom ("a shower bat at least, if not a tub, and also a cloak room"); work benches, storage cases, blackboards, and materials ("lumber, paper, reed and rafia, cloth, yarn, varnishes, stains, etc."); and gymnastic apparatus.[21] After critically assessing the recruitment and training of teachers in the ungraded classes and the supervision of the ungraded classes, Goddard moved to more familiar territory, that being the menace of the feebleminded and the importance of the Binet-Simon Scale.

"The most extensive study ever made of the children of an entire public-school system of two-thousand has shown that 2 per cent. of such children are so mentally defective as to preclude any possibility of their ever being made normal and able to take care of themselves as adults."

"According to this estimate of 2 per cent. there are 15,000 feeble-minded children in the public schools of New York," Goddard hypothesized. At the time, there were a mere 2,500 students served in ungraded classrooms. That the "actual" number was six times that amount was a bold estimate indeed.

"I have examined a number of children in the New York schools by this scale, and am entirely convinced that the 2 per cent. is well within the mark."[22] Goddard supervised the administration of the Binet-Simon Scale with students in three ungraded classes housing 46 children; 81 children in E classes, which were for students who had started late and were attempting to catch up, content wise, with their same-CA peers; and 22 children in D classes for older students who were slow learners. As was the case whenever Goddard looked for them, the putatively feebleminded children seemingly came out of the woodwork.

"In one high school, at the request of a teacher, we examined five cases that were selected by her. They all proved to be feeble-minded."[23]

Goddard's solution to this "problem," after ruling out segregation in institutions and surgical sterilization as "possible but not applicable solutions ... for the reasons that their parents will not consent,"[24] was the establishment of a separate school system for defective children. If they could not be segregated outside of the school system, segregate them inside it.

In a report prepared for the board of education subtitled "An Analysis of Dr. Goddard's School Inquiry Report on Ungraded Classes," subsequently pub-

---

[21] Goddard, 1914b, pp. 21-22.
[22] Goddard, 1914b, p. 44.
[23] Goddard, 1914b, p. 46.
[24] Goddard, 1914b, p. 53.

lished in three sections in *The Psychological Clinic*, Elizabeth Farrell provided a point-by-point rebuttal of Goddard's report. Because the wheels of bureaucracy turn slowly, particularly in politically charged situations such as the New York School Survey, Farrell's report ended up in front of the Board of Education Commissioners at the same time Goddard's report was officially submitted.

"Some criticisms of the report have appeared," Goddard later observed. "Some of these, written for political reasons, are of no value to the student. Others, written by enthusiasts who fear that their hobby has been attacked, only show the necessity of elaborating points that one is apt to pass over briefly, supposing they would be understood. Perhaps the reader may be interested to know also that New York has already carried out several of the recommendations, which may show that they are not without merit."[25]

That Goddard and Farrell would clash seems almost inevitable. They represented two different poles of Galton's nature–nurture dichotomy. Goddard was taking more and more extreme hereditarian positions because that was what was good for psychology and his continued prominence in the field. As such, the use of the Binet-Simon Scale to ferret out mentally defective children who were, in his view, uneducable and to segregate them in institutions like Vineland was the only viable option. Farrell, however, did not hold Goddard's hereditarian views, with her positions on society's response to human need driven by Jane Addams's settlement house ideology.

"The jails are full of your failures—all of you," Farrell charged teachers under her supervision. "I want every teacher here to think now of her failures, of the men and the women whose lives were cut short in their opportunity, because we were not well-trained enough, because the science of education was not an instrument in our hands. How many people are less than they should be because we lack the artistry of creating interest, because we lack the artistry of making attractive the knowledge of the world?"[26]

Hardly Goddard's notions.

"The Binet tests, upon which some part of our argument in the report is based, are still being condemned occasionally," Goddard explained in the preface to the release of his report in the *School Efficiency Series* in 1914. "They have been killed several times, but, in the spirit of Galileo, 'The world moves just the same.' The Binet tests are proving their value and accuracy every day."

In the Spring of 1913, Goddard turned his sights to the use of intelligence testing to screen immigrants coming into America. Among eugenicists, particularly Harry Laughlin, the threat of "race suicide" was propagated largely by the infusion of immigrants into the American breeding stock.

---

[25] Goddard, 1914b, pp. ix–x.
[26] Kode, 2002, p. 3.

The usual masses of humanity that flowed through Ellis Island were absent on that spring morning because of fog on the Upper New York Bay, but there were 100 or so immigrants who, having passed through the lengthy inspection process, were ready to depart Ellis Island for their new lives in the United States.

When immigrants disembarked at Ellis Island they were subject, after registration and baggage stowage, to a medical examination that became known as the "line inspection." Two medical officers of the U.S. Public Health Services (PHS) were posted at the front of the line, conducting a quick scan of immigrants, referred to as the six-second physical.[27] Once immigrants had run the gauntlet of the inspections, they returned to the first floor to await a ferry to transport them to Manhattan,[28] and it was among the 100 or so undoubtedly anxious, relieved, and excited immigrants milling about waiting to board the ferry that Goddard conducted his "experiment."

"We picked out one young man," Goddard recounted, "whom we suspected was defective, and, through the interpreter, proceeded to give him the test."

This young man, of course, had already passed the PHS and immigration officers' scrutiny.

"He tested eight by the Binet Scale," Goddard proudly proclaimed.

"I could not have done that when I came to this country," protested the interpreter who had translated the Binet-Simon Scale questions to the young man.

"We convinced him," Goddard stated flatly, "that the boy was defective."

One wonders if the young man was, literally, snatched from the cusp of emancipation and freedom and sent back to wherever he had sought to escape, as many later would be when labeled "defective."

William Williams, the Commissioner of Immigration at Ellis Island with whom Davenport had originally spoken was, according to Goddard, so impressed that he, Florence Mateer, and Catherine Bell were invited back the following Monday when the fog was to have lifted and the passenger ships were again delivering their human cargo.

Williams, held "jaundiced views on immigrants from Southern and Eastern Europe"[29] and, perhaps because of that or simply because he was under pressure from new immigration restrictions, he provided Goddard the opportunity to test his growing belief that professionals, including fieldworkers like Bell, Mateer, and Kite, could identify the feebleminded at a glance and that the Binet-Simon Scale could systematize the hunt for Goddard's degenerates.

"After a person has had considerable experience in this work, he almost gets a sense of what a feeble-minded person is so that he can tell one afar off," Goddard claimed as he reported his immigration testing accomplishments to his peers at a later meeting. "The people who are best at this work," he explained,

---

[27] Moreno, 2004, p. ix.
[28] Moreno, 2004, p. xv.
[29] Guzda, 1986.

"are women. Women seem to have closer observation than men. It was quite impossible for others," particularly, perhaps, the PHS doctors who were being upstaged by Goddard and his fieldworkers, "to see how these two young women could pick out the feeble-minded without the aid of the Binet test at all."[30]

And pick them out they did. On Monday, Goddard, Bell, and Mateer returned, spending the entire day at Ellis Island.

"We placed one young lady at the end of the line," Goddard explained, referring probably to the line in the registry hall that immigrants came to after they had cleared the line inspection by the PHS officers, "and as the immigrants passed, she pointed out the ones she thought defective. They were taken to the quiet room, and we proceeded to test them."[31]

That the 1911 Goddard version of the Binet-Simon Scale seems manifestly inappropriate for use with non-English speaking immigrants, many of whom had little or no formal education, seems patently obvious today.

Goddard did express some hesitation about use of the Binet-Simon Scale with immigrants, although his concern was not about the validity of the measure itself or the process with this population, but instead on difficulties associated with the translation and the translator.

"One reason why we had not taken up this work before was because it is exceedingly difficult to handle the Binet scale through an interpreter," he explained. "The interpreter was much inclined to say, 'that is all right,' when perhaps the questions were not answered just as they should have been."[32] One can only imagine how confused, frightened immigrants responded to the more morbid Binet-Simon Scale items. "That's all right" seems like a compassionate response to the hapless immigrant, although of course, Goddard wasn't interested in compassion—only "truth."

After the full day, Goddard and his associates claimed that the PHS doctors were ineffective at screening for feeblemindedness, as nine immigrants eyeballed by the research associate were all feebleminded according to the Binet-Simon Scale.[33]

Flush with success, Goddard's fieldworkers, Mateer and Bell, returned to Ellis Island in late September sans Goddard for a full week. This time the Vineland research associates tested 44 immigrants, one-quarter of whom had been identified by visual inspection by Bell or Mateer, the other two-thirds of whom had been selected by Ellis Island medical inspectors. The immigrants denoted by the medical inspectors tested in the feebleminded range less than half the time whereas those identified by Goddard's assistants tested feeble-minded 80 percent of the time. Further, on the basis of a tally generated by visual inspection on their final day at Ellis Island, Goddard estimated that the

---

[30] Goddard, 1913b, p. 106.
[31] Goddard, 1913b, p. 105.
[32] Goddard, 1913b, p. 106.
[33] Gelb, 1986, p. 327.

physicians were identifying only about 10 percent of the feebleminded coming through Ellis Island.[34]

Needless to say, the Ellis Island physicians were not ecstatic with Goddard's results, given that they called their own expertise and capacity into question. They were, however, intrigued by the potential for intelligence tests to enable them to identify feebleminded and imbecile immigrants. Several PHS officers began experimenting with mental testing, the most successful of whom was Howard A. Knox, assistant surgeon in the PHS to Ellis Island from 1910 to 1916. Knox tried out the standardized tests, but also developed and validated tests that purportedly took into account immigrants' cultural background and education level.

In a paper published in the *Journal of Heredity* in 1914, which included a criticism of psychology in general and, specifically, psychologists' use of the term "feebleminded"—"the term feeble-mindedness' is regarded by most alienists as a sort of waste basket for many forms and degrees of weakmindedness"[35]—Knox outlined his testing regimen, which used a combination of form board, puzzle, and general knowledge tests seen in the Binet-Simon Scale.

That the introduction of intelligence testing to the system impacted the lives of immigrants seems supported by the indirect evidence in the numbers of people excluded; indirect in that there is no way to assign causality to the testing as having been the sole or even primary cause of changes in the numbers of people excluded. In 1909, two years after the 1907 Immigration Act had explicitly identified feebleminded people and imbeciles as ineligible for entry into the country, there were only 121 persons rejected by U.S. Immigration Officers under those categories, and in 1912, only 110 were excluded. In 1914, however, after Goddard's experiments at Ellis Island and concurrent with the increased use of some form of mental testing, 995 people were excluded.[36]

Goddard's own intention in venturing to Ellis Island was, however, less an anti-immigrant manifesto than another battlefront in his crusade for the field of psychology, for the use of the Binet-Simon Scale, and for establishing the importance of institutionalization by emphasizing the menace of the feebleminded.

Later in the spring of 1913, Goddard secured minimal funding and was able to send his associates back to Ellis Island for several months, where they tested 165 immigrants. As social historian Steven Gelb observed, Goddard sat on his immigration data for a long time before publishing it in 1917, something that was uncharacteristic of the prolific psychologist. Goddard had even been approached by Paul Popenoe, then-editor of *American Breeders Magazine* (soon to become the *Journal of Heredity*), at Davenport's suggestion. Goddard

---

[34] Gelb, 1986, p. 327.
[35] Knox, 1914, p. 125.
[36] King, 2000, p. 172.

demurred, undoubtedly in part because his view on mental defectiveness in immigrants was that it was probably environmental and not hereditary.[37]

When he did present the data at the 1916 American Psychological Association meeting held in late December in New York City, followed by publication of a paper in the September 1917 issue of *Journal of Delinquency*, it was almost with a sense of hesitancy and an uncharacteristic level of equivocation.

"The reader familiar with the history of mental testing will realize something of the difficulty that we faced," began Goddard. "We were in fact most inadequately prepared for the task. There were scarcely any tests standardized at that time. Even the Binet-Simon Scale was so new as to be still largely in the experimental stage."[38]

Perhaps Goddard's experience in the New York Schools study had taught him to curtail his dogmatic language; perhaps the scientifically and psychometrically sophisticated work being done by Stanford University psychologist and mental tester Lewis Terman with the Stanford-Binet Intelligence Scale made Goddard recognize that his early work, although pioneering, was not up to the current scientific standard; perhaps the criticisms of people like J. E. Wallace Wallin and Samuel Kohs were beginning to influence him; or, perhaps, and most probably, his findings warranted that he approach them with caution.

"We have waited more than three years to present the results because not until recently have we had standards by which we could make even a tentative evaluation of the data,"[39] he vaguely explained.

"Two problems were set: First, whether persons trained in work with the feeble-minded could recognize, by simple inspection, the feeble-minded immigrant. Second to what extent if any could mental tests be successfully applied to the detection of defective immigrants.

"For the purpose of the first question, an investigator selected 39 cases—20 were Italians and 19 were Russians—who appeared to her to be feeble-minded. These were then tested by the investigator.

"For the second question, cases were picked who appeared to be representative of their respective groups. In this list we had 35 Jews, 22 Hungarians, 50 Italians and 45 Russians.

"In both instances the cases were selected after the government physicians had culled out all mental defectives that they had recognized as such."[40]

It is with the findings from the latter question, pertaining to the use of mental testing to identify immigrants, that Goddard sounded the "shot heard round the world" with regard to the mental capacity of immigrants. The results, presented in a table in the article, of testing the immigrants with the Binet-Simon Scale,

---

[37] Gelb, 1986, p. 328.
[38] Goddard, 1917, p. 243.
[39] Goddard, 1917, pp. 243–244.
[40] Goddard, 1917, p. 244.

were that 76 percent of Jews, 80 percent of Hungarians, 79 percent of Italians, and 82 percent of Russians were feebleminded.[41]

Even Goddard sensed that this finding invited incredulity. Before presenting the Binet-Simon Scale data in the table, he noted that even when omitting potentially "non-valid" questions, that is those that 75 percent or more of the immigrants had failed, nearly 40 percent of the immigrants would still be considered feebleminded.

"Are these results reasonable?" Goddard asked, rhetorically. "Doubtless the thought in every reader's mind is the same as in ours, that it is impossible that half of such a group of immigrants is feeble-minded, but it is never wise to discard a scientific result because of apparent absurdity."

"Assuming for the sake of argument that the percentages and mental levels shown in the foregoing results are approximately correct, what is to be done about it?"[42] Goddard asked.

In *The Kallikak Family*, published five years before this article, and in other publications, when Goddard posed the "what is to be done about it" question, it was a signal that he was to launch a diatribe about the menace of the degenerate. Not so, however, with his findings from his Ellis Island research.

"The fact seems to be that a very large percentage of these immigrants make good after a fashion," he argued. "At least it is true that they do a great deal of work that no one else will so. If some of them run amuck and make us trouble, then the wise solution of the problem would seem to be not to exclude them all but to take care of those who are not getting along well."[43]

"Here is a vital question which obviously our investigation does not answer. Are these immigrants of low mentality cases of hereditary defect or cases of apparent mental defect by deprivation?"[44]

"We know of no data on this point, but indirectly we may argue that it is far more probable that their condition is due to environment than that it is due to heredity. To mention only two considerations: First, we know their environment has been poor. It seems able to account for the result. Second, this kind of immigration has been going on for 20 years. If the condition were due to hereditary feeble-mindedness we should properly expect a noticeable increase in the proportion of the feeble-minded of foreign ancestry. This is not the case."[45]

"In contrast," suggested Gelb, "to psychologists Robert Yerkes, Lewis Terman, and Carl Brigham in the 1920s" and, parenthetically, in contrast to Ward, Hall, Laughlin, and Davenport in the 1910s, "Goddard was unoccupied with issues of race, nationality, and immigration restriction."[46]

---

[41] Goddard, 1917, p. 252.
[42] Goddard, 1917, p. 268.
[43] Goddard, 1917, p. 269.
[44] Goddard, 1917, p. 270.
[45] Goddard, 1917, p. 270.
[46] Gelb, 1986, p. 329.

Goddard was interested in the progress of psychology, the expansion of Binet-Simon Scale testing, and the identification of the feebleminded. And yet, his impact on the immigration restriction movement and the eugenic consequences for immigrants was writ large by two factors. First, as much as anyone else, Goddard had propelled the PHS and immigration officers to use mental testing, resulting, undoubtedly, in the identification of more immigrants as feebleminded or imbeciles. By 1918, the PHS had issued its own *Manual of the Mental Examination of Aliens*, published under the direction of the U.S. Surgeon General, intended to standardize the process of mental testing by health officers. The manual provided instructions as to what the officers should look for during the visual "line inspection," photographs of "low and high grade imbeciles," or a "constitutional inferior." Officers were provided information on the Binet-Simon Scale tests, the Healy-Fernald form board, and the Seguin form board, among numerous other tests of mental ability.[47] Goddard may not have succeeded in having psychologists take front-and-center in testing immigrants, but he certainly propelled the testing of immigrants forward.

Second, his findings that nearly 80 percent of immigrants were feebleminded was, like the Juke and Kallikak family narratives, ammunition for eugenicists to alarm the public and achieve their aims.

Speaking at the first meeting of the Department of Child Study of the National Education Association, held in San Francisco in July 1911, at the invitation of Terman, Goddard stated:

"We owe many things to France and the Frenchmen, but I predict that we shall find nothing that is of more value to us than this scale, which will enable us to understand children better than we have understood them before and to treat them more wisely."[48]

Goddard certainly owed a great deal to the Frenchmen, at least Binet and Simon. That he suggested it would be used to treat children more wisely is, from the perspective of women like Deborah Kallikak, more than a bit circumspect.

Meanwhile, Goddard's host in the city by the bay, Terman, was rapidly gaining on Goddard in prominence with regard to the use and revision of the Binet-Simon Scale tests. Although Goddard had to rely on the availability and skills of fieldworkers to conduct his studies of the Binet-Simon Scale, Terman had at his disposal the resources a university can offer, the primary one being bright, motivated graduate students. In 1912, working with one of those graduate students, H. G. Childs, Terman reported findings from a study of 396 schoolchildren from California. Published in the fledgling *Journal of Educational Psychology*, Terman and Childs found problems with the Binet-Simon Scale: it underesti-

[47] United States Treasury Department, 1918.
[48] Goddard, 1911b, p. 878.

mated MA for older students and overestimated such scores for younger children. Terman and Childs proposed alterations to the test to correct for these errors, but Terman recognized that the sample sizes he had been working with were insufficient, psychometrically, for a true revision. As such, Terman and his graduate students assembled about them all the data with regard to the use of the Binet-Simon Scale up to that point, "including percentages passing the test at various ages, conditions under which the results were secured, method of procedure, etc.," and generated 40 additional items that might be added to the scale. They then scoured California for children who were within two months of their birthday and who were native-born Americans, and administered the full Binet-Simon Scale with the 40 additional items, recording children's answers verbatim. They successfully tested nearly 1,000 children and, on the basis of these results, revised the scale. Eventually, Terman had a revision to his liking, with 27 of the 40 newly generated items now included in the test and the total number of items at 90, as opposed to Binet and Simons' original 54. Terman's revision, which also added items that provided MA scores for "average" and "superior" adults, was published as the Stanford-Revision to the Binet-Simon Scale (later just the Stanford-Binet test) in 1916.[49]

The Stanford revision was published, fully, in Terman's now-classic 1916 text, *The Measurement of Intelligence*. Not only did that text describe the test's revision, but Terman introduced the idea of an intelligence quotient, and it's now ubiquitous acronym IQ, as the ratio of MA to CA multiplied by 100. Actually, though, Terman was not the first to propose the idea of an intelligence quotient. German psychologist William Stern, a professor at the University of Breslau, made such a proposition in his book *The Psychological Methods of Intelligence Testing*, published in German in 1912 and translated into English in 1914. Stern had observed that the ratio between MA and CA remained constant across time, and proposed:

> Since feeble-mindedness consists essentially in a condition of development that is below the normal condition, the rate of development will also be a slower one, and thus every added year of age must magnify the difference in question, at least as long as there is anything present that could be called mental development at all. With this in mind it is but a step to the idea of measuring backwardness by the relative difference; i.e., by the ratio between mental and chronological age, instead of by the absolute difference.[50]

Terman's adaptation to Stern's original intelligence quotient was to multiply the quotient obtained from dividing the tested MA of the child (the dividend) by the child's CA (the divisor) by 100, so as to eliminate the decimal.

---

[49]Terman, 1916.
[50]Stern, 1914, p. 79.

The 1916 Stanford revision of the Binet-Simon Scale quickly became the gold standard for intelligence testing, the formula for determining an IQ score caught on rapidly, and Terman's reputation as the nation's premier intelligence tester eclipsed even Goddard's fame. And, although Goddard drew first blood in spreading the use of the Binet-Simon Scale beyond simply categorizing levels of feeblemindedness by applying the test to the New Jersey schoolchildren, it was Terman who moved the test firmly out of the marginalized realm of mental deficiency testing and into the realm of mental hygiene and the psychological study of individual differences.

"Thus far the Binet tests have been valued chiefly as an improved method for the exact grading of the degrees of deficiency present in feeble-minded children,"[51] observed Terman, speaking before the attendees to the Fourth International Congress of School Hygiene in Buffalo, New York, in August 1913. "The use of mental tests is fast emphasizing," he continued, "the extent of the individual difference to be found in the intelligence of children who are well above the borderline of feeble-mindedness. Hygiene demands that the school shall take account more seriously than it has yet done of the existence of individual difference in the ability of its pupils."[52]

"Mental tests are aiding us to understand better some of the moral peculiarities of children," Terman continued, "and the moral life, it hardly need be said, is full of possibilities for mental hygiene."[53]

And that is the problem with the seemingly innocuous notion of mental hygiene, which at its most benign simply refers to the promotion of mental health and the prevention of mental illness. It was co-opted by eugenicists to provide both scientific credibility and moral justification to their negative eugenic approaches, much as had been the ideas of social hygiene and social control.

"Mental tests will inform us," predicted Terman, "whether the so-called inferior races are really inferior or merely unfortunate in their lack of opportunity to learn. They will be able to give us meaningful norms of intellectual performance for different ages and thereby enable us to prevent the waste of untimely instruction."[54]

---

[51]Terman, 1914b, p. 120.
[52]Terman, 1914b, p. 121.
[53]Terman, 1914b, p. 126.
[54]Terman, 1914b, p. 127.

CHAPTER 6

Acceptance and Fame

The demand for the Vineland Training School summer teacher training program had grown steadily since its inauguration in 1904. For the 1911 summer session, Johnstone and Alice Morrison Nash received 100 applications, from which they could accept only 60 participants. For the first few years, summer school attendees resided in temporary cottages constructed solely for that purpose, but as demand grew, three buildings providing accommodations for 60 people were erected, thus setting the upper limit for annual enrollment. In 1911, these three-score women arrived in Vineland to begin classes on July 17 for a six-week stint that lasted until graduation day, August 25. They spent one week in courses surveying the general subject of feeblemindedness, another week on causes and classification, a third week on sociological issues and methods of care, and then three weeks in practical applications of these methods. During their period of stay, they heard from Dr. Carl Kelsey of the University of Pennsylvania; Dr. Walter Cornell, a Philadelphia physician who worked part time at the Training School; Alexander Johnson, Johnstone's brother-in-law; Dr. David Weeks of the Skillman New Jersey facility for epileptics; and, of course, Johnstone, Goddard, and Nash.

When graduation day arrived, the soon-to-be alumna were congratulated by New Jersey Governor Woodrow Wilson, who only a month earlier had been nominated the Democratic candidate for president of the United States.

Among the topics the summer school students studied during the three-week session was the use of the Binet-Simon Scale under the tutelage of the person most responsible for introducing intelligence testing to North America—Goddard.

Goddard's emergence as the preeminant mental tester in the United States occurred both because he was an early adopter and evaluator of the Binet-Simon Scale and because he was the first to suggest that intelligence tests might be useful in classifying people who were feebleminded. At the 1909 meeting of the American Association for the Study of the Feebleminded, held at the Wisconsin Home for the Feeble-Minded in Chippewa Falls, Goddard presented a paper titled "Suggestions for a Prognostical Classification of Mental Defectives," in which he recommended a classification system for feeblemindedness that, importantly, linked each classification group and level with mental age determinations from the Binet-Simon Scale. The ensuing discussion of Goddard's paper resulted in the establishment of the Committee on Classification of the Feeble-Minded for the association, with Walter Fernald, a physician influential in the early institutionalization movement who was superintendent of the Massachusetts School for Idiotic and Feeble-Minded Youth, as chair and Goddard as a member. At the American Association for the Study of the Feeble-Minded meeting of 1910, held in Lincoln, Illinois, Goddard presented the findings from his use of the Binet-Simon Scale with the 400 Vineland inmates.

Goddard recommended that children who did not establish a basal age be classified as idiots; children who scored a mental age from three to seven be classified as imbeciles, with low-grade imbeciles being children with mental ages of three or four years, children with a mental age of 5 years being middle-grade imbeciles, and children with mental ages of six or seven as high-grade imbeciles; and all others falling into the category of feebleminded, with children with mental ages of eight and nine being low-grade feebleminded, mental ages of ten as middle-grade feebleminded, and mental ages of eleven and twelve as high-grade feebleminded.

Goddard ended his presentation with the further suggestion that there was a need for a new term to be used instead of feebleminded for the higher group because that term was "universally used in the country now to cover the entire range of mental defectives."[1]

Of course, Goddard was a member of the Association's Committee on Classification, which during the past year had discussed this very topic and he knew that the committee's recommendation, presented at the same meeting, would include a new term for that higher grade, one coined by Goddard himself. In the Committee's report, Chairman Fernald recommended the adoption of the division of the feebleminded, as a class, into three subgroups. The first group, "Idiots," were defined as "those so deeply defective that their mental development does not exceed that of a normal child of about two years." The second group, "Imbeciles," were "those whose mental development is higher than that of an idiot but does not exceed that of a normal child of about seven years. The third group, "Morons," were those children "whose mental development is above that of an imbecile but does not exceed that of a child of about twelve years."[2]

Fernald had begun the discussion that resulted in this report with an April 1910 letter to committee members stating a preference for "something very much simpler than has been the vogue for a decade, something like . . . Idiocy, Imbecility, Feeble-mindedness."[3]

---

[1] Goddard, 1911, p. 26.
[2] Fernald, 1911, p. 61.
[3] Fernald, 1911, p. 62.

"My idea is that three, or possibly four, groups for our institution children would be sufficient and the terms idiocy, imbecility and feeble-mindedness are as good as any," responded Arthur Wylie, superintendent at the Institution for the Feeble-Minded in Grafton, North Dakota, although he also suggested the terms "psycho-asthenia," "amentia," and "mental debility" as alternatives. Wylie then proceeded to torpedo Fernald's suggestion to keep it simple by also recommending that clinical subgroups—"microcephalous," "hydrocephalous," "Mongolian," and "cretin," among others—be appended to the group terms, as well as adding the label "moral imbeciles" to the topmost group of the feebleminded.[4]

J. M. Murdoch, superintendent of the Western Pennsylvania Institution for the Feeble-Minded, took much the same trek, agreeing with Fernald, but then suggesting an expansion.

"I agree with you thoroughly in the ideas put forth in your letter" Murdoch responded. "I believe the classification should be made as simple as possible, and in the classification of any given case three things should be made clear— the etiology; the clinical variety or pathological condition; and the degree of mental defect."[5]

In other words, the simple three-tier classification of idiocy, imbecility, and feeblemindedness would account for only one of three domains used for classification. Classification systems similar to those proposed by both Wylie and Murdoch had been suggested in prior years. Goddard's response, mailed April 29, 1910, was both the longest and the only one to propose anything new.

"I have felt just exactly as you express it in regard to classification for some-time," he began, "but I feared that I was a heretic and that no one would agree with me. Now we have been carrying on here during the past year quite an elaborate study of our children for some scheme of classification. I hope to have this matter in suitable condition to present to the meeting at Lincoln, and if it comes out as it seems to me it will, I think it will be at least a small contribution to the problem, but for our committee work now, I think I may give you an outline sufficient for the present purpose."[6]

"First, I have been thinking all year of some way in which we could obviate the difficulty of having the term feeble-minded used in both the generic and specific sense. My first thought was to follow the English and call the generic word "amentia" but Prof. Johnstone reminds me that all our institutions are called institutions for the feeble-minded, which is the generic use of the term, and it would be impossible to change that because that would mean legal changes.

"The next best thing is, of course, to give up the specific use of the term and get something in its place. Various things have been suggested. The two most feasible ones seem to me to be, first, proximate (with the idea that these children

[4]Fernald, 1911, p. 64.
[5]Fernald, 1911, p. 64.
[6]Fernald, 1911, p. 64.

are nearly normal), for the group that are nearest. They might be called proximates. The other is to call them by the Greek word "moron.' It is defined as one
who is lacking in intelligence, one who is deficient in judgment or sense.

"Personally, I prefer the latter word," Goddard concluded. "It has the advantage also of not being already in use in English in any sense. Consequently we
would have no quarrel or no necessity for saying that we use it in a special way.
We would simply define its meaning once for all and by using it, make it stand
for what we want."[7]

At this juncture, Goddard had not worked out the specific Binet-Simon Scale
age ranges he would propose to populate the categories of idiot, imbecile, and
moron. "It is this correlation that I hope to work out and present in my paper,"
he explained.

He does note, however, that "in our complete testings we have found no children that test above the mentality of a twelve year old child."

"I think this brings out some very significant things in the development of
the mind," Goddard concluded. "In the first place, the fact that we have none
over twelve suggests the further fact that at twelve or thirteen we began the
period of reasoning with children and inasmuch as that is precisely the thing
that is lacking in our moron children, we have here a striking agreement, they do
grow up to that point. Or we may say, apparently, any child that develops beyond
the twelve year period has sufficient reasoning power to get along in the world
and does not pass as feeble-minded."[8]

And so it was. The cleverness of the Greek word and the simplicity of aligning levels of feeblemindedness with mental age scores on the Binet-Simon Scale
were too alluring. Fernald and the committee accepted Goddard's recommendation and it went before the association for a vote and was ratified. The issue
of the *Journal of Psych-Asthenics* that followed the Lincoln conference began
with an editorial from that year's president, A. C. Rogers, superintendent of the
Minnesota Institution for Feeble-Minded in Faribault.

"If it had been easy to devise a classification of general application it would
have been done long ago,"[9] noted Rogers, referring to the smorgasbord of classifications and definitions that had piled up like a train wreck over the years.

"As to the matter of emphasizing a psychological basis for classification rather
than a pathological one, we can see no serious objection to it, if thereby we can
secure a means of determining quickly even an approximate estimate of the
child's mental ability by some system that is of general application and that
presents to all, the physician, the teacher, the parent and the student, alike, the
same mental picture to be referred to a common mental standard. Who is there
that does not have a mental picture always in view, of the activities and capaci-

[7] Fernald, 1911, p. 65.
[8] Fernald, 1911, p. 66.
[9] Rogers, 1910, pp. 68–69.

ties of normal children at different ages? What more natural and rational than to compare the mind, backward in development, with a normal one?

"We have reason to congratulate the committee upon its work in laying so excellent a foundation,"[10] Rogers concluded.

The importance of Goddard's coinage of the term "moron" extends well beyond his personal satisfaction with this professional achievement, although he was quite pleased. Professors Harold Burtt and Stanley Pressey, Goddard's colleagues later in his career in the Department of Psychology at Ohio State University and authors of his obituary, noted that "perhaps of all his accomplishments he was most proud of his invention of the word moron, feeling that its becoming a part of popular speech meant an enlargement of understandings."[11]

According to J. E. Wallace Wallin, the term "moron" occurred to Goddard when he thought of the definition of "sophomore" used by his college professor of English, which meant "wise fool" (Greek, *sophos* = wise, *moros* = stupid). According to Wallin, when asked why he used the neuter form (e.g., gender neutral) of *moros*, Goddard replied, only partly tongue-in-cheek perhaps, "because they ought to be neuter."[12]

Writing more than 45 years later, Goddard's assistant at Vineland, Edgar A. Doll, observed that the term "moron" "technically refers to those so developmentally lacking in good sense of practical judgment as to be in need of social assistance or supervision."[13] *Moros* is perhaps more accurately translated as dull. Those in Goddard's moron class were not obviously disabled, like people in the idiot or imbecile classes, and that was, in the eyes of eugenicists, the most dangerous situation. People who were "morons" might not be easily detected and would be likely to procreate.

Beyond simply a personal triumph, though, the linkage between the administration of the Binet-Simon Scale and the classification of feeblemindness was the triumph for the discipline of psychology Goddard had been striving for since his days at Clark. It must have almost taken Goddard's breath away to see Rogers, himself a physician, state that he saw no reason not to emphasize a psychological basis for classification as opposed to a medical, pathological basis. It was a coup d'état, wrestling control over the diagnosis of feeblemindedness from physicians to psychologists.

Finally, the combined circumstances of discovering the Binet-Simon Scale tests, coining the term "moron," and linking with Davenport's eugenics movement set Goddard on a track for the remainder of his Vineland career to identify and deal with the "problem" of his "moron."

---

[10] Rogers, 1910, pp. 69–70.
[11] Burtt and Pressey, 1957, p. 657.
[12] Wallin, 1953.
[13] Doll, 1948, p. 495.

"The greatest menace to a proper understanding of feeble-mindedness," wrote Goddard in his June 1911 *Pediatrics* article titled "The Menace of the Feeble Minded," "is the preconceived notion of what a feeble minded person is. To most people this term is synonymous with idiot or imbecile and that means a human being who is so distorted mentally that it shows in his outward physical appearance. They are the pitiable wretches that one occasionally sees, or that one knows in his home community who passed along the street, known as 'Crazy Jane' or 'The Silly Boy' or by some such familiar term.

"While such persons as these exist and have always existed in every community, they are the least of our troubles. They are poor, unfortunate, miserable beings, a burden to all that have to do with them, but nevertheless, they do not constitute the great social problem that we find in the higher group of the feeble minded which we now call the Moron group.

"We have all known that there are people in the community who do not get along well. There are people who do things that make us call them "fools," but we have not yet realized that even that meant they were irresponsible, yet such is the case. They constitute the great army of ne'er-do-wells, the great mass of people who cannot learn to do things rightly."[14]

"A feeble minded person of this high grade is always a dangerous person to have about. The very nature of their condition means danger. They are lacking in self-control while at the same time they have the same impulses and the same passions as normal people so that had it happened that they had been aroused, had been excited or angered, they would have done the most atrocious things, bringing shame and disgrace upon people and causing the loss of life and property. One has only to read the morning paper with a discriminating thought and knowledge of this condition to realize that an immense amount of crime is committed by persons who are feeble minded."[15]

After discussing the "appalling power of heredity in this kind of stock" using standard unit-character, single trait inheritance language, Goddard closed the article answering his stock rhetorical question "What is to be done?"

"First, what can we do with those who are already born, these children are all about us. We have determined that at least two per cent. of the school population belongs to this class. With these there is only one thing, test them out by the Binet scale and determine who they are. Then place them in institutions, if possible, if this cannot be done then in special classes in the public schools where they will be trained to do hand work as well as they can and thus become happy and as little a burden upon society as possible."[16]

"But we must go further than this. This is a day of prevention. What can be done to prevent this stream of bad protoplasm from coming into the world and

---

[14] Goddard, 1911e, p. 1.
[15] Goddard, 1911e, p. 3.
[16] Goddard, 1911e, p. 7.

keeping us busy with social problems? We can, if we will, prevent the birth of feeble minded children, by first preventing the marriage of feeble minded people, second by putting in institutions where they may be kept for life, all persons who are capable of begetting or bearing children and who would be likely to give birth to feeble minded children. Thirdly, we can sterilize these persons who would become the parents of feeble minded children. Of these three methods the ideal one would be to place them all in colonies where they would be kept as long as they live. But inasmuch as this cannot be done entirely and is too slow, we must, I believe, resort to some form of either castration or vasectomy and it must be practiced on the female as well as on the male."

"If we would cope successfully with this menace of feeble mindedness, we must put aside sentiment and deal with the problem in a practical manner."[17]

In the *Oxford English Dictionary*'s entry for "moron," the adoption of which is attributed to the American Association for the Study of Feeble-Minded in 1910, the first illustrative quotation is from Goddard's 1910 response to Fernald's letter. The second is from *The Kallikak Family*, page 54, in which Goddard explained the advantage of his study over the Jukes study and writes "the type of feeble-mindedness of which we are speaking is the one to which Deborah belongs, that is, to the high grade, or moron."[18]

Deborah Kallikak quite literally, to this day, defines what is meant by Goddard's "moron."

Although Goddard's designation for those persons falling in the highest functioning group of feebleminded people trumped Superintendent Wylie's suggestion of "moral imbecile," Goddard's "menace of the feeble-minded" rhetoric propagated the same message associated with the term "moral imbecility," which referred to the putative "innate criminality of the feebleminded."[19] In fact, the quote selected from *The Kallikak Family* for the *Oxford English Dictionary* was from a section of the book discussing this very issue.

"The formerly much discussed question of the hereditary character of crime received no solution from the Jukes family," explained Goddard, "but in the light of present-day knowledge of the sciences of criminology and biology, there is every reason to conclude that criminals are made and not born. The best material out of which to make criminals, and perhaps the material from which they are most frequently made, is feeble-mindedness.

"The reader must remember that the type of feeble-mindedness of which we are speaking is the one to which Deborah belongs, that is, to the high grade, or

[17] Goddard, 1911e, p. 8.
[18] Simpson and Weiner, 1989, p. 1090.
[19] Rafter, 1997, p. 55.

moron. All the facts go to show that this type of people makes up a large percentage of our criminals."[20]

Eugenicists' assertion that the "material" from which criminals are made was
feeblemindedness was derived from a 19th-century doctrine called degeneracy (or degeneration) theory. The father of degeneration theory was Benedict
Augustin Morel (1809–1873), a French alienist who is best known as the first
person to introduce the term "dementia praecox" to describe the condition now
called schizophrenia. In fact, prior to the 20th century, schizophrenia was also
called Kraepelin-Morel disease, after Morel and Emil Kraepelin (1856–1926),
a German psychiatrist who further refined the description and definition of
"dementia praecox," and was the first person to describe Alzheimer's disease.
Morel, working as a resident at the Salpetriere, was smitten by Darwin's theories and in 1857 wrote an influential treatise titled *Traité des Dégénérescences
Physiques, Intellectuelles et Morales de l'espèce Humaine et des Causes qui Produisent
ces Variétés Maladives* [*Treatise on Physical, Intellectual, and Moral Degeneration in
Humans and the Conditions Producing These Detrimental States*].[21] In this he both
introduced the term "dementia praecox" and attributed it, and other conditions
such as cretinism and tuberculosis, to degeneration.

"Les degenerations sont des deviations maladives du type normal de
l'humanite hereditairement transmissibles et evoluant progressivement vers la
decheance" [Degenerations are deviations from the normal human type that
are transmissible by heredity and that deteriorate progressively toward extinc-
tion], explained Morel. Degeneration should be distinguished from our modern
understandings of the progress of a disease being accompanied by a gradual
decline in functioning or of the impact of a disease resulting in the *disintegration*
of neural and other systems. Degeneration was "roughly synonymous with *bad
heredity* and conceived as an invisible attribute of the 'germ plasm' or 'blood' . . .
a tendency to devolve to a lower, simpler, less civilized state."[22]

Ontogeny recapitulates phylogeny is the oft-quoted but nevertheless erroneous
hypothesis, also called recapitulation theory, which posits that the development of any individual within a species (ontogeny or ontogenesis) progresses
through stages that resemble developmental stages of its evolutionary ancestors (phylogeny). The law was proposed by German biologist and philosopher
Ernst Haeckel (1834–1919), a physician who abandoned his practice when
he read Darwin's *Origin* and devoted the remainder of his life to evolutionary
biology.

Haeckel wrote in the 1899 *Riddle of the Universe at the Close of the Nineteenth
Century*

---

[20] Goddard, 1912, pp. 53–54.
[21] Carlson, 2001, p. 40.
[22] Rafter, 1997, p. 36.

[The] history of the embryo must be completed by a second, equally valuable, and closely connected branch of thought, the history of race. Both of these branches of evolutionary science, are, in my opinion, in the closest causal connection; this arises from the reciprocal action of the laws of heredity and adaptation . . . ontogenesis is a brief and rapid recapitulation of phylogenesis, determined by the physiological functions of heredity (generation) and adaptation (maintenance).

Unfortunately, Haeckel was wrong. Although the field of comparative embryology has shown that embryos across species share common precursors that take on different developmental trajectories depending on the species, there's no evidence that human embryos pass through anything resembling stages that recapitulate ancestral or lower forms. This is unfortunate not principally because it was wrong, because science progresses by the proposal of hypotheses and theories that are tested and, almost always, eventually abandoned, but because of the consequences of its application to social sciences.

Haeckel himself was a proponent of "biogenic" theory, which proposed that the development of races paralleled the development of individuals and that some races, which he viewed as unique species, were inferior or less developed than others, sort of recaptiulation theory applied to races. His theory was represented by an oft-reprinted drawing. At one end were most advanced races, Europeans of course; at the other end were simians, with gradual steps from the lowest of simians (Baboon) up through the great apes and then to lower human races (species) beginning with a Tasmanian, followed by an African, an aboriginal Australian, a Fuegian, an East Asian and, finally, the European.

"The pictures were arranged to show a gradual change in skull shape, and the profile of the last human, the Tasmanian, looked very similar to the profile of the gorilla [in the picture immediately after the Tasmanian]," noted Richard Weikart, but "Haeckel made sure no one missed the point by commenting in his caption that his illustrations demonstrated graphically that 'the differences between the lowest humans and the highest apes are smaller than the differences between the lowest and highest humans.'"[23]

Haeckel "played a chief role in the acceptance and substantiation of Darwin's ideas in Germany, both within scientific discourses—particularly in his work on marine invertebrates—and in popular culture, which he helped to shape in best-selling books."[24] Further, he was a strong proponent for eliminating the unfit. "The only reason we do not kill 'defective' children at birth is because we are following emotion rather than reason,"[25] he wrote.

---

[23] Weikart, 2004, p. 106.
[24] Lustig, 2004, p. 2.
[25] Weikart, 2004, p. 147.

Degeneration theory can be thought of as rather the opposite of recapitulation theory. Instead of organisms passing through ancestral stages in the process of developing to a mature organism, degeneration theory held that under
certain circumstances, humans would, as Rafter mentioned, devolve to a lower,
simpler, less civilized state (though this is where the analogy with recapitulation
theory parts ways, as degeneration theory posits a devolution to a lower state,
but not a lower species or ancestral stage). This occurred over generations; was
hypothesized to be passed on through heredity; could be triggered by mental
impairments or, more associated with eugenicists' versions of degeneracy theory,
by such factors as alcoholism or immoral behavior; and could also be reversed by
moral behavior and righteous living.

Morel's degeneration theory was combined with social Darwinism by Caesar
Lombroso (1836–1909) in the development of an influential theory that criminals were born, not made, and, in fact, that this innate criminalism was a "throw-
back to the past line of descent from ape to man."[26]

Moral imbeciles or moral imbecility involved the application of degeneration
theory to the feebleminded.[27] "Every mentally backward person, they [super-
intendents] warned, is afflicted with moral imbecility, a congenital and inherited inability to tell right from wrong," Rafter observed. "In addition, there is a
particularly criminalistic subgroup of the feebleminded, moral imbeciles, whose
intellectual defects can be discerned only by experts."[28] It was to this group to
whom Wylie referred. In *The Kallikak Family*, Goddard does not refer to moral
imbeciles, yet he uses the word "immorality" or "immoral" 17 times, all in reference to members of Deborah's family. Virtually all of them were described, in
essence, as hereditary criminals, prostitutes, and other forms of ne'er-do-wells.
Eugenicists were not only concerned about the degeneration of physical traits,
but also equally, and perhaps more, concerned with moral degeneration—the
idea that one generation at a time, the Jukes, Kallikaks, Nams, and all the other
families charted by eugenicists were devolving to lower states of morality.

So, the association between the feebleminded and social ills, such as criminal
behavior, prostitution, and so forth, was, in the mind of eugenicists, not simply
a function of the types of behaviors that people of limited intellectual capacity
might engage in or even that these people might be more highly suggestible and
more prone to get into trouble, but that these "moral imbeciles" would create
more and more degenerate offspring who would, in turn, further degrade society.

"Every feeble-minded person, especially the higher-grade imbecile, is a
potential criminal," wrote Fernald in a presentation at the American Association
for the Study of the Feeble-Minded in Vineland in 1912, "needing only the
proper environment and opportunity for the development and expression of his

[26] Carlson, 2001, p. 45.
[27] Rafter, 1997, p. 55.
[28] Rafter, 1997, pp. 55–56.

criminal tendencies. The unrecognized imbecile is a most dangerous element in the community. There are many crimes committed by imbeciles for every one committed by an insane person. The average prison population includes more imbeciles than lunatics."[29]

Fernald's speech was a litany of the burdens imposed by the feebleminded:

"It is certain that the feeble-minded girl or woman in the city rarely escapes the sexual experiences that too often result in the birth of more defectives and degenerates . . ."

"The feeble-minded are a parasitic, predatory class . . ."

"They cause unutterable sorrow at home and are a menace and a danger to the community . . ."[30]

"Feeble-minded women are almost invariably immoral, and if at large usually become carriers of venereal disease or give birth to children who are as defective as themselves . . ."

"Many of the immoral and diseased girls found in rescue homes and shelters are defective and absolutely incapable of reform . . ."

"A majority of the parents prosecuted by the Society for the Prevention of Cruelty to Children for abuse of their own children are feeble-minded . . ."

"It has been truly said that feeble-mindedness is the mother of crime, pauperism and degeneracy. It is certain that the feeble-minded and the progeny of the feeble-minded constitute one of the great social and economic burdens of modern times . . ."[31]

When Goddard positioned his newly minted "moron class" in close approximation to the already well-known notions of moral imbecility and degeneracy theory, he was intentionally aligning that term with a way of thinking about the feebleminded guaranteed to strike fear into the hearts of progressive, socially minded Americans.

"When I use a word, it means just what I choose it to mean, neither more nor less," says Humpty Dumpty to Alice.

Goddard meant "moron" to mean "moral imbecile."

Goddard's emerging prominence as a leading expert in mental testing and the Binet-Simon Scale tests coincided with his growing involvement in Davenport's eugenics movement, and the two quickly melded into a consistent theme, that of the potential menace of the feebleminded. "All mental defectives would be delinquents in the very nature of the case," Goddard told the audience at the 38th Annual Meeting of the National Conference of Charities and Corrections

---

[29] Fernald, 1912, p. 91.
[30] Fernald, 1912, p. 90.
[31] Fernald, 1912, p. 92.

in Boston in early June 1911, "did not some one exercise some care over them."[32] "The Menace of the Feeble Minded" was published in that same month in the journal *Pediatrics*, emphasizing the menace of the moron, who, he argued, may look normal but whose germ plasm was a threat to the social stability of the nation. Goddard repeated the message time and again, arousing fear and anxiety like the sound of a far-off drumbeat sounding steadily through the dark night. The loudest and most clearly heard of these drumbeats was, of course, *The Kallikak Family*.

"The parallelism of two descendants from one common ancestor, makes the study one of the most enlightening and instructive contributions to heredity that has ever been made," wrote Rogers in his review of the book in the *Journal of Psycho-Asthenics* in December of 1912. "The illustrations showing the housing conditions of some of the 'bad' side, serve a good purpose in impressing upon the reader the nature of the usual environmental conditions in such cases, and into which such people always gravitate, and in which they always remain unless the stock is rehabilitated by the influx of better blood."

"The photo of the young descendant from which the study started," Rogers continued, "and the cuts representing hand work produced by her, with a description of her mental reactions to the laboratory tests, are well calculated to impress upon those unfamiliar with the moron grade, from which the bulk of all mental defectives come, the social and economic limitations of this class, despite their trained accomplishments in certain limited directions."[33]

And that was the point. *The Kallikak Family* was "well calculated to impress" on the American public the "menace of the feebleminded," and particularly the threat of Goddard's moron class. The pictures to which Rogers referred were, indeed, compelling. There were, first, the photographs of Deborah at the Training School. Posed shots, with Deborah coifed and groomed, these near-studio pictures of Deborah seated in a rocking chair reading a book; at a sewing machine, or posed as a waitress; in a garden or with a pet; were intended to deliver several messages. One such message pertained to Goddard's implications about the moron class. Deborah was not threatening looking in any way. In fact, she was attractive . . . perhaps too attractive, the reader was supposed to conclude. She was a menace . . . "a typical illustration of the mentality of a high-grade feeble-minded person, the moron, the delinquent, the kind of girl or woman that fills our reformatories,"[34] described Goddard in the narrative accompanying the photographs.

The proof of her status as a moron was, of course, based on her less-than-sterling performance on the Binet-Simon Scale.

"By the Binet Scale this girl showed, in April, 1910, the mentality of a nine-year-old child with two points over; January, 1911, 9 years, 1 point; September,

---

[32] Goddard, 1911f, p. 64.
[33] Rogers, 1912, pp. 83–84.
[34] Goddard, 1912, pp. 11.

1911, 9 years, 2 points; October, 1911, 9 years, 3 points. She answers correctly all of the questions up to age 7 except the repetition of five figures, where she transposes two of them. She does not read the selection in the required time, nor does she remember what she reads.

In counting the stamps, her first answer was "ten cents," which she later corrected. Under age nine, none of her definitions are *"better than by use"*—"Fork is to eat with," "Chair to sit on," and so forth. She can sometimes arrange the weights in their proper order and at other times not. The same is true of putting the three words into a sentence. She does not know money. Her definitions of abstract terms are very poor, in some cases barely passable, nor can she put together the dissected sentences. She rhymes "storm" with "spring," and "milk" with "mill," afterward using "bill," "will," and "till."[35]

The photos of Deborah also served to counter the deplorable conditions depicted in the photographic "evidence" of the degeneracy of Deborah's family that followed. "Deborah is pictured enjoying all the blessings of middle-class domesticity within her institution, while her less fortunate relatives still lived in dilapidated huts—a condition that Goddard interpreted as proof of their poor heredity and consequent inability to control their environment."[36]

These pictures are grainer, most probably because they were taken by Elizabeth Kite during her visits in the field. Martin Elks noted that a central theme in the photographs is that of the "hovel."

"The image of a hovel is a common representation associated with the feeble-minded,"[37] beginning, Elk's noted, with the Jukes. Degenerate families were posed in front of what can best be described as hovels, all looking as if they are about to fall down, "its construction from wood and scraps of building materials with holes and gaps in the walls; people posed in front of the hovel (thereby juxtaposing degenerate people with their degenerate homes); isolated location in rural settings (the house is usually a solitary edifice); and with animals nearby."[38]

"The image of the hovel is, therefore, one of poverty; squalor, and an animal-like, unhealthy, and disease-ridden lifestyle. It is a particularly powerful image because eugenicists believed that the feeble-minded created their own environment."[39]

The first photograph depicting the circumstances of Deborah's "Kallikak" ancestry is, appropriately then, the hovel identified as the last home of Millard Kallikak. Other pictures with strikingly poor looking children and adults standing out front include the picture labeled "Great Grandchildren of 'Old Sal,'" with three young children sitting on the crumbling porch of a wooden house that clearly fits the description of a hovel. The second picture depicts a family of

---

[35] Goddard, 1912, pp. 12.
[36] Zenderland, 1988, p. 743.
[37] Elks, 2005, p. 271.
[38] Elks, 2005, pp. 271–272.
[39] Elks, 2005, p. 272.

the supposed degenerates sitting or standing in front of an edifice that looks as if it's a mud or stone-plaster construction and, as such, none too secure. These images both contrast with the pictures of Deborah in the relative splendor of the Vineland Training School, but also as clear iconography indicating the "feeble-mindedness" of the Kallikaks.

Another image repeated in *The Kallikak Family* pictures, noted Elks, was that of the ruins of buildings. Again, these images are more than historical documentation for Goddard and Kite; their inclusion in the text was likely intended to send messages. The most obvious such message was that of the connection between ruin and feeblemindedness. Elks, however, suggested that pictures of ruins are, in one sense, pictures of old hovels, and thus symbolic of the same meaning as hovel pictures. Further, Elks suggested a biblical symbolism in the ruins pictures: that is, that ruin is the ultimate outcome of sin, à la Sodom, Gomorrah, and Babel; and the pictures of ruins depict the ultimate and, perhaps, inevitable outcome of the sin of Martin Kallikak, Jr. That the first such ruin picture is of a mountain hut supposedly built by Martin Kallikak, Jr. emphasizes who was the original sinner, or at least progeny of the original sinner.

With the publication of *The Kallikak Family*, then, Goddard provided the eugenic movement with its most powerful image of the menace of the moron.

The story of the Kallikaks was greeted with acclaim and achieved great popularity. Goddard's presentation of feeblemindedness as a hereditary problem was received with great enthusiasm by the general public and proponents of the eugenics movement alike. The simplistic explanation that social ills like poverty, prostitution, crime, and alcoholism were the result of feeblemindedness, particularly the high-grade moron type defined by Goddard, was appealing to the spirit of the time. To improve society, the "menace of the feeble-minded" must be recognized and controlled.

Shortly after its publication, the book was given very favorable reviews in a number of periodicals. The *Dial*, for example, proclaimed that the book was "a remarkable human document" and a "convincing sociological essay, a tragedy of incompetence, and a sermon with a shocking example as text."[40]

G. Stanley Hall's *American Journal of Psychology* called the study a "find" and self-congratulatorily praised Goddard for having "the training which enables him to utilize the discovery to the utmost."[41]

"An epoch-making study of the hereditary transmission of mental deficiency in a degenerate family,"[42] is how fellow mental tester Lewis Terman described the book.

---

[40] Goddard, 1914a, p. 603.
[41] Goddard, 1914a, p. 603.
[42] Terman, 1916, p. 354.

The popular appeal of the Kallikak story was perhaps best illustrated when, in 1913, Goddard was approached concerning the dramatic rights to the book.

"I want to apply for the dramatic rights of your book, *The Kallikak Family*," wrote New York agent Alice Kauser. "Joseph Medill Patterson, who has written plays with ideas back of them, is very much interested in it and has asked me to ascertain if an arrangement could not be entered into by which he could make a play out of your book."[43]

Joseph Medill Patterson was a Pulitzer Prize–winning newspaperman, novelist, and playwright. His grandfather founded the *Chicago Tribune* and Patterson himself established the *New York Daily News*. Patterson's politics were definitely left leaning. He was a proclaimed member of the Socialist Party, serving as campaign manager for Eugene V. Debs, the Socialist candidate in the 1908 presidential election. He wrote a novel and two plays on social topics, including alcoholism and divorce. As copublisher of the *Chicago Tribune*, Patterson forced Chester Gould to change the name of his new cartoon strip detective from *Plainclothes Tracy* to *Dick Tracy*.

"I am sure," Goddard replied, "we should have to be assured that the play would be one that would carry the moral lesson which the book is intended to convey. We would not consent to its being dramatized for any other purpose."[44]

Despite this rather cool reception, Goddard was interested enough to meet with Kauser in New York City. Apparently, however, the negotiations with Ms. Kauser and Patterson did not go well, as there is no evidence that the book was adapted for the stage. Interest in the dramatic properties of the story, however, did not die. In 1925, after Goddard had left the Training School, a Kansas City, Missouri, man contacted Superintendent Johnstone and described a play he had written based on the Kallikak book. He had titled it *The Seed*.

It was not just the general public that received the book well. The eminent Harvard professor of genetics, E. M. East, praised Goddard's hereditary work as it was reported in the Kallikak book and in Goddard's more extensive volume that followed, titled *Feeble-Mindedness: Its Causes and Consequences*. Noting that findings were consistent with Mendel's unit-trait inheritance (i.e., feeblemindedness is inherited through a single recessive gene), East stated:

Again, the results of unions between a feebleminded parent (nn) and a normal heterozygote, a carrier (Nn), or between two carriers (Nn x Nn), are remarkably in accord with theory. They are even more closely in accord with theory than Goddard makes out in his report, for he did not make the appropriate corrections when calculating the expected number of feeble-minded children. . . . When the proper mathematical corrections are made in such cases, by a simple and correct algebraic method, the correspondence

---

[43] Zenderland, 1998, p. 184.
[44] Zenderland, 1998, p. 185.

between the theoretical expectation and the actual result is so good as to be almost suspicious.[45]

Deborah's date with infamy had arrived.

By early 1914, *The Kallikak Family* had been translated into German and was being published in serial form in that country. On June 8 of that year, Goddard's wife Emma embarked as tour leader and chaperone for eight young women to Europe, starting with a night on the town in New York City. After dinner at the restaurant in the Martinique Hotel on 32nd Street, the women, accompanied by Dr. Goddard, took in a showing of Ziegfield's Follies at the New Amsterdam Theater. The following morning, the women boarded the Hoboken & Holland America Liner, the *SS Nieuw Amsterdam*, sailing from Hoboken to Rotterdam.

The luxury liner docked in Rotterdam on June 18 after an uneventful voyage. The group toured The Hague, Amsterdam and the Rijks Museum, and Hildesheim, Hanover, and Berlin, Germany. From Berlin the group moved to Potsdam, where the carefree tour began to take on a slightly more ominous tone. In Potsdam, they encountered a garrison of 7,000 German soldiers. From Potsdam the women traveled to Dresden and reveled in the historic city whose destruction through firebombing during World War II would be immortalized by Kurt Vonnegut. Then it was on to Munich and, appropriately, a Wagner concert. Munich was followed by Venice, Milano, and Bellagio, Italy, and up to Lucerne, Switzerland, and the Glacier Garden.

By July 24, the group was in Zurich, Switzerland, having traveled from Lucerne to Interlaken, Meiringen, Gletsch, and Zermatt. On the train from Zurich to Heidelberg, Germany, Emma Goddard was left behind, along with the baggage and tickets, but the group, their chaperone, and their baggage were reunited at the next train stop. When the tourists arrived in Heidelberg on July 28 though, they found the town in turmoil over the declaration of war between Austria and Serbia after the assassination of Archduke Franz Ferdinand, heir to the Austro-Hungarian throne. The weather portended the political climate, raining constantly. Emma Goddard had to be hospitalized briefly with typhoid fever, but recovered and shepherded the group to Paris, where their tour ended abruptly on the final day of July as Europe's attention turned to the Great War. By the next day, August 1, Germany had declared war on Russia and, two days later, on France. On August 4, the German Army invaded Belgium and Britain was drawn into the bloody conflict.

---

[45] East, 1927, pp. 104 – 105.

❧ ❧ ❧

While Emma Goddard experienced the turmoil of typhoid and the outbreak of World War I, Deborah Kallikak was experiencing her own turmoil, not as disruptive to the world, but completely disruptive to her own world. In July of 1914, at the age of 25 and after having lived at the Vineland Training School for 17 of those years, Deborah was transferred to the women's institution across the street.

In 1888, the same year the Training School was established, the Reverend Garrison also founded and became the first superintendent of the New Jersey State Institution for Feeble-Minded Women. Approved by New Jersey Governor Robert S. Green on March 27, 1888, the institution opened on May 1 in the former home of Professor Marcius Willson, across Landis Avenue from the Training School. Willson had been a pioneer in literacy instruction, authoring three early reading series, and had retired in Vineland. He sold his home, barn, and outbuildings for $10,000 to the state of New Jersey.

The new institution was intended by Garrison to provide a custodial situation in which feebleminded women could be placed to keep them from "propagating their kind."[46] The Training School was intended to "train children in the home-school, then move custodial females across the street."[47] That new institution across the street was to be Deborah's home for the rest of her life.

"When she was one of the group called in before the Superintendent and advised of her impending transfer to the State Home for Women, across the street, it was a blow from which she never recovered," wrote someone familiar with her at that time about the transfer.

Even 60 years after the event, Deborah's eyes still watered when recounting her walk across the street from the Training School, pausing at the Reverend Garrison's tomb to thank him for his kindness.

"The Training School. My home."[48]

---

[46] Doll, 1988, p. 4.
[47] Doll, 1988, p. 4.
[48] Reeves, 1938, p. 199.

CHAPTER 7

The Criminal Imbecile

"Born criminal" was a term that biologically-oriented theorists used to refer to their assumptions about the innate nature of criminal behavior; or more accurately, the inherited character of criminals themselves.[1] The father of the notion of the so-called born criminal was Cesare Lombroso (1836–1909). Lombroso—a psychiatrist on the medical school faculty at the University of Turin—combined elements of Morel's degeneration theory, physiognomy, and phrenology to create a theory of innate criminality.

Born in northern Italy in 1835, Lombroso graduated from medical school in 1858, and then served the revolutionary forces in the wars for Italian unification. By 1871, when Austrian rule in northern Italy had been subjugated and Rome had been established as the capital of the unified country, Lombroso had served as director of several insane asylums. In 1876 he was appointed to a distinguished chair of medicine at the University of Turin. By then he had also heard his calling.

In 1871, he was performing the autopsy of a prisoner he had known who had been a repeat offender.

"At the sight of that skull," Lombroso would later claim, "I seemed to see all of a sudden, lighted up as a vast plain under a flaming sky, the problem of the nature of the criminal—an atavistic being who reproduces in his person the ferocious instincts of primitive humanity and the inferior animals."[2] That Lombroso seems to have at worst fabricated and at best embellished this story of the revelatory nature of the birth of criminal anthropology seems apropos given its rapid disappearance as a credible science.[3]

From this apocryphal beginning, Lombroso constructed a detailed theory of the *Criminal Man* and *Criminal Woman*—titles from his two most popular books—that assimilated aspects of Morel's degeneration theory, suggesting that

---

[1] Rafter, 1997, p. 9.
[2] Gibson, 2002, p. 20.
[3] Gibson, 2002, p. 20.

acquired devolution of the species included both physical and moral traits, with
an emphasis on (1) physiognomy's premise that a person's internal character
could be deduced from external appearances; (2) phrenology's suggestion that
features of the head reflected internal psychological structures; and (3) atavistic
tendencies of criminals.[4]

Physiognomy underwent a renaissance during the 18th and 19th centuries,
in part attributable to writers like Charles Dickens, whose rich descriptions
of characters' facial countenances reinforced, in the Victorian reading public's
mind, physiognomist's linkages between certain facial features and human personality or character. In *A Christmas Carol*, Dickens described Ebenezer Scrooge
evoking images of ice and steel, with sharp facial features and thin lips.

> Oh! But he was a tight-fisted hand at the grind-stone, Scrooge! a squeez-
> ing, wrenching, grasping, scraping, clutching, covetous, old sinner! Hard and
> sharp as flint, from which no steel had ever struck out generous fire; secret,
> and self-contained, and solitary as an oyster. The cold within him froze his old
> features, nipped his pointed nose, shriveled his cheek, stiffened his gait; made
> his eyes red, his thin lips blue and spoke out shrewdly in his grating voice. A
> frosty rime was on his head, and on his eyebrows, and his wiry chin. He car-
> ried his own low temperature always about with him; he iced his office in the
> dog days; and didn't thaw it one degree at Christmas.[5]

Phrenology was also widely adopted by many Victorians, both in Britain and
America. Viennese physician Franz Joseph Gall (1758–1828), the founder of
phrenology, proposed that the brain was the seat of the mind; that the size of
one's brain was equated with its power or capacity; that the mind has "innate
faculties" that differ among people; that the shape of the brain correlated with
the development of these innate faculties; that the shape of the skull was determined by the size and shape of the brain itself; and, thus, that you could read the
surface of the skull to determine the development of brain areas that, in turn,
were correlated with personality characteristics.

Gall proposed 27 such faculties, including faculties for musical talent, words
and language, wit, ambition and vanity, morality, and valor. Not all of Gall's
proposed faculties were, however, desirable traits. Gall also included organs
for murder and carnivorousness, as well as larceny. Johann Gaspar Spurzheim
(1776–1832), a Gall devotee who later fell out with his mentor but was instrumental in popularizing phrenology, was the first of many to expand Gall's system
to include more and different brain faculties. Spurzhiem's list included locations
for combativeness, destructiveness, and covetiveness.

---

[4] Gibson, 2002, p. 20.
[5] Dickens, 1843, p. 2.

"The born criminal," wrote Lombroso, "shows in a proportion reaching 33% numerous specific characteristics that are almost always atavistic. Those who have followed us thus far have seen that many of the characteristics presented by savage races are very often found among born criminals."[6]

Atavism refers to the reappearance of characteristics associated with a species' remote ancestors. The spurious linkages between the presence of atavistic characteristics in primitive or "savage" races and criminality were central to Lombroso's theory of the born criminal.[7]

The "specific characteristics" born criminals supposedly exhibited were legion, and included a too-small or too-large head; a thick skull; strongly, arched brows; a low, retreating forehead; numerous Wormian bones (small bones found in-between cranial sutures); large and prominent zygomata (the bone commonly called the cheekbone); large, outstanding ears; facial asymmetry; strabismus; anomalies of bones of the nose; anomalies of teeth; prehensile feet (feet that posses the ability to grasp like a hand); left-handedness; simplicity of lines of the palm; abnormal wrinkles in the skin; and crispy hair.[8] The expression of a combination of peculiarities or anomalies in these various body features would, accordingly, signal that the person was a "born criminal"; someone whose morphological features were indicative of an atavistic individual who was predestined to be a criminal.

That the born criminal shared physical characteristics attributed to "savage peoples" was proof of degeneracy for Lombroso, as these more "primitive peoples" were seen by him and others to represent earlier stages in the development of the human species, much as Haeckel's biogenic theory had posited that the development of races paralleled the development of individuals and that some races were inferior or less developed than others. Morel himself had referred to the physical characteristics of supposedly degenerate people as the "stigmata of degeneration."[9]

"To those who . . . object that there are savage peoples who are honorable and chaste," Lombroso wrote, "we must reply that a certain degree of density of population and of association among men is necessary for crimes to develop. It is not possible for example, to steal when property does not exist, or to swindle when there is no trade. But the proof that these tendencies exist in germ in the savage, is that when they begin to pass from their stage of savagery and take on a little civilization they always develop the characteristics of criminality in exaggerated form. As Ferrero has pointed out to us, even when honor, chastity, and pity are found among savages, impulsiveness and laziness are never wanting.

---

[6] Lombroso, 1899, p. 365.
[7] Horn, 2003, p. 43.
[8] Lombroso, 1899, p. 371.
[9] Gelb, 1995, p. 2.

Savages have a horror of continuous work, so that for them the passage to active and methodical labor lies by the road of selection or of slavery only."[10]

Lombroso's atavism, however, attributed the germ of criminality to an even more ancient ancestral root: animal behavior.

"We may add that the atavism of the criminal . . . may go back far beyond the savage, even to the brutes themselves." Lombroso grounded his attribution of human criminality in a Darwinian view of nature, describing the evolution of insect-devouring plants as the first occurrence of criminality.[11]

Lombroso's theory of the born criminal changed over time. By the fourth edition of his influential book, *Criminal Man*, as Gibson has noted, Lombroso had revised his theory in several ways, including postulating that epilepsy was a "universal substructure of all criminal behavior."[12] Lombroso extended his conceptualization of the born criminal to include two subcategories, the epileptic criminal and the morally insane criminal. People who were morally insane "appeared normal in physique and intelligence, but were unable to distinguish between good and evil."[13] Alienist (an early term used for those who practiced a form of psychiatry) James Prichard (1786–1848) coined the term "moral insanity" prior to Lombroso's use of it, defining it as referring to a person whose impairment was of their capacity to behave in moral or ethical ways, but not to their intelligence.[14]

Lombroso's recommended remedies to crime varied according to the criminal's gender or age, and as much a function of the type of criminal as the type or nature of the crime. Most female criminals should, according to Lombroso, receive suspended sentences, except when the crime is homicide, in which case confinement in a convent was the preferred punishment. Petty offenses by women could be addressed by penalties "which will touch female vanity, such as cutting the hair."[15]

Children and the elderly were to be treated similarly. Children and adolescents should be placed with kindly families or charitable institutions, agricultural colonies, or reform schools. The elderly should be sent to a workhouse.

In the case of crimes of passion, Lombroso believed that remorse for the crime was punishment enough and that a fine, reprimand, or removal from the city in which the crime was perpetrated would be sufficient. This lenient approach was applied, as well, to political criminals and for some occasional criminals, with the exception that the latter was to also provide some restitution. Criminaloids (occasional criminals pulled into crime by their environments) should receive a suspended sentence for a first offense, with a requirement for

---

[10] Lombroso, 1899, p. 366–367.
[11] Horn, 2003, p. 39.
[12] Gibson, 2002, p. 25.
[13] Gibson, 2002, p. 25.
[14] Rafter, 1997, p. 75.
[15] Lombroso, 1899, p. 407.

restitution. Criminaloids who repeatedly offended would need to be committed to workhouses or agricultural colonies.

For the criminally insane, Lombroso recommended confinement to a criminal asylum—hardly a surprise given he had himself directed several such institutions. Depending on the nature and type of the crime, Lombroso suggested that "those who are affected with a transitory or intermittent form of insanity and show signs of a perfect cure should be selected for discharge after one or two years of observation and subjected after their release to monthly medical visits."[16]

Lombroso's tolerance ended, however, with the born criminal.

"It would be a mistake," Lombroso argued, "to imagine that the measures which have been shown to be effective with other criminals could be successfully applied to born criminals; for these are, for the most part, refractory to all treatment, even to the most affectionate care begun at the very cradle."[17]

"There are many jurists, who are deeply versed in scientific matters and in the current of the scientific movement with regard to the criminal, who have not been able to gauge its depth accurately for want of physiological ideas or of direct contact," Lombroso lamented. "These men have maintained that the great numbers of insane and feeble-minded to be found among criminals, and consequently the limited responsibility of many criminals for their crime, lead inevitably to the reduction of the penalty. They do not understand that the new anthropological notions, while diminishing the guilt of the born criminal, imposes upon us at the same time the duty of prolonging his sentence, because the more irresponsible criminals are the more they are to be dreaded, since their innate and atavistic criminal tendencies can be neutralized only by selection and sequestration."[18]

As such, born criminals who engaged in crimes not reaching the status of a capital offense should, according to Lombroso, be permanently segregated on an island or outside the city with mandatory work to offset the cost of their incarceration. To those born criminals who were engaged in violent crimes, he recommended the death penalty.[19]

"The fact that there exist such beings as born criminals," wrote Lombroso in 1899, "organically fitted for evil, atavistic reproductions, not simply of savage men but even of the fiercest animals, far from making us more compassionate towards them, as has been maintained, steels us against all pity. Our love for animals . . . has not reached such a point that we are willing to sacrifice our own lives for their benefit."[20]

---

[16]Lombroso, 1899, p. 424.
[17]Lombroso, 1899, p. 432.
[18]Lombroso, 1899, p. 361.
[19]Gibson, 2002, pp. 26–27.
[20]Lombroso, 1899, pp. 427–428.

❧ ❧ ❧

The 1911 English translation of Lombroso's *Crime: Its Causes and Remedies* was instrumental in spreading his theory to an American audience, although his work was familiar to the superintendents of institutions for the feebleminded earlier, mainly from a partial English translation titled *The Female Delinquent* and through Havelock Ellis's popular text, *The Criminal*, which through four printings and over more than 20 years presented Lombroso's theory of the born criminal to an English-speaking audience. Lombroso's theory was tantalizingly close to what eugenicists were seeking to promote their social control agenda. His message, that born criminals could not be rehabilitated, as their criminality was innate, certainly fit their eugenic message. His inclusion of epilepsy as a universal substrate also fed into eugenic rhetoric. There were, however, several problems prohibiting Davenport, Goddard, and others from adopting Lombroso's theory wholesale. First, although Lombroso identified heredity as a cause of criminal behavior, his articulation of specific hereditary mechanisms for that transmission was confusing and overly generic.

"The organic type is constantly being fixed by heredity," he wrote in 1899. "The children themselves have a large part in the manifestation of heredity, by the fact that they can assimilate more or less actively the hereditary characteristics. Hereditary influences are not all manifested at any given moment, or once for all. They are latent in the organism and manifest themselves gradually throughout the whole period of development. Everything organic is subject to the general laws of heredity; the characteristics inherited by any part of the organism follow the general course of the development of that organ, and reaches its highest point at the period of the organ's greatest development."[21]

Second, and perhaps more important, Lombroso said next to nothing about the link between feeblemindedness and criminality. He did devote several pages in *Crime: Its Cause and Remedies* to the Juke family narrative as proof of the hereditary nature of crime, but saw prostitution and atavism as the hereditary components in the Jukes equation, mentioning idiocy only among a number of "diseases, malformations, and injuries" connected with criminals. In large part, the viability of the eugenicists' message concerning the menace of the feebleminded was contingent on a causal relationship between feeblemindedness and criminal behavior, and this did not exist in Lombroso's theory of the born criminal. Granted, Lombroso spoke of the criminally insane, but by the late 19th century, the class was being viewed with a great deal of skepticism by the general public as "a euphemism for reckless, irresponsible, and selfish behavior."[22]

Goddard's attribution of the cause of criminality was surprisingly not nature, but nurture. "In the light of present-day knowledge of the sciences of criminol-

---

[21] Lombroso, 1899, p. 174.
[22] Gelb, 1989, p. 367.

ogy and biology," Goddard wrote in *The Kallikak Family*, "there is every reason to conclude that criminals are made and not born."[23]

It was the relationship between feeblemindedness and criminal behavior that was important to Goddard, eugenicists, and institution superintendents. "In regard to criminality," Goddard continued in *The Kallikak Family*, "we now have enough studies to make us certain that at least 25 per cent of this class is feeble-minded."[24]

"Nearly every case," intoned Walter Fernald, referring to case studies of 19 inmates from his Waverly, Massachusetts, institution at the 1908 meeting of the American Medico-Psychological Association in Cincinnati, "presents various physical stigmata of degeneracy in the skull, ears, face, teeth, palate or physiognomy. All of these patients boast of their evil acts and eagerly discuss the criminal experiences of a new-comer. They gloat over newspaper stories of crime and shame. The cases described fairly represent the criminal imbecile type."[25]

By the time the idea of the "morally insane" had fallen into disfavor, however, the institution superintendents had modified it to fit their needs and applied it to the feebleminded as the "moral imbecile," and it was this term that eugenicists appropriated to create the class of people they called the "criminal imbecile." According to social historian Steven Gelb, among the first of the superintendents to suggest a subclass of the feebleminded who were, in essence, congenital criminals, was Isaac Kerlin. Kerlin, who in 1876, as director of the Pennsylvania Training School for Idiotic and Feeble-minded Children, convened the first meeting of what became the Association of Medical Officers of American Institutions for Idiotic and Feeble-Minded Persons, was among the first generation of superintendents of institutions for the feebleminded and tailored his message to emphasize the need for these fledgling asylums.

"Kerlin combined zeal with an inflexible will, administrative brilliance with a need to control, and sentimentality with shrewdness,"[26] described Rafter. According to his successor, Martin Barr, Kerlin was genial but had an abhorrence of sloth and self-indulgence, including "excessive use of the organs . . . of procreation."[27] Rafter suggested that his personality may have predisposed him to eugenics; he had a desire for purity that stemmed from his Quaker beliefs and was a perfectionist, so much so that he kept a notebook recording his secretary's spelling errors.[28] That he approached the habilitation of the feebleminded with an emphasis on criticizing the unproductive, impure nature of idiots is, then, not surprising.

---

[23] Goddard, 1912, p. 54.
[24] Goddard, 1912, p. 57.
[25] Fernald, 1909, p. 30.
[26] Rafter, 1997, p. 60.
[27] Rafter, 1997, p. 60.
[28] Rafter, 1997, p. 60.

"To show that a burdensome, unproductive idiot properly trained in a special facility could become a productive, law-abiding worker was a crucial task for superintendents seeking private and public funds,"[29] observed historian James Trent. Kerlin did this by emphasizing the burden of the feebleminded on the family and society, and the linkages between feeblemindedness and social problems. To make this link, he suggested that there were, among feebleminded people, those who were not just intellectually impaired, but morally impaired as well. He described this group as "moral idiots."

"He was a moral idiot," wrote Kerlin in 1858 of a Pennsylvania inmate. "He recognized no obligation to God nor man, and having some appreciation of the value of money and property, nothing that could be appropriated, was safe from his reach."[30]

"Steeped and seethed in crime," he wrote about a second inmate, "from the moment they enter the world, and hardened as steel by brutality; what surprise is it, that before their tongues cease lisping, they commence swearing, and before [they are] men, they are murderers; and while we tolerate a nursery of crime, why wonder and regret, that annually our criminal records, expose such a large percentage of juvenile theft, outrage, arson, and murder?"[31]

Kerlin's moral idiot was born and raised in poverty and among criminals: "steeped and seethed in crime" and brutality. His use of the term "moral idiot" was distinguished from the earlier term, "moral insanity," in that moral idiots were people identified most importantly as idiots or feebleminded; in essence the group Goddard would eventually label as "morons."

In 1884, Kerlin had proposed a classification system that added a fourth categorical area, "moral imbecile," to the three categories of feeblemindedness (e.g., idiot, imbecile, feebleminded) most frequently used. A moral imbecile was someone who lacked "the willpower to be other than they are, or to do otherwise than they do."

"These moral monstrosities," Kerlin wrote, "are often conceived and born in the best of families; inheriting graces of body and precocious in accomplishments, there is an inherent failure to recognize the claims of others, which is the foundation of duty, truth, respect for property, prudence, discretion and all the primary virtues of civilized societies; in this declension consists the essence of moral insanity and imbecility."[32]

By 1884, however, Kerlin had abandoned his contextualization of the moral imbecile as "steeped and seethed" in poverty and deplorable environmental conditions. Instead, his conceptualization of the moral imbecile embodied both the emerging (as it was in the 1880s) presumption that all forms of feebleminded-

---

[29] Trent, 1994, p. 20.
[30] Kerlin, 1858, pp. 48–49 quoted in Trent, 1994, p. 21.
[31] Kerlin, 1858, pp. 98–101 quoted in Trent, 1994, p. 21.
[32] Kerlin, 1887, p. 37 as quoted in Scheerenberger, 1983, p. 111.

ness were hereditary and the degenerative nature of the born criminal. "The moral sense being the latest and highest attribute of our rising humanity," he wrote in 1887, "it is the first and most to suffer from the law of reversion to the lower type, when from any cause the progressive development of a family is broken by the birth of a defective child."[33] In other words, because morality was the most recent, evolutionary, trait of humanity, it was the first to degenerate.

By the end of the century, superintendents had incorporated under their umbrella of feeblemindedness the condition of moral imbecility, even though the construct had, like moral insanity, come to refer to people without obvious intellectual impairments. A moral imbecile was someone with the characteristics of the degenerate born criminal, but without the physical stigmata. Rafter noted that this had practical applications as well as making good sense, politically, for the superintendents. They could use the fear factor of the moral imbecile to justify the need for the growth of institutions and to petition for more money from legislators, but they could also use these fairly capable inmates as, in essence, free labor. "Moral imbeciles . . . make first-class foremen," noted Faribault superintendent A. C. Rogers.[34]

Led mostly by Kerlin's protégés, including his successor at Elwyn, Martin Barr, the moral imbecile became a fixture in classification schemes of feeblemindedness. Barr's 1904 text *Mental Defectives* listed "Moral Imbeciles" as one of four educational classifications of the feebleminded, recommending "custodial life and perpetual guardianship" for this class and describing them now as mentally *and* morally deficient and identifiable in three grades; low, middle, and high—the former with a "bestial" temperament and the latter with "a genius for evil."[35]

As illustrated by Barr's definition, the notion of moral imbecility had morphed from its roots in moral insanity, which posited impairment in morality but not intelligence, to the co-occurrence of both mental and moral impairments. When, in 1910, Goddard linked the moron class to Binet-Simon Scale mental age (MA) scores of 12 years, he essentially completed the conversion of Lombroso's morally insane into the moral imbecile.

The moral imbecile and, later, Goddard's moron, was a much more effective vehicle through which eugenicists could convey their message to the public.

One aspect of Lombroso's work that was particularly useful for eugenicists, and devastating to women like Deborah Kallikak, was his application of the born criminal theory to women. Lombroso's *The Female Offender* was published in Italian in 1893. A partial English translation appeared in the United States

---

[33] Kerlin, 1887, p. 37 as quoted in Gelb, 1989, p. 370.
[34] Rogers, 1894, p. 477 as quoted in Rafter, 1997, p. 66.
[35] Barr, 1904, p. 90.

that same year. A full translation of the book's title is *Criminal Woman, the Prostitute, and the Normal Woman*. As Nicole Rafter and Mary Gibson observed, women presented a conundrum for Lombroso's born criminal theory. Lombroso, emblematic of most men of his era, viewed women as inferior to men. Among criminals, however, men far outnumbered women, suggesting, according to the born criminal theory, that they should be less atavistic then men. Because atavism refers to degeneration to a less developed level of the species, women could not be inferior to men and less atavistic at the same time. Lombroso's solution to the dilemma was to argue that women "were less criminal than men because of their inferiority to men."[36] That is, women were less developed than men to begin with, thus had comparatively fewer traits that could become "degenerative" and, as such, women who were born criminals were relatively more scarce than were men.[37]

True to his belief that born criminals harbor an animal atavism, Lombroso began his recitation of the crimes of women with an examination of the "crimes" of females in the animal world: crimes of passion and frenzy as demonstrated by female warrior ants; crimes of banditry and robbery as demonstrated by the actions of bandit bees; envy and malevolence, as illustrated by behaviors of doves and orangutans; sexual aberrations as attested to by supposedly homosexual behavior in cows, geese, ducks and pheasants; adultery among female pigeons and storks; crimes of maternal malfeasance as exhibited by cows, horses, and dogs who abandoned their maternal responsibilities or by infanticide among doves, goshawks, and crocodiles; and alcoholism, somewhat incredulously evidenced by bees drunk on fermented honey or cows crazed by a mixture of cannabis and opium.[38]

Next, Lombroso discussed the criminal acts of "savages and primitive women." These included women breaking gender-specific cultural prohibitions or taboos, many of which he felt were bizarre or irrational, but violations of which he counted as criminal behavior nonetheless. These included prohibitions against eating with men, entering male-only spaces, and various taboos pertaining to women during menstruation. Adultery and prostitution were next, followed by abortion and infanticide. Lombroso even identified witchcraft as a serious crime of women in the middle ages, and closed with poisoning as a frequent crime of savage women. Of all female offenses, however, Lombroso emphasized prostitution, writing in 1899 that "we may conclude that the true born criminal exists among women only in the form of the prostitute."[39]

Female born criminals evinced many of the same physical attributions that constituted the stigmata for male born criminals, although Lombroso identi-

[36] Rafter and Gibson, 2004, p. 9.
[37] Rafter and Gibson, 2004, p. 10.
[38] Lombroso, 1893, pp. 91–93.
[39] Lombroso, 1899, p. 406.

fied several other anomalies that he claimed bespoke degeneration in females, including moles; extreme hairiness; cleft palate; and anomalies of the breasts, nipples, and genitalia.

The crimes performed by female born criminals were described as crueler than even male born criminals, frequently multiple in nature, and often revolving around eroticism and passions. Further, female born criminals, observed Lombroso, had a propensity to commit crimes to obtain clothing and jewelry and were frequently motivated by jealousy and a desire for revenge.[40]

Lombroso's emphasis on the female born criminal played well with the eugenic fixation on feebleminded women, particularly women of childbearing age. Prostitution was one of the social ills most frequently discussed by eugenicists, in part because it was a social issue of great concern to progressives in the early 20th century. The Roosevelt era rhetoric pertaining to race suicide and changes in the role of women, fears about immigration, and white slavery threats kept the public on the edge about the threat to the American family and American values from prostitution.

The white slavery crusades of the early 20th-century were efforts to "eradicate forced prostitution."[41] So-called "white slavery narratives" issued frightening warnings of the thousands of innocent, and of course white, girls who were being forced into prostitution. These narratives focused on the rising number of young women, emancipated from previous generations' restrictions on women, who were entering the labor market in urban areas. Alone and on their own, according to white slave alarmists, they became potential victims for white slave procurers; to be abducted, supposedly, from dance halls, train stations, and the streets of the city.[42]

Eugenicists played on these fears to link white slavery and prostitution to feeblemindedness and heredity. Massachusetts superintendent Walter Fernald was particularly active in the white slavery crusades, chairing the Commonwealth of Massachusetts's Commission for the Investigation of the White Slave Traffic, So Called. Issuing a report in February of 1914, Fernald's commission "found" that in addition to the desultory nature of the youth of the time; the decadence of postindustrial-era urban areas; the supposedly crumbling family structure and moral training; and the explosion of single, young working women, feeblemindedness played a significant part in prostitution and the white slavery problem.

"The fact that one-half of the women examined were actually feeble-minded," Fernald and colleagues wrote, "clears the way for successful treatment of this portion of this class. The mental status of the prostitutes under arrest should

---

[40] Lombroso, 1893, pp. 182–192.
[41] Donovan, 2006, p. 1.
[42] Donovan, 2006, p. 23.

be determined and such of them as are found to be feeble-minded or defective delinquents should be placed under custodial treatment."[43]

The links among prostitution, white slavery, feeblemindedness, and the female born criminal, along with the subsequent construction of the moral imbecile and moron, made incarcerating women like Deborah all the more appealing to political and social progressives.

Goddard's own research on delinquency began with a small grant from the New Jersey legislature in 1911. Over the next few years, he tested criminals in the New Jersey State Hospital for the Insane and, on the request of a probation officer, 56 delinquent girls, ages 14–20. Of the latter, Goddard found that almost half belonged either to the 9- or 10-year level of intelligence and only four could pass the tests at the 13-year-old level.[44]

"Twenty-five per cent of delinquents are mentally defective," claimed Goddard in a presentation in Boston to the delegates of the National Conference on Charities and Correction in June of 1911. "All mental defectives would be delinquents in the very nature of the case, did not someone one exercise some care over them."

Goddard had just published his study of the use of the Binet-Simon Scale with public schoolchildren, and was seeking ways to validate the utility of the scale to identify the moron class. Goddard's solution to the problem of the mentally defective delinquent was predictable. "We must have enough institutions or colonies for the feebleminded to care for all the feebleminded delinquents at least."[45]

The real problem, he asserted, was identifying these potential delinquents and segregating them before they had the opportunity to commit their inevitable crime. "How shall we recognize this feeble-minded child of high type, this moron grade, as we now call them? Until recently, we have been more or less helpless in this matter, but now we may say with perfect assurance that the Binet tests of intelligence are entirely satisfactory and can be relied upon to pick out the mental defective at least up to the age of twelve years."[46]

And, predictably, Goddard attributed to Deborah the same qualities of potential criminality he attributed to all of the "moron grade." "To-day if this young woman were to leave the Institution," he wrote in reference to Deborah in *The Kallikak Family*, "she would at once become a prey to the designs of evil men or evil women and would lead a life that would be vicious, immoral, and criminal, though because of her mentality she herself would not be responsible. There is

---

[43] Fernald, 1914, p. 68.
[44] Zenderland, 1998, p. 186.
[45] Goddard, 1911f, p. 64.
[46] Goddard, 1911f, p. 64.

nothing that she might not be led into, because she has no power of control, and all her instincts and appetites are in the direction that would lead to vice."[47]

"For a few years after 1910 Goddard was the most powerful criminologist in the country, the national expert on the causes of crime,"[48] observed sociologist and criminologist Nicole Rafter. Goddard's status as one of the most important criminologists in the nation, however, came about because of two murders, two criminal imbeciles, and another best selling book, titled *The Criminal Imbecile*. On May 17, 1914, Goddard testified as an expert witness in the case of the *People of the State of New York v. Jean Gianini*. Gianini had been charged with the murder of his former teacher, Ms. Lida Beecher, and Goddard was called in to administer the early version of the Binet-Simon test to the 16-year-old Gianini and to testify as to the adolescent's mental condition.

"I gave him the Binet-Simon test and he showed a mentality of between 10 and 11,"[49] Goddard told his colleagues at the June 1914 meeting of the American Association for the Study of the Feebleminded, held in Columbus, Ohio.

Goddard certainly believed the event was noteworthy. "These cases [referring to both trials in which he testified] are probably epoch-making in that they are the first instances in judicial procedure in which so high a grade of mental defectiveness has been recognized by the court,"[50] Goddard confidently proclaimed at the Ohio meeting.

It was not the first time a psychologist had testified as an expert witness in a court, although it was a rare enough occasion that this alone would have stood out as an accomplishment. It was, however, the first time that Binet-Simon Scale testing results had been entered as court evidence.[51] The resulting book, published in 1915 by MacMillan in the same format as the highly successful Kallikak narrative, kept Goddard's mission with regard to the moron front and center of the public's attention.

"On the morning of March 28th, 1914," explained Goddard, "Henry Fitch, a farmer of Herkimer County, accompanied by his son, started on his usual work to deliver milk. At a point in the highway, approximately one mile from the village of Poland, Mr. Fitch saw blood and signs of a struggle in the snow and slush in the road; he also found an umbrella and a hat. A bloody path led out of the road to a point some hundred and thirty feet away. Following the tracks he found the body of Lida Beecher, one of the school-teachers in the village of Poland. She lay at full length on her face, both arms under her.

"On the same morning Jean Gianini, sixteen years old, left his father's house on the edge of the village to go to the home of Sam Hutchinson, where he

---

[47] Goddard, 1912, p. 12.
[48] Rafter, 1997, p. 146.
[49] Goddard, 1914c, p. 31.
[50] Goddard, 1914c, p. 31.
[51] Gelb, 1997, p. 124.

was working and taking his meals. He had his breakfast, went to the barn, and worked a short time. When Mr. Hutchinson went out a little later, he could not find Jean. A Mr. Smith said he had seen him going down the tracks toward Newport. William Taylor, the track foreman, said he passed Jean near the bridge. Mr. Hutchinson then sent word to the boy's father that he had gone. The father, supposing his son had run away as he frequently did, telephoned to Newport asking that he be apprehended and sent home."[52]

Gianini was located at the Newport train station apparently attempting to take a train out of town, and he was whisked home to Poland, then to the Herkimer County Justice of the Peace. Here, he was stripped and searched, whereupon he confessed to the brutal murder of Miss Beecher who, he claimed, had humiliated him in school. Jean was booked and on the strength of the confession and circumstantial evidence, charged with murder in the first degree.

Gianini had been out of school for over a year. According to Goddard, his time in school had been neither productive nor, it seems, pleasant. Unable to perform the academic work required, he had become disruptive. Before his suspension from school, Miss Beecher had seated him facing the wall with his back to the rest of the class and, when that didn't work, had sent him to the principal who "sometimes flogged him."[53]

Witnesses for the prosecution told a different story, however. One of Lida Beecher's colleagues described Gianini as a good student, earning above-average marks across all subjects and performing exceptionally well in others. Ms. Lida, in a recommendation letter to another school, referred to Gianini as "not a bad boy by any means" and needing only "a little guidance to show him that he really could amount to something if he chooses to."[54]

For his part, Gianini appeared anxious to be reinstated in school. He was seen frequently badgering Ms. Lida about coming to his house to talk with his father about his return to school, and on the night before her murder, Jean was observed once more pleading his case with Miss Beecher in the street near her house.

After his conversation with Miss Beecher, Jean returned home, and then was sent on an errand, from which he returned quickly and retired to his room for the evening. This, of course, placed suspicion on him immediately.

"The fact that he was the last person to be seen with her, that the monkey wrench was found at the scene of the deed, that he left his place of work and went down the railroad track toward Newport, was sufficient to arouse suspicion,"[55] observed Goddard.

Well, yes—that and the fact that Jean had frequently confronted her about returning to school; had told others, braggingly, that he would get revenge on

---

[52] Goddard, 1915, pp. 3–4.
[53] Goddard, 1915, p. 7.
[54] Gelb, 1997, pp. 124–125.
[55] Goddard, 1915, p. 8.

her or that if he had a revolver he would shoot her; had actually tried to obtain a gun; and had noted to others that he "had a use for it," in reference to the monkey wrench in his pocket.

Steven Gelb has noted that given the evidence and the brutality of the crime, it was probably only the fact that Miss Beecher's father, a minister in Sennett, New York, refused to sanction vigilante justice that kept Gianini from being dragged from his cell and hung from a nearby oak tree.

Gianini's confession was particularly damning to his defense.

"I met her above the hotel," Jean told Fred Moore, the Justice of the Peace for the Town of Russia, near Poland, "and walked up the street with her up beyond the stone quarry; she had been a coming to see my folks about school and was a coming up to see them last night and I told her they lived up the hill, and when we got up there on the left side of the road, I hit her with a monkey wrench that I got out of my father's barn. I had the wrench in my pocket when I went up.

"After I had hit her about three times with the wrench, I hit her with a knife several times, to be sure to finish her, and then I took her over in the lot; I dragged her by the foot; and then I went home and got there about 7:30.

"The knife I stabbed her with was one that belonged to my father and I took it home and put it in the pantry drawer.

"I left the wrench somewhere near where I hit her. When I hit her first, she did not scream, but moaned."[56]

"In its main points the confession must be accepted as true," Goddard concedes. "It is accepted then by all that Jean Gianini killed Lida Beecher on the night of March 27, 1914. There is no difference of opinion on that point."

"It is now only a question of his responsibility."[57]

With that, Goddard built his case; a case more about proving the menace of the moron, the importance of the psychologist, and the value of the Binet-Simon Scale than, perhaps, about fairness to the brutally murdered Miss Beecher and her family. As Gelb noted, "once Goddard had determined that Gianini was feeble-minded, he was able to reinterpret all apparently purposeful behavior as being consistent with that condition."[58] Gelb has pointed out that the conditions under which Goddard administered his version of the Binet-Simon Scale—in Gianini's jail cell with two physicians, Goddard himself, and a stenographer— were far from the distraction-free environment needed for intelligence testing. Further, Terman pointed out that Goddard's version of the Binet-Simon Scale was unreliable in differentiating between "high-grade imbeciles" and "low functioning but normally intelligent" people, which was exactly the task Goddard was trying to achieve.

---

[56] Goddard, 1915, pp. 9–10.
[57] Goddard, 1915, p. 11.
[58] Gelb, 1997, p. 125.

"To refuse to accept [Gianini's confession] would be to admit at once without further proof that the boy was crazy or an imbecile. Is Jean Gianini an imbecile?" Goddard asked rhetorically. "What is an imbecile?"[59]

"The high grade imbecile, such as the person under discussion, feeble-minded as he is called in England, or the moron as we are coming to call him in the United States . . . has the mentality of a normal child of from three to twelve years of age. These age limits have been determined by examining thousands of the inmates of institutions for the feeble-minded and comparing with normal children.

"In the case of Jean Gianini, although he is sixteen years old, he has only the mentality of a child of ten; he is a high-grade imbecile; he is of the grade that is only recognized by those who are intimately familiar with imbeciles of all types. He is only discovered when we make a close comparison between him and the normal boys of the various ages."[60]

He is, in other words, a perfect example of the menace of the moron about which Goddard and his fellow eugenicists had been warning society.

Gianini's behavior and his characteristics spoke volumes, at least to Goddard, about his true nature, starting with the confession. "Nobody but an imbecile would have confessed under those circumstances," Goddard proposed. "But we do not have to rely upon the fact that it looks foolish to us for him to have confessed, because we have the fact, well known to all who have to deal with imbeciles, that it is characteristic of them to do just this thing. They do not always confess, it is true. It seems to depend largely upon how proud they are of their deeds—and frequently the more atrocious these are, the prouder they are of them."[61]

The next detail that was indicative of Gianini's status as an imbecile to Goddard was his wanderlust. Recalling Davenport's description of the hereditary nature of wanderlust as a recessive trait—because according to Davenport's family records it skipped generations—Goddard described Gianini's sojourn down the railroad tracks to Newport as indicative of the "wanderlust which is also characteristic of imbeciles."[62]

Another of the hereditary traits attributed to criminals by Davenport was an abnormal erotic instinct, and Goddard saw this in Jean Gianini's actions as well. Although Goddard argued that the gist of Gianini's confession was true, he also suggested that one could not invest much confidence in the details of the account and, thus, that it was unlikely that the act was premeditated.

"Jean being an imbecile, it is entirely possible that he had no premeditation of murder at all," explained Goddard. "On the contrary, it is possible that as he

---

[59] Goddard, 1915, pp. 10–11.
[60] Goddard, 1915, pp 12–16.
[61] Goddard, 1915, p 16.
[62] Goddard, 1915, p 16.

walked up the hill with Lida Beecher he had no more thought of killing her than of committing suicide. Indeed, it is much more plausible form all we know of imbeciles . . . that there was an entirely different purpose. That purpose was probably sexual."[63]

In attributing causality to criminal behavior, Goddard and Davenport part ways slightly, although their paths merge again eventually. Cesar Lombroso believed that what was inherited was the degenerative, atavistic nature that created a born criminal. It wasn't that the born criminal inherited traits that resulted in one becoming a criminal, but that he or she was born as a criminal and the traits were simply evidence thereof. Davenport believed that what made a criminal was the heritability of criminal characteristics, like temper, wanderlust, and the abnormal erotic instinct. These, in turn, led inevitably to criminals. Both were born criminals, but Davenport's theory was built to strengthen his stance regarding the heritability of characteristics that led to certain, inevitable outcomes. For both, the criminal was born and criminality was inevitable. Goddard, though, posited that what was hereditary was feeblemindedness and that it was in the nature of being a moron that created the criminal. The moron was born, as it were, but the criminal was made by his (or her) exposure to the world, and criminality could be prevented only by segregation and institutionalization.

"The best material out of which to make criminals, and perhaps the material from which they are most frequently made, is feeble-mindedness,"[64] Goddard wrote in *The Kallikak Family*. "In the good branch of the Kallikak family there were no criminals. There were not many in the other side, but there were some, and, had their environment been different, no one who is familiar with feeble-minded persons, their characteristics and tendencies, would doubt that a large percentage of them might have become criminal. Lombroso's famous criminal types," Goddard suggested, "in so far as they were types, may have been types of feeble-mindedness on which criminality was grafted by the circumstances of their environment."[65]

"Feeble-mindedness is hereditary and transmitted as surely as any other character. We cannot successfully cope with these conditions until we recognize feeble-mindedness and its hereditary nature, recognize it early, and take care of it,"[66] Goddard summarized in *The Kallikak Family*. "The kind of criminality into which they fall seems to depend largely upon their environment. If they are associated with vicious but intelligent people, they become the dupes for carrying out any of the hazardous schemes that their more intelligent associates plan for them. Because of their stupidity, they are very apt to be caught quickly and sent to the reformatory or prison. If they are girls, one of the easiest things for

---

[63] Goddard, 1915, p. 21.
[64] Goddard, 1912, p. 54.
[65] Goddard, 1912, p. 59.
[66] Goddard, 1912, p. 117.

them to fall into is a life of prostitution, because they have natural instincts with no power of control and no intelligence to understand the wiles and schemes of the white slaver, the cadet, or the individual seducer. All this, we say, is what is to be expected. These are the people of good outward appearance, but of low intelligence, who pass through school without acquiring any efficiency, then go out into the world and must inevitably fall into some such life as we have pictured."[67]

Goddard and Davenport's views coalesced again, though, in attributing to the moron and criminal imbecile, respectively, the ultimate characteristic of a lack of control or inhibition. In a paper presented to the superintendents at their annual meeting in Lapeer, Michigan, in June of 1913 titled "Feeble Inhibitionedness," Davenport argued that ultimately it was this quality that created criminals. "The moral imbecile . . . seems to lack these inhibitions; they have never developed with the development of his mind; he remains childlike in respect to his control of the emotions. Our first impulse is to say he lacks training . . . but the experience of those in charge of institutions for wayward boys and girls indicates that the trouble is much deeper; they lack the capacity for inhibitions in one or all directions."[68]

So, too, does Goddard ultimately attribute Jean Gianini's actions to the lack of inhibition. "With the imbecile the case is different. The fires of sexual passion may burn as vigorously as in the better endowed, but he lacks both the power of control and the courage and ingenuity to overcome the social barriers."[69]

"Now, Doctor," began defense attorney John McIntyre, questioning Goddard on the witness stand, "from your experience in the treatment and knowledge of imbeciles and idiots, and from your knowledge and skill as an expert, can you express an opinion as to the condition of Jean Gianini at the time of the killing of Lida Beecher on the 27th day of March, 1914?"

"I can," Goddard replied after several objections from the prosecutor were overruled by the judge.

"What is your opinion?"

"That he is an imbecile."

"Now, Doctor," continued McIntyre, "in conjunction with the physical and mental examination made by you in the County Jail on the 17th day of May this year,—from your experience and knowledge of imbeciles and idiots, in your opinion was Jean Gianini at the time of the killing of Lida Beecher in such a mental condition as to know the nature and quality of the act he was doing or that the act was wrong?"

[67] Goddard, 1912, pp. 55–56.
[68] Davenport, 1914, p. 148.
[69] Goddard, 1915, pp. 21–22.

"He was not in such condition."[70]

Before the jury left the jury box to deliberate, they were instructed by the presiding judge with the following charges: "that, if the jury cannot say, beyond a reasonable doubt, that the defendant was sane at the time of the commission of the act, and cannot say whether, at that time, he was sane or insane, the defendant must be acquitted.

"That, although sanity is assured and presumed to be the normal state of the human mind, when imbecility is once shown to exist in a person, it is presumed to exist and continue until the presumption is overcome by contrary or repelling evidence proving sanity.

"That if, at the time of the commission of the act, the defendant was under the influence of a diseased mind, and was really unconscious that he was committing a crime, this defendant must be acquitted.

"That the law does not require that the insanity, imbecility, or mental aberration which absolves from crime should exist for any definite period, and only that it existed at the moment when the act occurred.

"That if the insanity, imbecility, or mental aberration which absolves from crime operated at the moment that the act was committed, that is sufficient in law to absolve from guilt, and this defendant cannot be convicted of the offense charged in the indictment, or any other offense.

"That if the jury acquit the defendant upon the ground of insanity, it will become the duty of the Court to order him committed to a State Asylum."[71]

"We find," returned the Foreman on the return of the jury, "the defendant in this case not guilty as charged; we acquit the defendant on the ground of criminal imbecility."[72]

Gianini was committed to the Matteawan State Hospital for the Criminally Insane in New York where he lived for 52 years.[73] Goddard combined the narrative for the case against Gianini with two other narratives in *The Criminal Imbecile*. In one, the case against Roland Pennington, who was accused of participating in the murder of his employer, Goddard had testified about the defendant's imbecility, this time to no avail, as Pennington was found guilty. That may account for why the Pennington narrative is half again as long as the Gianini section. The final case, against Fred Tronson—a Portland, Oregon, man who gunned down his girlfriend when she refused to marry him—was not one in which Goddard directly participated, and like Pennington, Tronson did not get off on the imbecility defense.

---

[70] Goddard, 1915, p. 24.
[71] Goddard, 1915, p. 25-26.
[72] Goddard, 1915, p. 26.
[73] Gelb, 1997, p. 123.

Goddard's treatise on criminal imbecility concludes with the predictable estimations that half of all criminals are feebleminded; that all feebleminded people could become criminals; that two-thirds of all feebleminded people inherited their impairment; and that society must act to colonize, segregate, and sterilize this population.

Not all psychologists greeted Goddard's triumph in criminology with equal avidity. Among the dissenters was J. E. Wallace Wallin, whose somewhat vagabond career (he held academic appointments at 22 universities or colleges alone) had, by 1915, taken him to St. Louis, where he was director of the Psycho-Educational Clinic for the St. Louis Board of Education. Given his previous criticisms of the Binet-Simon Scale, it is not surprising that he would be among the first to criticize its use in criminology.

"Now," Wallin said to attendees at the 1915 American Psychological Association meeting held in Chicago, "if we are justified in pronouncing older-adolescent or adult prostitutes, murderers, or other criminals, or grade and high school retardates as feeble-minded on the basis of these standards [e.g., the standard of scores under the MA of 12 years], we must be equally ready to call law-abiding, respectable and successful farmers, laborers or business men who have had no more school training than most prostitutes and criminals are claimed to have had, feeble-minded precisely on the same standards."[74]

To which end, he administered the 1908 and 1911 Goddard translations of the Binet-Simon Scale to upstanding members of an Iowa farming community. Wallin's grandparents had immigrated from Kinneved, Västergötland, Sweden, and his family, and those of his paternal uncles, settled in southeastern Iowa. In a trip back to his family home, Wallin gave the two versions of the Binet-Simon Scale to several successful farmers, a businessman, and a housewife. Each was described as an upstanding citizen; each had raised children who were equally successful; and, each performed miserably on the Binet-Simon Scale tests. Every one of these six solid citizens tested in the feebleminded range. He also gave the same versions to half a dozen college and high school students, whose performance was better than their elderly counterparts, although not a great deal.

"The present-day tendency to play fast and loose with such vague and undefined concepts as 'defective children,' 'mental deficiency,' 'mental defect,' 'defectiveness,' 'subnormality,' and 'feeble-mindedness,' 'moronity' and 'criminal imbecility,'" concluded Wallin, "when applied to mentalities of X and over and to base vital practical action on diagnoses based on such vague concepts is not only inexcusable but it constitutes a positive bar to sane progress in the study of the problem of mental deviation."[75]

"The more we learn," Wallin stated, "of psychological diagnosis the more evident it becomes that psychological tests are just like many of the tests of

---

[74]Wallin, 1916, p. 707.
[75]Wallin, 1916, p. 715.

the physician (temperature, pulse Wassermann, Moguchi, etc.): they are simply one means for aiding the clinician in arriving at a guarded diagnosis. They do not constitute an automatic diagnosticon, which will enable the examiner to dispense with a thorough clinical examination or to disregard other clinical findings, nor do they obviate the need of technical training on the part of the examiner."[76]

Wallin's APA remarks were reprinted in early 1916 in the *Journal of the American Institute of Criminal Law and Criminology*, resulting in an exchange reminiscent of Wallin's row in the *Journal of Psycho-Asthenics* with Frederick Kuhlmann over the latter's review of a previous Wallin text critical of the Binet-Simon Scale. Wallin's article was responded to by Samuel Kohs in, albeit, a less vitriolic manner. Unlike Kuhlmann, Samuel Kohs, who had spent time with Goddard in Vineland and who designed a block-test of intelligence that later was incorporated into the Wechsler Scales of Intelligence, was not a Clark graduate, but instead had obtained his doctorate at Stanford under the direction of Lewis Terman.

Kohs rebutted many of Wallin's major conclusions, but began the article with a single refutation that spoke to the changing of the guard with regard to intelligence testing.

"A particular object of recurrent attack in Wallin's paper," began Kohs, "is Goddard's 1911 revision of the Binet Scale. But the 1911 scale as the author of that article [e.g., Wallin] uses it and as he speaks of it is a matter of history."[77]

Goddard's versions of the Binet-Simon Scale were history. Goddard's reign as America's leading expert in the Binet-Simon Scale had nearly run its course by 1916. In a widely used 1923 text surveying the field of intelligence testing by Rudolf Pintner at Columbia University, Goddard's role had already been relegated to a historical note, and it was Terman's work that was the focus of attention.[78]

It was with the 1916 publication of *The Measurement of Intelligence* that Lewis Terman took center stage as the nation's guru in intelligence testing. Subtitled *An Explanation of and a Complete Guide for the use of the Stanford Revision and Extension of The Binet-Simon Intelligence Scale*, the book was, in essence, the manual for administering the Stanford Revision of the Binet-Simon Scale, or eventually the Stanford-Binet Scale. Goddard had translated the 1908 and 1911 versions of the Binet-Simon Scale and had done more to popularize its use than any other person. He had even modified some items in the 1911 version to create a Goddard-Binet Scale. Terman's revisions, however, were psychometri-

---

[76]Wallin, 1916, p. 706.
[77]Kohs, 1916, p. 860.
[78]Pintner, 1923, pp. 41–42.

cally stronger and the 1916 Stanford-Binet Scale constituted the first version of the Binet-Simon Scale that had truly been revised for and normed with an American audience. The additional items had been validated from studies with large samples of children without intellectual impairments. The final version was standardized on more than 2,300 people. This version allowed for testing past the original age of 13, all the way to 22 years of age. Plus, the adoption of the Intelligence Quotient, instead of relying on MA equivalents, gave the test an immediate power it lacked before.

"The Stanford-Binet quickly dominated the field," observed historian Raymond Fancher, "and became the standard against which all subsequent American intelligence tests—whether group or individual—would be measured."[79]

"I was a little surprised that my publications in the test field were so favorably received," noted Terman. "I knew that my revision of Binet's tests was superior to others then available, but I did not foresee the vogue it was to have and imagined that it would probably be displaced by something much better within a few years."[80]

Goddard's version was, indeed, history by 1916, although the Binet-Simon Scale tests themselves were not.

Goddard's continued insistence that practitioners in the field of feeblemindedness could provide reliable judgments of the intellectual capacity of people by administering mental tests, by assessing historical facts (as in *The Kallikak Family*), or even by visual inspection perpetuated his diminishing influence in intelligence testing. And it brought about a rising storm of criticism of his methods in *The Kallikak Family*. Goddard's fall from the precipice of premier intelligence tester precipitated a decline in fortunes as rapid as his ascent to that precipice.

---

[79] Fancher, 1985, p. 48.
[80] Terman, 1930, p. 324.

CHAPTER 8

The Rise and Fall of Goddard

Although his plinipotency as America's mental testing guru was waning, Goddard had one more triumph for himself with regard to mental testing before his final fall. In 1923, Carl Brigham, a young, relatively unknown assistant professor of psychology at Princeton, published *A Study of American Intelligence*, a book that concluded that the 'Nordic' race was intellectually superior to all others. The data for Brigham's book was derived from the U.S. Army Alpha and Army Beta intelligence testing program, which, between 1917 and the war's end in November of 1918, administered to 1.75 million American soldiers the first group intelligence tests. Brigham was a member of the committee that created the army tests, a committee chaired by Robert Yerkes, the president of the American Psychological Association (APA) for 1917. The Army Alpha and Army Beta testing program took intelligence testing from a relatively obscure activity to become the widely known phenomenon it is today. Among the other members of that committee was Goddard.

When the United States entered World War I, psychologists sought to find ways they could contribute to the cause and, not coincidentally, for that cause to contribute to the prestige of the profession. As president of APA, Yerkes had considerable power to wield to achieve this.

"Wars always generate their retinue of camp followers with ulterior motives," observed evolutionary biologist Stephen J. Gould, "Many are simply scoundrels and profiteers, but a few are spurred by higher ideals. As mobilization for World War I approached, Yerkes got one of those 'big ideas' that propel the history of science: could psychologists possibly persuade the army to test all its recruits? If so, the philosopher's stone of psychology might be constructed: the copious, useful and uniform body of number that would fuel a transition from dubious art to respected science."[1]

---

[1] Gould, 1981, pp. 223–224.

Robert Yerkes earned his Ph.D. in psychology from Harvard in 1902, where Charles Davenport was his biology professor, with a focus on comparative animal psychology. He was appointed as a professor at Harvard on graduation. He would later go on to found the Yale Laboratories of Primate Biology, the first primate research center in the United States, and performed groundbreaking research with chimpanzees and gorillas.

When the United States entered the War, Yerkes immediately contacted psychologists involved in intelligence testing, including Goddard, Terman, Brigham (whom Yerkes had met when the younger man was serving as a military psychologist), Thomas Haines, and Guy Whipple, to form the APA Committee on the Psychological Examining of Recruits.[2] These men were charged with the development of a means to screen army recruits to weed out unfit soldiers and, more specifically, according to Yerkes, to classify men "in order that they may be properly placed in the military service."[3] Their approach was three-pronged. Army recruits who could read would take one test, the Army Alpha test; those who could not were given a nonverbal test composed of pictures, called the Army Beta test; if a recruit failed the Army Beta test, he would be retested with a version of the Binet-Simon Scale. Each recruit would then be rated from $A+$ to $E-$ as a function of his testing results. This, in turn, was equated with a suitable role in the military. A grade of "A" denoted officer material, a "B" was "splendid sergeant material," "C" denoted a private-type, a "D" was just fit for service, and a recruit rated as "E" was to be declared intellectually unqualified.[4]

The Training School's contribution to this effort went beyond Goddard's participation on the committee. In early 1915, Edward Johnstone had consolidated several activities emanating from Vineland under the umbrella of the Training School at Vineland Committee on Provision, which, in essence, was established to take the Training School message and mission to a national audience. Directed by Joseph Byers, the committee was originally housed at the Training School, but then moved to Philadelphia, where Byers and the committee secretary, Johnstone's brother-in-law and mentor Alexander Johnson, sought to conduct a national effort to disseminate information about feeblemindedness.

When the war started, Byers contacted Yerkes to offer the committee's assistance in the mental testing effort. In May of that year, Yerkes met with Byers and Vineland board of director member Milton Greenman, during which Byers offered to fund the committee's meetings if held at the Training School.

On May 28, the committee met in the Research Laboratory on the Vineland Training School campus, with the Committee on Provisions paying travel expenses and hosting the committee members for two months while they gen-

[2] Zenderland, 1998, p. 282.
[3] Fancher, 1985, p. 118.
[4] Fancher, 1985, p. 124.

erated items for the tests.[5] The items, though, suffered from many of the same woes bedeviling intelligence testing up to that point; they were often culturally biased, lacked the scientific sophistication of factor analysis and item-evaluation statistics, and discriminated against those recruits—perhaps Iowa farmers like those J. E. Wallace Wallin tested—who had limited educational opportunities. The items included:

> Crisco is: patent medicine, disinfectant, toothpaste, food product?
> The number of a Kaffir's legs is: 2, 4, 6, 8?
> Christy Mathewson is famous as a: writer, artist, baseball player, comedian?[6]

One must remember, of course, that in 1917 and 1918, the capacity for mass advertising was limited, by and large, to magazines and radio. Crisco, an all-vegetable shortening used for cooking, was introduced in 1911 by Procter and Gamble as an alternative to animal fats and butters. Radio advertising for the product did not even begin until 1923. Kaffir is a now-obsolete name for a Black Crowned Crane (thus, two legs), found in the dry savannah in Africa. Kaffir is also a pejorative term used to refer to people in southern Africa, and as an adjective can refer to a type of melon, bread, orange, antelope (Kaffir Duiker), or a harp. And if you were not a baseball fan, you likely did not know that Christy Mathewson was the dominant pitcher of the first two decades of the 20th Century (who would, in 1936, be in the first class of players inducted, along with Babe Ruth and Ty Cobb, into the baseball hall of fame).

As Leila Zenderland observed, however, the tests' cultural biases transcended simply race, educational experience, or geography. The tests reflected the cultural biases inherent in the progressive society. "Equally revealing of the culture of the day was the subtest designed to gauge 'Practical Judgment' . . . commonsense judgements most prized by Progressive America—judgements, in other words, that emphasized utility, efficiency, and pragmatism. 'Why are doctors useful?' 'Why are cats useful animals?' 'Why is agriculture valuable?' 'Why is tennis good exercise?'"[7]

The most progressive of items, noted Zenderland, asked why every man ought to be educated. Recruits could select 'it makes a man more useful,' 'it costs money,' 'some educated people are wise,' and because 'Roosevelt was educated.'[8] The progressives' penchant for utility makes the first of those options the right pick, although the latter could just as well be argued as the best option. Roosevelt was educated. He was an American. In these times, citizens must embody a

---

[5] Doll, 1988, p. 10.

[6] Gould, 1981, p. 230.

[7] Zenderland, 1998, p. 286.

[8] Zenderland, 1998, p. 286.

Rooseveltian Americanism. Only then will they be useful; not to themselves, but to their country and their nation.

Nevertheless, the war waited for no man, let alone a group of psychologists developing a test, and by early July the committee had produced five versions of the Army Alpha for use with recruits who could read, and one version of Army Beta for use with illiterate recruits.[9] Although once in place, more than 200,000 recruits per month were tested using the Army Alpha or Army Beta tests, the real impact was not on the army itself, but in post hoc analyses of the massive amount of data collected and conclusions drawn from those analyses, including those in Bingham's book. According to Gould, the army itself seemed equivocal about the tests, and in many cases the army psychologists were simply tolerated.

"I do not think the Army ever made much use of the tests," wrote Gould. "One can well imagine how professional officers felt about smart-assed young psychologists who arrived without invitation, often assumed an officer's rank without undergoing basic training, commandeered a building to give the tests, . . . saw each recruit for an hour in a large group, and then proceeded to usurp an officer's traditional role in judging the worthiness of men for various military tasks."[10]

When President Woodrow Wilson signed the armistice ending armed conflict on November 11, 1918, it also signaled the end of the grand experiment with intelligence testing in the armed forces, as the army discontinued the program almost immediately.[11]

It was, however, the postwar analysis of this extensive data set that was most important to the widespread adoption of intelligence testing in American society. Both Yerkes and Brigham produced books from the data, *Psychological Examining in the United States Army*, a ponderous tome published by Yerkes in 1921, and *A Study of American Intelligence*, authored by Brigham in 1923. Edwin G. Boring, who at the time was a professor of psychology at Clark University and who would later move to Harvard and become a distinguished historian of psychology, was Yerkes's second-in-command and managed the data conversion and analysis for Yerkes's book. Boring's data set contained 160-thousand cases, from which Yerkes drew startling conclusions that bolstered the eugenicists' warnings that the population was degenerating as a function of the proliferation of morons.

First, Yerkes's treatise reported the shocking finding that the average mental age of a white American male—and because of the size of the Army Alpha database and the wide representation of American males in the military during World War I, Yerkes's and Brigham's findings were soon generalized to represent

---

[9] Zenderland, 1998, p. 285.

[10] Gould, 1981, p. 224.

[11] Fancher, 1985, p. 126.

all Americans, not just Americans in the military—was 13 years. Because the "average adult mental age" was 16, the average American, then, stood, intellectually, on the threshold of moronity.

"If 13.08 is the white average," interpreted Gould, "and everyone from mental age 8 through 12 is a moron, then we are nation of nearly half-morons."[12]

If these results were surprising, and embarrassing, pertaining to white recruits, things were worse with regard to black recruits, whose average mental age was 10.4. Similarly, immigrant American soldiers fared poorly.

"Yerkes also lent support to Goddard's Ellis Island data," observed psychology historian Morton Hunt, "by reporting that the Alpha and Beta showed the peoples of southern Europe and the Slavs of eastern Europe to be less intelligent than the peoples of northern and western Europe."[13] The reverberations from these findings were significant, starting with educational and social policy.

"It is an unfortunate but stubborn fact of American cultural history that for more than a half century following the administration of intelligence tests to 1,726,966 recruits of World War I," Social Historian Allen Chase observed, "the educational policies of this nation were to be based—at their core—on the astonishingly long-lived credibility of the pseudo-fact that the results of these very 'scientific' mental tests provided that 'the average mental age of all Americans is only about 14.'"[14]

Second, the data were a gold mine for eugenicists, who by the early 1920s were engaged in increasingly racist rhetoric. Readers of Brigham's text had an inkling of the potential racial tone it would take from the author's acknowledgements section, in which he indicated that his treatment of the race hypothesis was based, in part, on Madison Grant's *Passing of the Great Race*. Hardly an unbiased source.

Brigham selected just under 100,000 cases from white draftees, nearly 25,000 cases from black draftees, as well as 15,000 white officers as the "primary sample." The black cases were included, basically, to set the parameters with which to test the non-native white cases, because previous analyses, particularly those by Yerkes, had already established the putative inferiority of the black recruits' intellect. As such, the white group was subdivided into foreign and native born, and into Nordic, Alpine, and Mediterranean racial groups; foreign-born recruits were further divided by years of residence in the United States.

"The results of the examination of the nativity groups suggest immediately that the race factor may underlie the large differences found," wrote Brigham.[15]

---

[12] Gould, 1981, p. 227.

[13] Hunt, 1994, p. 239.

[14] Chase, 1977, p. 226.

[15] Brigham, 1922, p. 157.

That race "factor" was that members of the Nordic group outperformed either of the other two groups.

"Our study of the army tests of foreign born individuals," Brigham concluded, "has pointed at every step to the conclusion that the average intelligence of our immigrants is declining. This deterioration in the intellectual level of immigrants has been found to be due to two causes. The migrations of the Alpine and Mediterranean races have increased to such an extent in the last thirty or forty years that this blood now constitutes 70% or 75% of the total immigration."[16]

Bad blood.

On February 21, 1918, Goddard sent a letter to the Board of Directors of the Ohio Bureau of Juvenile Research accepting their offer to become the director of that agency. He would replace Thomas Haines, who like Goddard, was, at the time, serving on the army testing committee. "In leaving my little corner in the laboratory," Goddard wrote in his final report at Vineland, "my fondest hope is that I can spread the Vineland spirit all over the state of Ohio."[17]

Goddard's decision to leave the Training School was, according to his own version of the story, a difficult one. Zenderland described the personal and professional tug-of-war waged by Goddard as he considered whether to leave the comfort and prestige of Vineland for the position in Columbus, particularly a list Goddard drafted of the pros and cons associated with his move. One undeniable advantage of the move was that the new position would pay considerably more than Goddard was earning at Vineland. He would, in fact, be the second highest–paid employee in the state of Ohio, surpassed only by the governor.[18] In the end, according to Goddard's version, the promise of the challenge, the pay, and the opportunity to direct his own agency swayed him to leave Vineland.

Even weighing these advantages, Goddard's departure from Vineland in May of 1918 was surprising. The previous few years had been busy and, seemingly, productive ones. In 1915, he served as President of the American Association for the Scientific Study of the Feeble-Minded, delivering his keynote address at the association's annual meeting in Berkeley, California. He served on the Mental Hygiene Committee of National Conference of Charities and Corrections throughout 1917, and during the previous summer had hosted fellow intelligence testers Yerkes, Terman, Haines, and Brigham as they developed the Army Alpha and Army Beta tests; work that continued, primarily at Vineland, through 1918.

In a little more than a decade, Goddard had risen from an underappreciated psychologist at a state Normal School for Teachers, to the pinnacle of the field

---

[16] Brigham, 1922, p. 197.

[17] Zenderland, 1998, p. 302.

[18] Zenderland, 1998, p. 303.

of psychology and eugenics. He was there, largely, under the auspices of Samuel Fels. Goddard acknowledged his debt to Fels by dedicating *The Kallikak Family* to the soap magnate:

> To Mr. Samuel S. Fels, Friend and philanthropist. A layman with the scientist's love of truth and the true citizen's love of humanity who made possible this study and who has followed the work from its incipiency with kindly criticism and advice this book is dedicated.

In an era before federal agencies funded psychological, medical, and educational research, the psychological laboratory at Vineland was almost completely dependent on Fels for support. Johnstone and Goddard, particularly the former, spent a significant amount of time and energy trying to raise even small sums for the department's operation, and thus Fels's largesse was critical, if not at times a lot of trouble. Goddard's successor at Vineland, Stanley Porteus, described Fels as philanthropic, but having "a practical urge to see that he got value for his money."[19] Fels required Johnstone to meet regularly with him, Earl Barnes, and Wistar's Milton Greenman. Johnstone was, much of the time, almost obliged to grovel for his funds.

Johnstone wrote in November 1912 a letter typical of the type he often wrote:

> My dear Mr. Fels,
>
> Both Dr. Goddard and I were disappointed that you and Mrs. Fels did not get down last week—not that we expected you, for the weather at that time was so very bad that we knew, even if you had planned to come, you would hardly do so in such a storm, but because we had hoped the weather would be good and you would be here.
>   We shall appreciate it if you will send us a check on the current expenditures. The account to date is as follows below.
>   With kindest regards, I am,
>
> Sincerely yours,
>
> E. R. Johnstone.
>
> P.S. Won't you set another date to come down?"[20]

---

[19] Porteus, 1969, p. 72.
[20] Johnstone, 1912.

Most of Johnstone's communications with Samuel Fels during Goddard's tenure are similar to this; fawning tributes to the benefactor and the good work his dollars supported; and requests for more of those precious dollars. Goddard's work was frequently mentioned by Johnstone in a favorable light in these correspondences, often with an emphasis on how busy Goddard was—implying, of course, how beneficial more funds would be to alleviate that workload. Goddard's relationship with Fels appeared stable. Johnstone frequently alluded to discussions among Fels, himself, and Goddard, suggesting that Goddard was part of Johnstone's ongoing efforts to please Fels and secure greater levels of funding. Fels clearly was personally involved in many of Goddard's efforts, even to the extent that Goddard hired Elizabeth Kite on the direct recommendation of Fels.

In late 1915, for example, Goddard wrote to Fels personally on behalf of Florence Mateer, one of the research aides who had worked with Goddard on the immigration studies before starting her doctorate at Clark University. Mateer was seeking funding from Fels to complete her doctorate, and Goddard apparently felt comfortable enough to make the request directly himself. For his part, Fels felt positively enough about Goddard to make the loan to Mateer.

On April 17, 1917, Johnstone sent a letter to Fels discussing several hiring issues and attaching a "new suggested budget" kept within the Training School's "prospective income, as suggested." In this plan, Goddard remained in his role as director, with the salary of $4,060 annually. Johnstone's proposed budget included a projected $12,000 from Fels, $1,000 from prominent New York attorney and eugenecist Bleeker Van Wagenen, $3,000 from the Training School, and $1,600 from "sales, etc."[21]

On October 17, 1917, Johnstone wrote again, thanking Fels for the latest quarterly payment, and "enclosing a copy of program for year as Goddard and I laid it out." That attachment, which Johnstone referred to as a program of research on the "Psychology of the Undeveloped Mind" was, in essence, a continuance of the research in which Goddard had been engaged over the years leading up to that time.[22]

The next correspondence between Johnstone and Fels, however, signaled anything but the status quo, beginning with its date: December 31, 1917.

What might be so important as to compel Johnstone to spend New Year's Eve writing to Fels? By all appearances, nothing less than the fate of Fels's funding for the research laboratory was at stake. After communicating yet another request for "the latest quarterly payment," Johnstone stated: "I am enclosing outline of the new plans. Goddard is acquainted with what I am saying here and while he has not expressed a definite opinion I think he is going to be satisfied with it as it stands."[23]

---

[21] Johnstone, 1917a.
[22] Johnstone, 1917b.
[23] Johnstone, 1917c.

One has to question either Goddard's acquaintance or satisfaction with the new plan based on Johnstone's next sentence.

"Before it is formally presented to him, however, I think that you and Dr. Greenman and perhaps Mr. Van Wagenen, if you think best, should go over it with the idea of making such changes or emphasizing such points as are needed."[24]

The "new plan" dramatically altered Goddard's role.

"The following is an endeavor to put into form the results of our last conference," Johnstone wrote to Fels that New Years Eve. "The lines are purposely sharply drawn in order that there may be no misunderstanding of the division of activity, but I have not greatly elaborated the plan in order that it may be enlarged or modified—as seems best.

"In view of the present unsettled condition of affairs and the uncertainty of the future, it is deemed advisable to make a complete revision for the plans for the Research Department to be in effect with the opening of the new fiscal year—May 1, 1918.

"The whole field of study of the feeble-minded is too great for us to attempt to cover it at one time. We shall however pursue such lines as our finances may permit and it shall be our policy to separate into broad divisions the various lines of investigation.

"To this end the Research Department shall be divided into Laboratories. The Training School shall furnish the place, the facilities, and the materials. Each Laboratory head shall work under the direction of the institution or individual that sends him here or shall pursue his own studies if he comes here of his own accord, and the various laboratories shall be autonomous.

"The heads of the laboratories shall be undisturbed by administrative duties, and all shall work under the general direction of the Superintendent of the Training School in all matters related to the institution. It shall be the duty of the Superintendent of the Training School to administer the affairs of the Department in letter and in spirit in order that Dr. Goddard, or any other scientist who may in the future come into the laboratory, may be free to pursue his studies without giving attention to petty details and annoyances."[25]

Prior to this, all department heads had reported to Goddard who, in turn, reported to Johnstone. Now, all heads were to report to Johnstone, not Goddard. Yet, so far the only explanation for the reorganization was that Goddard had been annoyed by petty details, presumably of an administrative nature. The possible reasons for the overhaul appeared later in the letter:

"From now until the close of the fiscal year," continued Johnstone, referring to April 30, 1918, because the new plan was to be in place May 1, "Dr. Goddard will

---

[24]Johnstone, 1917c.

[25]Johnstone, 1917c.

develop all of the time necessary to get his book in shape, using the present staff. Beginning with the new year we shall employ as assistants to Dr. Goddard only people who have good training along psychological lines—preferably men- and we shall have in mind two things. [First], that they shall not continue in the laboratory longer tham one year unless by vote of the Research Committee. (It is the intention to set a policy of training good psychologists along the special lines relating to feeble-mindedness and then send them out to –if possible- develop other centers.).

"[Second], these assistants shall be selected with a view to their being able to work with as little expenditure of Dr. Goddard's time as may be. They shall pursue definite studies on the children which shall continue or initiate such lines of psychological research as Dr. Goddard shall direct, working only on problems that will be of really use to him in his larger studies.

"It is recognized," Johnstone's amended plan concluded, "that each investigator has the first right to publish his researches over his own name and in such scientific journals as may appear to him desirable, provided any desired number of reprints may of such articles may be purchased by the Training School and provided also that such researches may be published by the Training School in any form desired. No responsibility for statements made in such scientific publications shall be assumed by the Training School.

"The Superintendent as heretofore shall always have control of the children and no scientific work shall be conducted on the children without his knowledge and consent."[26]

It was clear, then, that Goddard was being dislodged from many of his responsibilities as director and supervisor. Why? Did the reference to hiring "preferably men" allude to some inappropriate conduct on Goddard's behalf? This seems more than unlikely given Goddard's lifelong devotion to his wife, Emma. Perhaps, then, it refers to difficulties Goddard had with supervising women, or might simply reflect the gender bias so common to that era. Did the reference to "control of the children" and consent indicate some problem with Goddard's methods? Perhaps some of the Vineland inmates' parents were becoming less enamored with their children as scientific guinea pigs. Or, did Fels or others see Goddard as a glory hound, snapping up all the credit? Finally, was Goddard's eugenic rhetoric wearing thin with Fels, who was Jewish, or with Greenman?

If the December 31 letter from Johnstone to Fels signaled a problem, two letters from February of 1918 clearly indicated that Goddard was in serious trouble. The first was from Greenman to Fels, dated February 16, 1918, communicating that "a plan for the cooperation of the Wistar Institute and the Training School at Vineland in the scientific study of defectives"[27] had been approved at a meeting of the Board of Managers of the Wistar Institute held two days earlier.

---

[26] Johnstone, 1917c.

[27] Greenman, 1918.

By all appearances, then, Johnstone's late hour effort to rescue the research at Vineland had failed.

The next letter is, however, the most poignant and informative. It is a handwritten letter from Goddard dated February 21, 1918.

My Dear Mr. Fels

Life is a strange mixture of pain and pleasure. We learn to bear the pain that as we say is inevitable with a fair degree of complacency. It is when we feel that the unpleasant could have been avoided that <u>regret</u> comes in and takes away all the fortitude that we could have shown in the face of the disaster.

It was painful for you to come to the decision that you made known in your letter: It is painful to me to have you come to such a decision but it is vastly more painful to realize that I am largely responsible for your decision and to always have to regret that I was not able to make the work appeal to you.

Had you seen fit to go on with the programs we started five years ago-and had it not been for outside influences I think you would have gone on- we would by now have had results that would have satisfied you. No one could appreciate as I did the fatal error of that decision of the committee not to go on.

I am responsible, I know. I should have been able to <u>convince</u>, but I believe there were subtle influences at work that I did not understand and hence could not counteract.

But in such cases one cannot always walk by sight. It takes faith. You must find some one in whom you have faith and then trust all to him. I sincerely hope that my leaving Vineland will clear the way for some one in whom you have such faith to come in and that you will trust him implicitly and turn your entire income if need be to the solution of this problem. There is no place in the world so fitted for this as Vineland.

I have written freely, because it no longer concerns me personally and so I cannot be accused of pleading my own cause. I am pleading your cause and Vineland's, but most of all the cause of humanity.

Sincerely,

Goddard[28]

Goddard's letter accepting the position in Ohio was dated the same day he wrote to Fels. Something had gone terribly wrong for Goddard. Someone on the committee—Fels, Barnes, Greenman, or Johnstone—had lost trust in Goddard's work. Barnes and Johnstone were Goddard's colleagues and confidants. Fels

---

[28] Goddard, 1918a.

ultimately held the purse strings, so Fels must have lost trust. Goddard makes it clear that it was Fels's painful decision and not his own.

Stanley Porteus, writing in his autobiography 50 years after the fact, recalled that Goddard had submitted his letter of resignation in advance of accepting the Ohio position to Fels and the committee as a ruse to get a raise. "When an invitation came to Goddard to head the newly established Bureau of Juvenile Research in Ohio," wrote Porteus, "an offer carrying with it the then princely salary of $7,500 a year, this demand for his services was no great surprise. That came when Goddard laid the flattering proposal in the Vineland Committee's lap. Instead of meeting those terms, as he no doubt expected they would, Greenman and Fels congratulated him on the honor and suggested that he accept."[29]

Could the fateful decision to which Goddard referred have been to accept Goddard's resignation instead of making a counteroffer, as Porteus contends? The timing of the acceptance letter to Ohio certainly supports this. Goddard had an offer on the table if he wrote that letter the same day he penned Fels. It is also clear, however, that whatever the decision was, and even if it was to accept Goddard's resignation and not counter it, Goddard viewed it as a failure on his part to convince Fels to go on with the work. His letter referred to "outside influences" (Wistar and Greenman?) compelling "the committee" to come to the "fatal error" of not going on with the research program.

As Goddard prepared for his departure, he began to hear from colleagues, among them Davenport, wishing him success.

"My dear Dr. Davenport," Goddard wrote on March 25 in response to a letter from Davenport wishing him well. "Thank you for your kind note in regard to my new move. It has been a long and difficult problem to settle. Have been considering it since last July and only recently made up my mind. It is exceedingly difficult to leave Vineland, but on the whole it seems as though it were the proper thing to do. I trust I may be useful in the new work."[30]

In May 1918, just short of 12 years from the day in September 1906 when he'd walked the dusty path toward Maxham Hall into the unknown venture of a psychological laboratory in an institution for the feebleminded, Goddard walked away.

Goddard ultimately lost on several fronts that had motivated him to achieve such dramatic heights while at Vineland. For one, he lost his battle to usurp medicine's hold on research on the feebleminded, at least at Vineland. The impetus for the research moved from Goddard's psychological and eugenic agenda to Wistar's medical agenda.

---

[29] Porteus, 1969, p. 68.
[30] Goddard, 1918b.

"In the first group," wrote Greenman to Fels in March of 1918, referring to the first series of research questions to be addressed by a Wistar–Vineland collaboration, "it is proposed to include all Psychological problems and Behavior phenomena (as defined by psychologists). These observations are to be determined by the psychologist in consultation with the Superintendent of the Training School and members of the Wistar Institute staff engaged in the research."[31] In other words, it was to be much like it was when Goddard began, the psychologists were to be subservient to the medical doctors.

Strides had certainly been made for the discipline of psychology, many in which Goddard played a part. Intelligence testing had wrested some of the responsibility for diagnosis and treatment from psychiatrists to psychologists. But medical physicians still headed up the institutions for the feebleminded, a trend that continued through the midcentury. Medical doctors still dominated in the professional associations in the field as well. Of the first 35 presidents of the American Association for the Scientific Study of the Feeble-Minded, up to and including Goddard, 32 were medical doctors; Goddard and Johnstone were two of only three presidents who did not hold the M.D. in that stretch. Of the 35 presidents after Goddard, up to 1950, 30 were medical doctors. Among the five exceptions were Johnstone, serving his second term; Goddard assistant and eventual Vineland laboratory director Edgar Doll; and Meta Anderson and Fred Kuhlman, both of whom had spent time at Vineland.

The old physician versus psychologist struggles even followed Goddard to his new position in Ohio. When Goddard moved, he recruited Florence Mateer, who by that time had finished her doctorate at Clark and had been working as Walter Fernald's chief assistant at the Massachusetts institution, to follow him. Soon a not-friendly rivalry emerged between Mateer, the psychologist, and the Ohio Bureau of Juvenile Research's chief physician, Gertrude Transeau. In the spring of 1921, this rivalry essentially ended Goddard's stint at the Bureau of Juvenile Research. "On April 4, 1921," documented Zenderland, "this rivalry erupted into a public scandal when Transeau convinced ten other women employees to join her in resigning, as a protest against Mateer's power. Two weeks later, Mateer offered her resignation as well."[32]

The scandal provided the state legislature the opportunity to slash the agency's budget and cut Goddard's salary, ironically to $500 below what he had been earning when he left Vineland. Goddard's resignation followed one year later.[33]

He was replaced by a physician.[34]

---

[31] Greenman, 1918.

[32] Zenderland, 1998, p. 306.

[33] Zenderland, 1998, p. 307.

[34] Zenderland, 1998, p. 307.

❧ ❧ ❧

The final shot from the bow of Goddard's not-so-good ship the "S.S.Eugenics" occurred in April 1919, when he delivered the Vanuxem Lecture at Princeton University.

Founded in 1912 from a $25,000 bequest in the will of 1879 Princeton University graduate and insurance lawyer Louis Clark Vanuxem, the list of scientists who have delivered the Vanuxem Lecture is truly a litany of the brightest, most capable scientists in the world: Sir Roger Penrose, Oxford Mathematician who in 1988 shared the Wolf Prize in Physics with Stephen Hawking; Richard Leakey, renowned anthropologist and (with his mother and father, Louis and Mary) named among the 100 most influential scientists in the 20th century by *Time Magazine*; Carl Sagan, astronomer and one of the most widely recognized science popularizers of the last century; Eric Kandel, 2000 Nobel Laureate in Medicine whose groundbreaking work in memory storage is charting the brain; David Hubel, 1981 Nobel Laureate in Physiology or Medicine for his work, with Torsten Weisel, on the visual system; Francis H. C. Crick, 1962 Nobel Laureate for his discovery, with J.D. Watson, of the structure of DNA; Renowned neurologist Wilder Penfield, among the first to map out the function of the brain; J. Robert Oppenheimer, head of the Manhattan Project and father of the atomic bomb; Edwin Hubble, famed astronomer after whom the Hubble Telescope is named.

And Goddard. Actually delivered across four days from April 7 to 11, Goddard's lectures were published in 1920 under the title *Human Efficiency and Levels of Intelligence*.

Goddard's lectures echoed a theme that had been emerging through his writing with regard to the "role of the moron" in society.

"The fact seems to be that a very large percentage of these immigrants make good after a fashion," Goddard had argued, referring to immigrants who were morons. "At least it is true that they do a great deal of work that no one else will so. If some of them run amuck and make us trouble, then the wise solution of the problem would seem to be not to exclude them all but to take care of those who are not getting along well. It is perfectly true that there is an immense amount of drudgery to be done, an immense amount of work for which we do not wish to pay enough to secure more intelligent workers. May it be that the moron has his place?"[35]

It was this theme, the "place" of people in society as a function of their intellectual level that formed the basis of Goddard's Vanuxem lecture.

"Stated in its boldest form," began Goddard, "our thesis is that the chief determiner of human conduct is a unitary mental process which we call intelligence: that this process is conditioned by a nervous mechanism that is inborn: that the

---

[35] Goddard, 1917, p. 269.

degree of efficiency to be attained by that nervous mechanism and the consequent grade of intelligence or mental level for each individual is determined by
the kind chromosomes that come together with the union of the germ cells: that
it is but little affected by any later influence except such serious accident as may
destroy part of the mechanism.

"As a consequence any attempt at social adjustment which fails to take into
account the determining character of the intelligence and its unalterable grade
in each individual is illogical and inefficient."[36]

If any of Goddard's colleagues in the eugenics movement had feared—on the
basis of his proclamation that criminals were not born but made from feeble-
minded people, and that immigrants were likely feebleminded as a function
of environment—that Goddard had gone soft on hereditary determinism, his
Vanuxem lectures would have assured them that this was anything but the case.

"The theory of mental levels," Goddard explained, "holds that every human
being comes into the world with a potentiality for mental development that will
carry him just so far and that barring those accidents that may stop a person
from reaching the development which would have been normal to him, nothing
can, to any great extent, effect the mental level to which he will finally attain."[37]

Goddard distinguished between knowledge, which he argued was acquired,
and intelligence, which he conceptualized as innate. If, however, knowledge is
acquired, might not people become more efficient with advanced knowledge
and education, despite a low "mental level" as determined by intelligence tests?

"Knowledge is to intelligence what the raw material is to the machine,"
explained Goddard. "Low grade intelligence cannot use much knowledge."[38]

As such, Goddard's thesis puts the role of education at simply making sure
people had the right amount of knowledge they could use pertaining to their
intelligence, and made the education of the feebleminded and morons an exercise in futility.

Goddard then trotted out the Army Alpha findings. Suggesting that "no one
will deny that this distribution based on the examination of a million, seven
hundred thousand drafted men, may be applied to the entire population of the
United States,"[39] Goddard laid out the distribution of Army Alpha scores as a
function of the A through E rankings linking intelligence to suitability for military assignment, and argued that the army's efficiency was greatly aided by being
able to use mental levels to match soldiers to roles.

"Our army abroad had a well earned reputation for efficiency and no small
part of the result may be attributed to the fact that the lowest 10 per cent in

---

[36] Goddard, 1920, p. 1.

[37] Goddard, 1920, p. 7.

[38] Goddard, 1920, p. 11.

[39] Goddard, 1920, p. 35.

intelligence were not sent overseas and that 83 per cent of the officers came from the 'A' and 'B' classes—superior and very superior intelligence."[40]

Goddard then expanded this thesis, which of course had no evidence to support it, to society at large. "There can be no question that if a similar condition prevailed in our social groups a corresponding gain in efficiency would result. It is a maxim in engineering that a bridge is not stronger than its weakest part. The same is largely true of society. It must be understood, however, that weakness is not determined by the size of the part but by the relation the size or strength of the part bears to the work it has to do.

"Similarly, the efficiency of the human group is not so much a question of the absolute numbers of persons of high and low intelligence as it is whether each grade of intelligence is assigned a part, in the whole organization, that is within its capacity."[41]

After spending one lecture discussing the problem of the moron, its relationship to delinquency, and the threat of girls who are delinquents and who "show an incapacity for controlling themselves and acting properly"[42]—all well-traveled territory for Goddard—he moved on to his major thesis in his final lecture, titled *Mental Levels and Democracy*.

Goddard began his discussion of mental levels and democracy by returning to the army data, asking rhetorically if society can "hope to have a successful democracy when the average mentality is thirteen?"[43]

"Now it is a question," Goddard expanded, "of whether a people whose average intelligence is that of a thirteen year old child can make a sufficiently wise choice of rulers to insure the success of a democracy."[44]

"Lower intelligence will invariably," he continued, "and inevitably seek and follow the advice of higher intelligence so long as it has confidence in the individuals having the higher intelligence."[45]

"Socialism is a beautiful theory but the facts must be faced," Goddard observed, getting to the crux of his argument. "One of the facts is that people differ in mentality and that *each mentality requires its own kind of life for its success and happiness.*"[46]

"We have in the past allowed the idea of individual freedom to encroach heavily upon the domain of social efficiency. Why should we not ascertain the

---

[40] Goddard, 1920, p. 34.

[41] Goddard, 1920, pp. 34–35.

[42] Goddard, 1920, p. 88.

[43] Goddard, 1920, p. 95.

[44] Goddard, 1920, p. 96.

[45] Goddard, 1920, p. 97.

[46] Goddard, 1920, p. 102.

Figure 1. Goddard's Research Laboratory at the Vineland Training School. Contemporary undated postcard from author's collection.

Figure 2. "Deborah" (foreground left) on an outing. Contemporary undated postcard from author's collection.

Figure 3. "Deborah" identified as "A pupil who can neither read nor write, but who pays her way by useful work (she is a waitress in the school dining room, does beautiful woodwork, and plays the cornet in the band)" in Bjorkman (1911).

Figure 4. The Band. "Deborah" is the woman seated on the ground to the left (between the drummers). Photograph from the Twenty-First Annual Report of the New Jersey Training School for Feeble-Minded Girls and Boys in Vineland for the Year 1909. From author's collection.

THE BURGOMASTER AND
FRAU SAUERKRAUT

THE BEADLE

THE TYPICAL OBSTRUCTIONIST

THE CHIEF USHER

SOME CHARACTERS IN THE CHRISTMAS PLAY "THE PAY OF THE PIED PIPER OF HAMELIN"

Figure 5. Characters from annual Christmas play. "Deborah" is pictured, with a male actor, in the top, left oval titled "The Burgomaster and Frau Sauerkraut." Photograph from the Twenty-First Annual Report of the New Jersey Training School for Feeble-minded Girls and Boys in Vineland for the Year 1909. From author's collection.

Figure 6. Christmas entertainments. Photograph from the Twenty-Second Annual Report of the New Jersey Training School for Feeble-minded Girls and Boys in Vineland for the Year 1910. From author's collection.

Figure 7. The Girls' Band. "Deborah" is seated second row, third from the viewer's right, holding her cornet. Photograph from the Twenty-Second Annual Report of the New Jersey Training School for Feeble-Minded Girls and Boys in Vineland for the Year 1910. From author's collection.

Figure 8. Children playing in the southern lawn on and a playground near Garrison Hall. Originally Assembly Hall, it was renamed in honor of the founder, Olin Garrison. Photograph from the Twenty-Seventh Annual Report of the New Jersey Training School for Feeble-Minded Girls and Boys in Vineland for the Year 1915. From author's collection.

Figure 9. Aerial view of Training School campus, including the poultry plant. Photograph from the Twenty-Seventh Annual Report of the New Jersey Training School for Feeble-Minded Girls and Boys in Vineland for the Year 1915. From author's collection.

Figure 10. Animal photographs. "Deborah" is pictured in the top panel, labeled Pets, with a dog. The same photograph was used in *The Kallikak Family* and identified as Deborah "Age 17." Photograph from the Eighteenth Annual Report of the New Jersey Training School for Feeble-Minded Girls and Boys in Vineland for the Year 1906. From author's collection.

State Home for Girls and Women

ADMINISTRATION BUILDING   LAUNDRY   GYMNASIUM
MAIN ENTRANCE   WATER TOWER AND POWER HOUSE

Figure 11. New Jersey State Institution for Feeble-Minded Women, "Deborah's" home after 1914 and for most of her life. Photograph from Beautiful Vineland 1907 publication.

Figure 12. Horse and buggy in front of Maxham Hall at Vineland Training School circa 1900. From author's collection.

Figure 13. Panoramic view of the Training School campus circa 1900. To the left is Maxham Hall, with Garrison Hall to the right, the laundry with its brick chimney, and Cattell and Robinson cottages. From author's collection.

Figure 14. Maxham Hall circa 1900. The original Maxham Hall was destroyed by fire in December, 1896. The Goddard era Maxham Hall was completed in 1900, probably shortly before this photograph. This building was also destroyed by fire in 1925. From author's collection.

Figure 15. Training School staff circa 1900. E. R. Johnstone, who was appointed superintendent in late 1898, stand's at the viewer's farthest left. Olin Garrison, the founder, who died in April of 1900, is seated on a chair in the front row. From author's collection.

Figure 16. "Deborah," identified as "A girl aged twenty-two with the mentality of a child of nine years" from a photograph accompanying an article titled The State and the Fool (Sloss, 1912), which appeared in the February 3, 1912 issue of *Harper's Weekly*. The same picture was used in *The Kallikak Family* identifying her at "Age 15." From author's collection.

Figure 17. "She was able to count the number of her children so long as she had no more than ten . . ." (Doll, 1917). From author's collection.

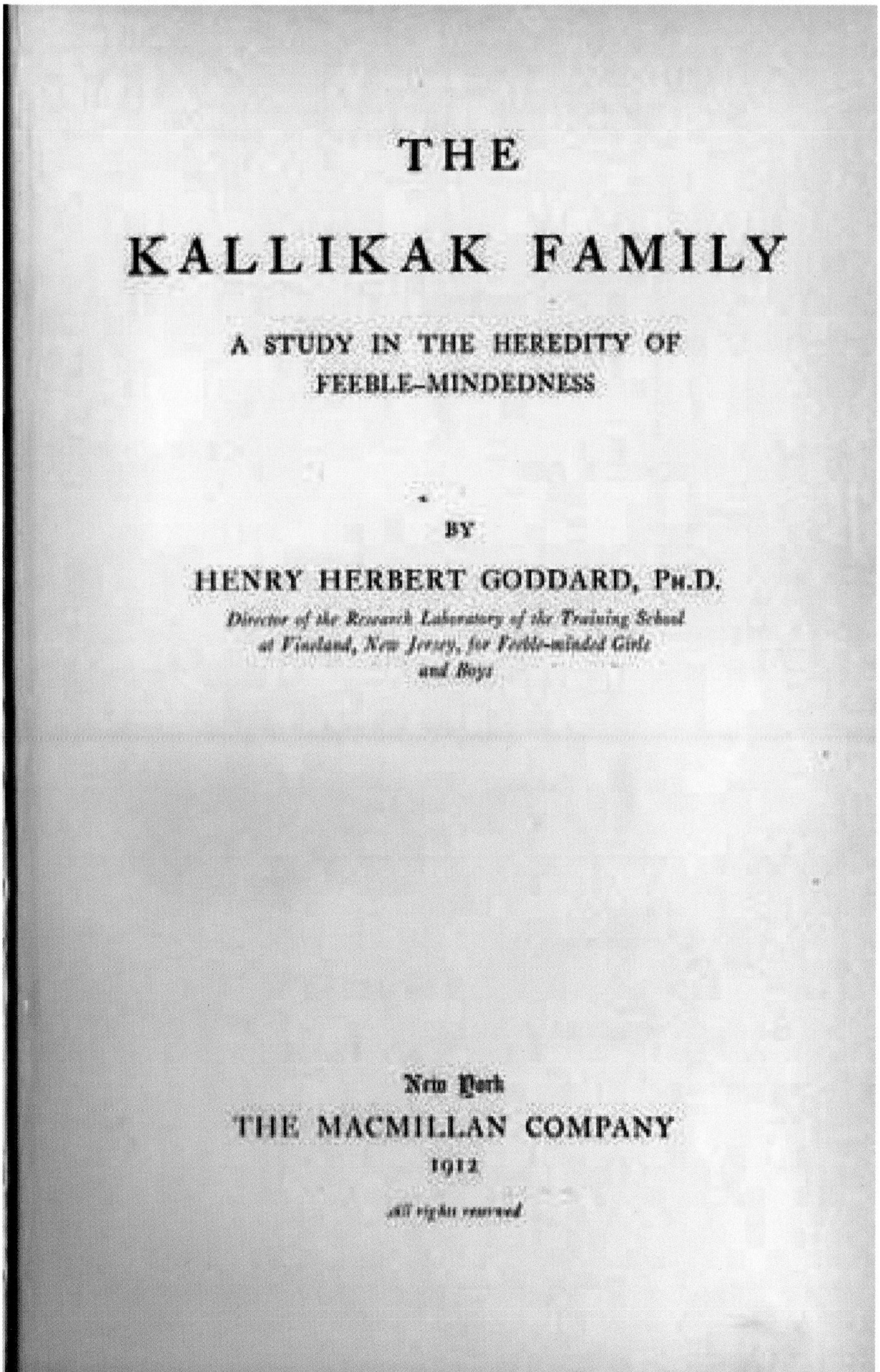

THE

KALLIKAK FAMILY

A STUDY IN THE HEREDITY OF
FEEBLE-MINDEDNESS

BY

HENRY HERBERT GODDARD, PH.D.

*Director of the Research Laboratory of the Training School
at Vineland, New Jersey, for Feeble-minded Girls
and Boys*

New York
THE MACMILLAN COMPANY
1912

All rights reserved

Figure 18. Title page for first printing of *The Kallikak Family* (Goddard, 1912). From author's collection.

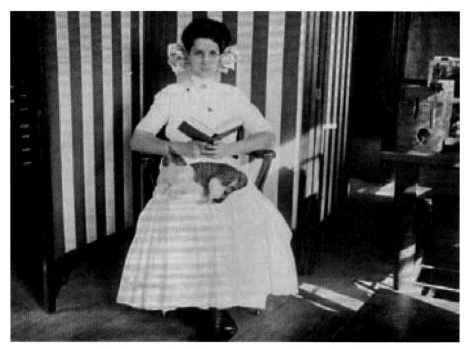

Figure 19. Frontispiece photograph of "Deborah" seated in the Psychological Laboratory from *The Kallikak Family* (Goddard, 1912). From author's collection.

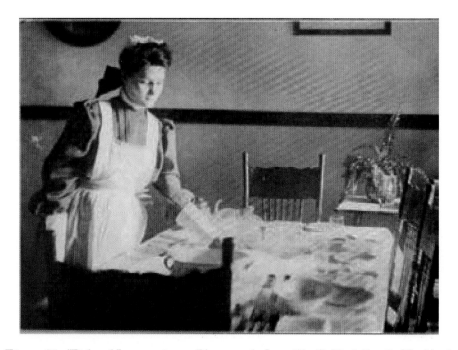

Figure 20. "Deborah" as a waitress. Photograph from *The Kallikak Family* (Goddard, 1912). From author's collection.

Figure 21. "Deborah" at the sewing machine. Photograph from *The Kallikak Family* (Goddard, 1912). From author's collection.

SPECIMENS OF DEBORAH'S HANDIWORK.

Figure 22. Specimens of "Deborah's" handiwork. Photograph from *The Kallikak Family* (Goddard, 1912). From author's collection.

Figure 23. "Deborah" at ages 15 and 17. Photograph from *The Kallikak Family* (Goddard, 1912). From author's collection.

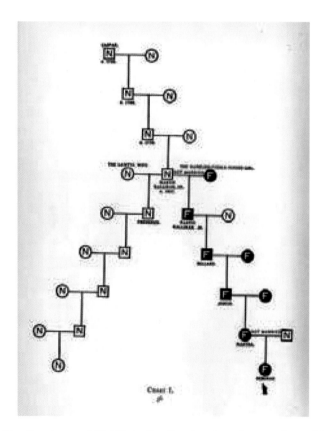

Figure 24. Family chart of Kallikak family showing lineage from Martin Sr. to "Deborah." The charts were, fundamentally, family trees depicting the genealogy and the hereditary nature, of inmates' families. From *The Kallikak Family* (Goddard, 1912). From author's collection.

Figure 25. The Training School Band from The Responsibility of Feebleminded Children by Alice Morrison Nash (1915). "Deborah" is in the middle row, third from viewer's right (behind drum on ground) holding her cornet in her hand. From author's collection.

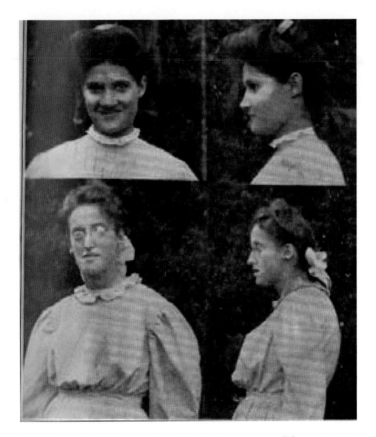

Figure 26. "High-grade feeble-minded girls, institution cases" from *Health and Medical Inspection of School Children* (Cornell, 1912). "Deborah" is shown in the upper front/side view photographs. From author's collection.

Figure 27. "Deborah" in 1962 (age 67) from *Charity and Correction in New Jersey: A History of State Welfare Institutions* (1967, Rutgers University Press) by Jame Leiby. From author's collection.

Figure 28. "Deborah" in 1931, age 42 (Used by permission Arthur Estabrook Papers, University at Albany Libraries' M. E. Grenander Department of Special Collections and Archives.).

Figure 29. Henry Herbert Goddard circa 1910s. (Image in public domain.)

Figure 30. View of the Hadamar Institute, one of six killing centers established by the Tiergarten Strasse 4, or just T4, Nazi killing program targeting adults with disabilities. (Used by permission, United States Holocaust Memorial Museum. The views or opinions expressed in this book and the context in which the images are used do not necessarily reflect the views or policy of, nor imply approval or endorsement by, the U.S. Holocaust Memorial Museum.)

Figure 31. Photograph of Charles Benedict Davenport, President of the Third International Congress of Eugenics, from *A Decade of Progress in Eugenics: Scientific Papers of the Third International Congress of Eugenics* (Perkins et al., 1934). From the author's collection.

grade of intelligence necessary in every essential occupation and then entrust to that work only those people who have the necessary intelligence?"[47]

"The plan recently announced by a few colleges, notably Columbia University, to give mental tests to their entering class is a great step forward."[48]

Aldous Huxley's *Brave New World* was still 13 years off, but Goddard seemed to presage Huxley's thesis.

❧ ❧ ❧

By 1919, when Goddard delivered his Vanuxem lecture, the field of genetics had expanded and matured and left his, and Davenport's, simplistic notions of unit-characters behind.

"The science of genetics changed enormously from about 1910 to the early 1930s," noted historian Hamilton Cravens. "In the 1910s and early 1920s a scientific gulf appeared between working biologists and geneticists on the one hand and eugenicists on the other. Of the leading genetics workers of the 1910s, only [Thomas] Morgan was doubtful of eugenics . . . the only recognized biologist who [criticized eugenics] before the early 1920s was Wesleyan University bacteriologist Herbert W. Conn."[49]

By 1920, the field of genetics was rethinking genetics and heredity, led by the research of future Nobel laureate Thomas Hunt Morgan and his research with *Drosophila melangastor*, the fruit fly.

"Results came rapidly from the Columbia fly-room," observed Cravens, referring to the laboratory at Columbia created by Morgan. "Within a few years a mosaic of interpretation emerged that did much to undercut simplistic views of Mendelism and extreme hereditarian views of human development. Morgan reported that sex was inherited in ways irreconcilable with the earlier idea of segregation of independent unit-characters, that the so-called unit characters were not always inherited independently, and that environment could influence the development of traits."[50]

In 1915, Morgan, along with three of his students—Alfred Sturtevant, Calvin Bridges, and H. J. Muller, who would win his own Nobel prize in 1946—published *The Mechanism of Mendelian Heredity*.

The 2000 winner of the Nobel Prize for Medicine, Eric Kandel, described *The Mechanism of Mendelian Heredity* as "a book that proved to be of historic importance," noting that "it set forth the physical basis for the new science of genetics . . . provided the first experimental basis for a modern biology, transforming it from a descriptive science that relied heavily on morphology" to "an

---

[47] Goddard, 1920, pp. 116 & 118.

[48] Goddard, 1920, p. 113.

[49] Cravens, 1978, pp. 159, 174–175.

[50] Cravens, 1978, p. 163.

exact, rigorous, quantitative experimental science that could exist on an equal footing with physics and chemistry."[51]

Morgan's new "gene theory" radically altered how heredity would be understood.

"For the unit-character idea," explained Craven, "they substituted the gene, which was not necessarily an independent building block responsible for but one trait. Genes could and were influenced by the behavior of other genes, the cytoplasm, by their arrangement on the chromosomes, by various environmental factors. And the facts of genetic linkage, of crossing-over (or interchange of blocks of genes between homologous pairs of chromosomes) and multiple factors for traits . . . meant that so-called unit-characters were not randomly and independently inherited."

"The development of traits," Craven summarized, "was not a simple matter of a single unit-character leading ineluctably to the formation of a fixed trait."[52]

Of course, Davenport's whole eugenic message was predicated on a single unit-character leading to the formation of a fixed trait, as was Goddard's thesis about the hereditary nature of feeblemindedness.

"The new picture of heredity and environment made it increasingly difficult for those with extreme hereditarian views," argued Cravens, "to maintain their scientific respectability."[53]

And yet, change happens slowly. If Morgan and company were redefining the field of genetics and moving it away from eugenically popularized notions of unit-characters in the mid-1910s, there were still plenty of scientists, like Henry Fairfield Osborn, perfectly willing to lend their aura of credibility to the movement. Although Morgan urged geneticists not to participate in the Second International Eugenic Congress in 1921, enough did, including Morgan's own student, H. J. Muller, that there was still an air of respectability to the proceedings.

"At least fifteen prominent working geneticists participated in the meeting by reading papers," noted Cravens, "but largely on their terms; all but two of them ignored eugenic issues entirely and gave detailed reports of their own genetics research."[54]

Yes, but they were there, nonetheless.

Working geneticists were increasingly mortified by the inflammatory nature of eugenics, exemplified by Harry Hamilton Laughlin's charades as an "expert" scientist in front of the House Immigration Committee.[55]

---

[51] Kandel, 1999.

[52] Cravens, 1978, p. 164.

[53] Cravens, 1978, p. 158.

[54] Cravens, 1978, p. 176.

[55] Cravens, 1978, p. 176.

Meanwhile, the eugenic rhetoric became increasingly racialist; involuntary sterilization went into high gear, culminating in a 1927 U.S. Supreme Court blessing of the practice; and the anti-immigration movement achieved restrictions in 1924 and 1927 that they had failed to achieve in the first two decades of the movement.

If the field of genetics was leaving eugenics behind as a credible science, then eugenics was also no longer as much in need of the credibility legitimate scientists provided the movement; it had risen to visibility using the credentials of the first generation of genetic scientists, including Davenport himself, and then caught the wave of the social discontent, anxiety, and beliefs held by mainstream Americans to take it even higher. If Madison Grant had Roosevelt's endorsement for his racialist screed, the *Passing of the Great Race*, why did he need Morgan's approval?

Additionally, even if individual scientists were drifting away from mainline eugenics, too many textbooks retained important vestiges of eugenic thought.

W. E. Castle, the Harvard professor of zoology who had advised Morgan that he try genetic experiments on the fruit fly, wrote about feeblemindedness in his 1916 text *Genetics and Eugenics*. "The most complete study of the inheritance of feeble-mindedness that has ever been made is that published by Dr. H. H. Goddard of the Vineland New Jersey Training School for Feeble-minded," referring to Goddard's 1914 *Feeble-Mindedness: Its Causes and Consequences*. "The information was obtained from the parents of pupils, from the family physicians, friends or neighbors, partly through printed questionnaires, partly through personal interviews by trained investigators. This method of obtaining information is of course capable of uncritical use . . . but seems to have been employed with circumspection and in some cases with independent verification by Dr. Goddard."[56]

After that misjudgment, Castle then summarized Goddard's work for his readers: feeblemindedness was more common than one would think; many criminals and social outcasts are feebleminded; the Binet-Simon Scales are the way to identify the feebleminded; and the feebleminded should be segregated as much as possible, sterilized if absolutely necessary.

There were other texts throughout the 1920s that buttressed the mythology created by Goddard, Davenport, and other eugenicists. Arthur Ward Lindsey's *Textbook of Evolution and Genetics*, published in 1929, included a recitation of the Kallikak saga, concluding that "the record of this family is even more convincing evidence of the potency of heredity in determining the value of human beings."[57]

---

[56] Castle, 1916, pp. 253–254.
[57] Lindsey, 1929, p. 370.

And because the universal education movement meant more of America's children were being educated in the public schools, the Kallikak mythology moved to high school textbooks. As late as 1951, the widely used high school science textbook *Modern Biology*, written by Truman Moon, Paul Mann, and James Otto, contained, in the chapter on genetics applied to human inheritance, the Jukes and the Kallikak stories. They were told uncritically and accompanied by Goddard's original Kallikak family chart and a picture of a "modern" slum, reminiscent of Goddard's use of the shack images in *The Kallikak Family*, with the caption "Criminals and social misfits are often the result of squalor and slum environments."[58]

Further, if genetic textbooks continued to contain information from eugenically oriented researchers, these same eugenicists were themselves writing textbooks for use in the growing number of eugenics courses taught in universities and colleges.

"Eugenics rocketed through academia, becoming an institution virtually overnight," stated Edwin Black. "By 1914, some forty-four major institutions offered eugenic instruction. Within a decade, that number would swell to hundreds, reaching some 20,000 students annually."[59]

One the most popular of these texts was Paul Popenoe and Rosewell Hill Johnson's *Applied Eugenics*, published first in 1918. Not surprisingly, the text was a manual for negative eugenics: the Jukes and the Kallikaks were highlighted, with the admonition that "if it were possible to improve or eradicate these defective strains by giving them better surroundings, the nation might easily get rid of this burden. But we have given reasons . . . for believing that the problem can not be solved in this way."[60] It was reprinted in 1920, 1923, and 1924. A revised edition was issued in 1933, and reprinted in 1935 and 1931. Yet another updated edition appeared in 1941, and the book was in print as late as 1949.

By the mid-1920s and into the 1930s, the attacks on eugenics became increasingly more frequent. Although many scientists had doubts about eugenics prior to 1920, as historian James Trent has noted, their opposition tended "to be private and cautious."[61] There were a few exceptions who made their opposition public, though, including Herbert W. Conn.

Conn was a professor of biology at Wesleyan University, a pioneering bacteriologist, and a cofounder of the American Society of Microbiology. In 1914, Conn published *Social Heredity and Social Evolution: The Other Side of Eugenics.*

"The teaching of eugenics," Conn argued, "leads to two unfortunate results. The first is a feeling of hopelessness and pessimism. As long as it was possible to

---

[58] Moon, Mann, and Otto, 1951, pp. 649–650.

[59] Black, 2003, p. 75.

[60] Popenoe and Johnson, 1918, p. 160.

[61] Trent, 2001, p. 38.

believe that the inheritance which we transmit to our offspring might be modified by our own actions, it was possible to see a hope in the future.

"But if we are forced to believe that by nothing that we do we can influence
the inheritance which we hand down to our children, we are landed almost in
despair. By this new view of heredity we learn that the inheritance which we are
to transmit into our offspring is fixed when we select our husband or wife, and
that nothing that we may do subsequently can possibly modify it. There seems to
be little hope for the future with such a view, for we cannot believe that even the
most extended discussion will have any material effect upon the mating habits
of mankind. The choice of husband and wife is bound up in the complex social
conditions in such a way that it is determined by an indefinite number of artificial factors of which physical fitness hardly plays even a minor part."[62]

"The second unfortunate tendency of the emphasis placed on eugenics is
that it inevitably makes us neglect certain other phases of the inheritance question which in reality have had greater influence on the evolution of mankind.
Reference is here made to phenomena which in the subsequent pages of this
work are together called social heredity."[63]

"The conclusions of eugenics," Conn summarized, "are all based upon the
assumption that mankind is controlled by the same laws as the rest of the
organic world, but . . . it must be pointed out that man stands in a unique position. The human animal may be controlled by the same laws of heredity as other
animals; but the human being is more than an animal, and the characteristics
which isolate him so sharply from the rest of organic nature are not features of
his animal functions at all, but are something quite distinct. It is quite possible
that, while his animal characteristics are under the dominion of the common
laws of heredity, those characteristics which make him stand forth so sharply
in contrast to other animals are under the influence of a different set of laws. If
so, these conclusions of helplessness which come from the eugenics may not be
well founded."[64]

Conn then went on to elaborate on the laws of social heredity that might
make the eugenic message an overly simplistic one, discussing the origin of language, the evolution of moral codes and moral sense, the development of social-
izations and cultures, and issues of egoism and altruism in the human race.

Conn dismissed the role of intelligence rather summarily, contrasting intelligence not with knowledge, as had Goddard in his Vanuxem Lecture, but with
instinct. "We call the actions of the brain that becomes molded by experience,
but is not preformed, by the name of intelligence, and we find that this is

---

[62] Conn, 1914, pp. 12–13.

[63] Conn, 1914, p. 13.

[64] Conn, 1914, pp. 16–17.

not handed on by heredity, but is acquired anew by each individual after years of training."[65]

Conn's sociobiological look at human evolution presaged many of the issues that biologists and anthropologists would grapple with in the coming decades. His refutation of the primacy of heredity and eugenics also put him ahead of his era, and in the next decade the ripple that was Conn's criticism would be become a surging wave.

Why was Conn's the nearly lone voice against the eugenic dogma that dominated the early 1910s? Perhaps it was because Conn had personal experience with disability. His second child, and only son, Herbert J. Conn—who like his father became a bacteriologist and served as president of the Society of American Bacteriologists—was deaf.

Conn's attacks, although prescient, did not carry the weight to significantly slow down the steam engine that was the American eugenics movement. Neither did a similar dart shot by psychologist Samuel Kohs in 1915. Writing in the *Journal of Heredity* in an article titled "New Light on Eugenics," Kohs argued that research in the psychological area of "unconscious phenomena," led by Freudian and Adlerian schools of psychiatry, suggested that many human traits are the function of early life experiences and not heredity, and thus called into question some eugenic research.[66]

R. C. Punnett, whose classic text on genetics, *Mendelism*, had so influenced Davenport and Goddard, was of such higher status in the field, however, that his opinions, which were strongly eugenic in 1907, could influence the thinking of others. Writing in the *Journal of Heredity* in 1917, Punnett questioned the presumption of many eugenicists that feeblemindedness could be eliminated through better breeding.

"If the proportion of feeble-minded in the United States is 3 per 1,000 today," Punnett pointed out, "it would require something over 250 generations, or about 8,000 years, before the proportion was reduced to 1 in 100,000, and nearly four times this length of time before the feebleminded were as few as 1 in a million. Clearly if that most desirable goal of a world rid of the feebleminded is to be reached in a reasonable time some method other than that of the elimination of the feebleminded themselves must eventually be found."[67]

Punnett's arguments buttressed those of Alexander Graham Bell, who was increasingly frustrated with Davenport's focus only on negative eugenics and who, toward the end of his life, began to fade out of active involvement in the eugenics movement. Neither man, however, repudiated eugenics per se, simply Davenport's brand of it.

---

[65] Conn, 1914, pp. 34–35.

[66] Kohs, 1915, p. 450.

[67] Punnett, 1917, p. 465.

More than any other voice before 1920, it was that of Franz Boas that carried the most weight and began to turn the tide of scientific opinion against the eugenics movement. Franz Boas was, by general consensus, the most important American anthropologist of the early 20th century and is often referred to as the father of American Anthropology. Born in Germany in 1858, Boas assumed a faculty position at Columbia University in anthropology in 1896 and became a full professor there in 1899. Boas's influences were many and varied, but his voice was most influential, at least with regard to eugenics, through his research and writing on the concepts of race and culture. He is, essentially, the most important person in repudiating the eugenics movement's theories and statements about racial superiority. It was because Boas had control over the existing professional anthropology association, the American Anthropological Association (AAA), in fact, that Davenport had to form an alternative organization, the Galton Society.

By the 1920s, Boas would lead the movement of anthropologists who dismissed the race-superiority theories of eugenics through the auspices of the AAA, but even as early as 1916 he was speaking of the dangers of eugenics. Writing in *Scientific Monthly* that year, Boas called eugenics "a dangerous sword that may turn its edge against those who rely on its strength."[68] As both Boas and Morgan disassociated themselves with the American eugenics movement in the early to mid-1920s, the movement lost scientific credibility. As evidenced by the spreading adoption of eugenic principles by the masses that occurred in the 1920s, however, the loss of scientific credibility was not immediately detrimental to the movement's vitality and viability.

The pre-1920 censures of eugenics were, essentially, private; they were voiced to members of the scientific community, not to the general public. The first attacks on eugenics in the public sphere began in the early 1920s. Among the most important of these were by novelist G. K. Chesterton and popular journalist Walter Lippmann.

Chesterton was a British literary icon, equally facile at writing fiction, poetry, biography, or political commentary. He is best remembered today, however, for the Father Brown mysteries, collections of short stories whose main character was a priest who also acted as a private investigator. In 1922, Chesterton published *Eugenics and Other Evils*, a collection of essays that served as a rebuttal to the false ideas propagated through the eugenics movement.

"Chesterton linked eugenics to Prussianism," summarized Daniel Kevles, "to the 'same stuffy science, the same bullying bureaucracy and the same terrorism by tenth-rate professors that have led the German Empire to it recent conspicuous triumphs.' In his view, science had long aimed to tyrannize. Through eugenics, it proposed to extend its tyranny 'to reach the secret and sacred places

---

[68] Boas, 1916, p. 471.

of freedom, where no sane man ever dreamed of seeing it; and especially the sanctuary of sex.' He predicted that eugenics would mean forcible marriage by the police."[69]

"In the first chapter," Chesterton summarized in *Eugenics and Other Evils*, "I attempted to define the essential point in which Eugenics can claim, and does claim, to be a new morality. That point is that it is possible to consider the baby in considering the bride. I do not adopt the ideal irresponsibility of the man who said, 'What has posterity done for us?' But I do say, to start with, 'What can we do for posterity, except deal fairly with our contemporaries?' Unless a man love his wife whom he has seen, how shall he love his child whom he has not seen?"

"In [a later chapter] I point out how this impatience has burst through the narrow channel of the Lunacy Laws, and has obliterated them by extending them. The whole point of the madman is that he is the exception that proves the rule. But Eugenics seeks to treat the whole rule as a series of exceptions—to make all men mad. And on that ground there is hope for nobody; for all opinions have an author, and all authors have a heredity."[70]

Chesterton's ironic style and cutting sarcasm may not, however, have played well in the Peoria of public opinion, and it is hard to judge the impact of *Eugenics and Other Evils* on American eugenics, although his is clearly the most literate of 1920s denunciations of eugenics. More influential in the United States was Walter Lippmann's criticism of intelligence testing and intelligence testers, which was also published in 1922. Lippmann was founding editor of and a frequent columnist for *The New Republic* magazine, a primary voice of the progressive movement. He was an advisor to Woodrow Wilson and helped the president craft his 14-points speech. He left *The New Republic*, as an editor, in 1920 and moved to the *New York Herald-Tribune*, where his column eventually won two Pulitzer Prizes.

Beginning in November 1922, in a series of six articles in *The New Republic*, Lippmann took aim at the eugenics movement through, primarily, a scathing critique of the army testing data and the use of results from that data set.

"A startling bit of news has recently been unearthed and is now being retailed by the credulous to the gullible," Lippmann began. "'The average mental age of Americans,' says Mr. Lothrop Stoddard in *The Revolt Against Civilization*, 'is only about fourteen.'

"Mr. Stoddard did not invent this astonishing conclusion. He found it ready-made in the writings of a number of other writers. They in their turn got the conclusion by misreading the data collected in the army intelligence tests. . . . The average adult intelligence cannot be less than the average adult intelligence, and to anyone who knows what the words 'mental age' mean, Mr. Stoddard's

---

[69] Kevles, 1985, p. 120.
[70] Chesterton, 1922, p. 84.

remark is precisely as silly as if he had written that the average mile was three quarters of a mile long.

"The trouble is that Mr. Stoddard uses the words 'mental age' without explaining either to himself or to his readers how the conception of 'mental age' is derived. He was in such an enormous hurry to predict the downfall of civilization that he could not pause long enough to straighten out a few simple ideas. The result is that he snatches a few scarifying statistics and uses them as a base upon which to erect a glittering tower of generalities. For the statement that the average mental age of Americans is only about fourteen is not inaccurate. It is not incorrect. It is nonsense."[71]

"Mental age," Lippman explained, "is a yard stick invented by a school of psychologists to measure 'intelligence.' It is not easy, however, to make a measure of intelligence and the psychologists have never agreed on a definition.

"Remembering this, we come to the army tests. Here we are dealing at once with men all of whom are over the age of the mental scale."[72]

Lippmann is referring to Stoddard's and others transformation of the army test measures to putative mental ages for comparison with mental ages calculated by Terman's Stanford-Binet scale.

"For the Stanford-Binet scale ends at 'sixteen years,'" Lippman continued. "It assumes that intelligence stops developing at sixteen and everybody sixteen and over is therefore treated as 'adult' or as 'superior adult.' Now the adult Stanford-Binet tests were 'standardized chiefly on the basis of results from 400 adults' 'of moderate success and of very limited educational advantages' and also thirty-two high school pupils from sixteen to twenty years of age. Among these adults those who tested close together have the honor of being considered the standard of average adult intelligence.[73]

"Before the army tests came along, when anyone talked about the average adult he was talking about a few hundred Californians. The army tested about 1,700,000 adult men. But it did not use the Binet system of scoring the mental ages. Naturally enough everyone interested in mental testing wanted to know whether the army tests agreed in any way with the Stanford-Binet mental age standard. So, by another process . . . the results of the army tests were translated into Binet terms. The result of this translation is the table which has so badly misled poor Mr. Stoddard. This table showed that the average of the army did not agree at all with the average of Mr. Terman's Californians. There were then two things to do. One was to say that the average intelligence of 1,700,000 men was a more representative average than that of four hundred men. The other was to pin your faith to the four hundred men and insist they gave the true average.

---

[71] Lippman, 1922a, p. 213.

[72] Lippman, 1922a, p. 214.

[73] Lippman, 1922a, p. 214.

"Mr. Stoddard chose the average of four hundred rather than the average of 1,700,000 because he was in such haste to write his own book that he never reached page 785 of *Psychological Examining in the United States Army*, the volume of the data edited by Major [Robert] Yerkes. He would have found there a clear warning against the blunder he was about to commit, the blunder of treating the average of a small number of instances as more valid than the average of a large number.

"But instead of pausing to realize that the army tests had knocked the Stanford-Binet measure of adult intelligence into a cocked hat, he wrote his book in the belief that the Stanford measure is as good as it ever was. This is not intelligent. It leads one to suspect that Mr. Stoddard is a propagandist with a tendency to put truth not in the first place but in the second. It leads one to suspect, after such a beginning that the real promise and value of the investigation which Binet started is in danger of gross perversion by muddleheaded and prejudiced men."[74]

With that, Lippmann proceeded to describe how the Army Alpha was used to classify officers, and to impugn the integrity of intelligence testing.

"It is not possible, I think," wrote Lippmann, "to imagine a more contemptible proceeding than to confront a child with a set of puzzles, and after an hour's monkeying with them, proclaim to the child, or to his parents, that here is a C-individual. It would not only be a contemptible thing to do. It would be a crazy thing to do, because there is nothing in these tests to warrant a judgment of this kind. All that can be claimed for the tests is that they can be used to classify into a homogeneous group the children whose capacities for school work are at a particular moment fairly similar. The intelligence test shows nothing as to why those capacities at any moment are what they are, and nothing as to the individual treatment which a temporarily retarded child may require. . . . Readers who have not examined the literature of mental testing may wonder why there is reason to fear such an abuse of an invention which has many practical uses. The answer, I think, is that most of the more prominent testers have committed themselves to a dogma which must lead to such abuse. They claim not only that they are really measuring intelligence, but that intelligence is innate, hereditary, and predetermined. They believe that they are measuring the capacity of a human being for all time and that his capacity is fatally fixed by the child's heredity. Intelligence testing in the hands of men who hold this dogma could not but lead to an intellectual caste system in which the task of education had given way to the doctrine of predestination and infant damnation. If the intelligence test really measured the unchangeable hereditary capacity of human beings, as so many assert, it would inevitably evolve from an administrative convenience into a basis for hereditary caste."[75]

---

[74] Lippman, 1922a, p. 215.
[75] Lippman, 1922d, p. 297.

Lippmann then aims his sights on the Kallikak study.

"There is," observed Lippman, "some doubt as to the Kallikaks. It will be recalled that during the Revolutionary War a young soldier, known under the pseudonym of Martin Kallikak, had an illegitimate feeble-minded son by a feeble-minded girl. The descendants of this union have been criminals and degenerates. But after the war was over Martin married respectably. The descendants of this union have been successful people. This is powerful evidence, but it would, as Professor [James McKeen] Cattell points out, be more powerful, and more interesting scientifically, if the wife of the respectable marriage had been feeble-minded, and the girl in the tavern had been a healthy, normal person. Then only would it have been possible to say with complete confidence that this was a pure case of biological rather than of social heredity."[76]

"It is possible, of course, to deny that the early environment has any important influence on the growth of intelligence," concluded Lippman. "Men like Stoddard and McDougall do deny it, and so does Mr. Terman. But on the basis of the mental tests they have no right to an opinion. Mr. Terman's observations begin at four years of age. He publishes no data on infancy and he is, therefore, generalizing about the heredity factor after four years of immensely significant development have already taken place. On his own showing as to the high importance of the earlier years, he is hardly justified in ignoring them. He cannot simply lump together the net result of natural endowment and infantile education and ascribe it to the germplasm."[77]

"A general measure of intelligence valid for all people everywhere at all times may be an interesting toy for the psychologist in his laboratory. But just because the tests are so general, just because they are made so abstract in the vain effort to discount training and industry. Instead, therefore, of trying to find a test which will with equal success discover artillery officers, Methodist ministers, and branch managers for the rubber business, the psychologists would far better work out special and specific examinations for artillery officers, divinity school candidates and branch managers in the rubber business. On that line they may ultimately make a serious contribution to a civilization which is constantly searching for more successful ways of classifying people for specialized jobs. And in the meantime the psychologists will save themselves from the reproach of having opened up a new chance for quackery in a field where quacks breed like rabbits, and they will save themselves from the humiliation of having furnished doped evidence to the exponents of the New Snobbery."[78]

Terman responded to Lippman in an article in a following issue of *The New Republic*, "comparing Lippmann to William Jennings Bryan, then the leading

---

[76] Lippman, 1922e, p. 328.

[77] Lippman, 1922d, p. 329.

[78] Lippman, 1922f, p. 11.

opponent of the Theory of Evolution, and to Wilbur Voliva, head of the Flat Earth Society."[79]

As Steven Selden noted, "Lippmann's most powerful criticisms were not of the technology of testing but of the test constructors' major assumptions."[80] Further, he had cast aspersions on the Kallikak study in the public arena.

Perhaps most detrimental to Goddard's tenure at Vineland, there were concerns about the Kallikak data from some people closely associated with Vineland. Australian psychologist Stanley D. Porteus, who succeeded Goddard as the research laboratory director and is best known as the developer of the Porteus Maze test, a nonverbal measure of intelligence, published in his autobiography in 1969, "About 1917, doubts began to creep in regarding the validity of the evidence gathered for Goddard, on which he based his book *The Kallikak Family*. It is quite possible that Dr. Greenman was one of those who decided Goddard's findings were both too good and too bad to be true; the descendants of the revolutionary officer through marriage with a woman of his own social class included no feebleminded as compared with the terrific load of mental defectives that hung from the limbs of the Kallikak family tree."[81]

Milton Greenman was, of course, both a physician and director of the Wistar Institute, which, in essence, took over much of the Fels-funded research after Goddard left.

By the early 1920s, others in the field were noting similar problems. Leta Stetter Hollingworth was a Columbia University graduate who earned her doctorate under psychologists and mental testing advocates Edward Thorndike and Naomi Norsworthy who went on to champion the cause of gifted education, earning the title of the mother of gifted education.[82] Hollingworth—who was a friend of Elizabeth Farrell, Goddard's combatant in the New York Schools Survey—had worked with Goddard's version of the Binet-Simon Scale. In 1920, she published *Psychology of Subnormal Children*.

"It detracts somewhat from the value of these studies," Hollingworth noted about the Kallikak family narrative, "that they rest upon the opinions of neighbors and field workers to so great an extent, and that mental deficiency has to be inferred from undesirable behavior. There still remains to be made a study of equal scope, in which all relatives shall actually be measured intellectually, by the psychological method."[83]

Wallin also entered the fray. In his introduction to a special education textbook in 1924, he wrote, "it must be frankly admitted, that family histories cannot, in

---

[79] Chase, 1975, p. 306.

[80] Selden, 1999, p. 122.

[81] Porteus, 1969, p. 68.

[82] Klein, 2002.

[83] Hollingworth, 1920, p. 213.

the very nature of the case, be made very accurate, particularly so far as concerns the record of minor social and moral lapses and the diagnosis of mental defect. The differential diagnoses of the dead of past generations are almost entirely conjectural, based almost solely on hearsay information, or traditional lore, or the record of lawless behavior. Moreover, when the investigator has started out with preconceived conclusions regarding the absolute dominance of heredity (Possibly as an avowed protagonist of the Mendelian theory of inheritance), the inevitable tendency has been to ignore or minimize the incident factors of the environment. But it is probable that a bad environment usually has hampered the advancement of the cacogenic strains, while a good environment has promoted the progress of the 'eugenic' strains. The heredity and environmental forces supplement and reinforce one another.

"Although an unfavorable environment will drag down the weaker strains more than the stronger ones, it is conceivable that if the progeny of Martin, Sr., had grown up in the environment of Martin, Jr., the character of the ancestral line of the former might have been different from what it is. The environment always supplies the soil, the opportunities for advancement or for deterioration."[84]

No one, however, was more critical over such a sustained period of time of the eugenic family narratives in general and the Kallikak narrative in particular, than was psychiatrist Abraham Myerson and, perhaps, no one was more successful in challenging the myth created by such narratives. Like Conn, Myerson voiced his opposition to eugenics early, although these criticisms became more widely recognized in the mid-1920s when he summarized them in a book on psychiatry. Myerson was a Columbia University graduate and received his medical degree from Tufts College Medical School in 1908, moving eventually to Boston, where he served, for a time, as a professor of clinical psychiatry at Harvard's Medical School. In 1913, Myerson became clinical director of the Taunton State Hospital in the Boston area. Opened in 1851 as the Massachusetts State Lunatic Hospital at Taunton, the campus boasted an impressive Kirkbride building topped by a majestic dome.

Almost as soon as he arrived, Myerson began to study the records of the inmates of his insane asylum. "It was hoped that it would be possible, to ascertain the fate of the descents of the insane. Such a method would be based on the fact that certain descendants of the insane become themselves inmates of insane hospitals, but the great majority do not. What happens to these last, that is, those descendants of the insane who disappear into society? What is their fate? In how far do they contribute to society's problems—insanity, criminality, feeble-mindedness, pauperism, disease?"[85]

[84]Wallin, 1924, pp. 281–282.
[85]Myerson, 1917, p. 355.

Myerson's interests were not, however, parallel to those of others tracking family histories, like Goddard or Davenport. Myerson was interested in testing the "classical doctrine" of the transmission of insanity as forwarded by Esquirol and Morel, referred to as the doctrine of the polymorphism of insanity.

"First," Myerson explained, "all forms of mental disease and a large part of nervous disorders, together with some constitutional states, and various and interchangeable manifestations of hereditary degeneracy. Thus, the central doctrine assumes that such varied diseases as idiocy, cretinism, moral insanity, hebephrenia (now 'disorganized schizophrenia'), catatonia, mania, melancholia, involution (progressive decline of functioning as a function of age) and senile diseases, neurasthenia, hysteria, epilepsy, criminality, and eccentricity in all its thousand and one forms, are not really separate conditions but merely manifestations of one condition; to-wit, inherited and inheritable degeneracy."[86]

Myerson's purpose, then, was to test the eugenically valued idea that various forms of mental illness and feeblemindedness simply reflected different points along a continuum of degeneracy.

The outcome of Myerson's study was a two-part, 188-page report published in the *American Journal of Insanity*, the first American psychiatric journal, which became the *American Journal of Psychiatry* in 1922. Most of these 188 pages were filled with the generational history of 98 family groups, which included at least three generations of which members from two generations had been hospitalized for mental illness at Taunton. Through this, Myerson began to sketch out the degree to which specific mental disorders, such as dementia praecox, paranoia, manic depression, and senile dementia, appeared and reappeared across generations. What Myerson found—not surprisingly, because we now know that many of these diseases do, in fact, have a strong hereditary component—was that, in many cases, like begat like. Dementia praecox appeared across generations; manic-depressives passed their condition on to the next generation, and so on. What he didn't find was that bad begat worse.

"How does this compare with the classical theory of Esquirol and Morel?" Myerson asked. "It may be stated that the schema of these writers is too rigid, too formal to fit the facts. A psychosis may repeat itself for three or four generations without changing its general character."[87]

Further, criminality didn't seem to be related to mental illness, per se. Insanity did not, according to Myerson, begat criminality, in the same way that Goddard had claimed that feeblemindedness begat criminality. "Criminality in the families here studied has been a very inconspicuous feature. It is true that some of these insane have committed crimes while insane. That, however, does not make

---

[86] Myerson, 1917, pp. 356–357.
[87] Myerson, 1917, p. 484.

them criminals since the crime was brought about by the insane delusions etc. Criminal relatives either in the fore or after generations have been infrequent."[88]

"The 1917–1918 articles [parts I and II of Myerson's study] pointed to what Myerson believed were methodological, logical, and interpretive flaws in the eugenicists' claims," observed Trent. "His use of the very methodology—pedigree studies from case records so revered by Davenport, Goddard and Rosanoff— enhanced his criticism."[89]

In the years following the publication of his Taunton study, Myerson published a series of book reviews—mainly in the journal *Mental Hygiene*—that were critical of eugenically oriented texts. In 1922, he critiqued Samuel J. Holmes's *The Trend of the Race* and Caleb Saleeby's *The Eugenic Prospect: National and Racial*, both of which had been published the previous year. In 1923, Myerson's target was Wiggam's *The New Decalogue of Science*, and the following year, Myerson and Maurice Hexter (director of the Federated Jewish Charities of Boston)[90] castigated Brigham's *A Study of American Intelligence*. In 1926, Arthur Estabrook and Ivan McDougle's eugenic family study *Mongrel Virginians: The Win Tribe*, and A. M. Carr-Sanders's *Eugenics* came under attack by Myerson's withering pen.

Myerson's 1922 critical review of Holmes's *The Trend of the Race* also, however, included an attack on Goddard's Kallikak study. Holmes, a professor of Zoology at the University of California at Berkeley, had been active with fellow eugenicist C. W. Goethe in the anti-immigration campaigns in California. Holmes was not a subtle eugenicist, titling one of his papers *Perils of the Mexican Invasion*, in which he "assailed Mexicans as undemocratic, mentally retarded, and wildly procreative carriers of the plague, typhus, and hookworm."[91]

Holmes's *The Trend of the Race* was, even when compared with other eugenic texts of the era, particularly enamored with "Goddard's fascinating book."[92] He provided a three-page summary of the Kallikak narrative, then returned to the Kallikak family as reference eight more times.

Myerson used Holmes's fixation on the Kallikak saga to launch an attack of Goddard's eugenic family narrative. "And here we meet the famous Kallikak family. The reviewer must confess that a sense of incredulity is raised to the *n*th power whenever he hears of the two lines of descendants of Martin Kallikak. On the one hand, he bred a family absolutely bad, and on the other hand a family absolutely good. The whole story is too good to be true. Nothing like it is seen anywhere else. Everywhere else one finds, instead, good people breeding bad people and bad people breeding good people. Saints are descendants of prosti-

---

[88] Myerson, 1917, p. 484.

[89] Trent, 2001, p. 38.

[90] Trent, 2001, p. 42.

[91] Stern, 2005, p. 90.

[92] Myerson, 1922, p. 625.

tutes and prostitutes are sprung from the loins of saints, but not so with Martin Kallikak."[93]

Myerson's incredulity that bad bred only bad and good bred only good mirrored what Porteus attributed to Wistar's Milton Greenman: that the Kallikak findings were both too good and too bad to be true.

In 1925, Myerson published *The Inheritance of Mental Disease*, which although not the first venue in which he had challenged the validity of the Kallikak study, quickly became the most widely read. "I confess to a feeling of shame in the presence of the work done by the field worker in this case. I have had charge of a clinic where alleged feeble-minded persons were brought every day and I see in my practice and hospital work murderers, thieves, sex offenders, failures, etc. Many of these are brought to me by social workers, keen intelligent women, who are in grave doubt as to the mental condition of their charges *after months of daily relationship*, after intimate knowledge, and prolonged effort to understand. Many a time it has happened that one of these excellent women has declared that her charge must be feeble-minded or insane, and yet the mental tests and psychological examinations have shown the contrary, that the patient was of full average mentality or better; often it has happened that the social worker (or the informant) has believed that the "social problem" was not feeble-minded, and yet the thorough examination has disclosed undoubted feeble-mindedness. And I have to say of myself, with due humility, that I have had to reverse my first impressions many and many a time.

"Judge how superior the field workers trained by Dr. Goddard were! Not only do their 'first glance' tell them that a person is feeble-minded, but they even know, without a shadow of doubt in so far as the book intimated, without the faintest misgiving, that 'a nameless girl' living over a hundred years before in a primitive community, is feeble-minded. They know this, and Dr. Goddard acting on this superior female intuition, founds an important theory of feeble-mindedness, and draws sweeping generalizations, with a fine moral undertone, from their work. Now, I am frank to say that the matter is an unexplained miracle to me."[94]

Goddard did not respond to Myerson's criticisms, although he was aware of them. Shortly thereafter, he wrote to Elizabeth Kite complaining that a few people were attempting to discredit the Kallikak story and asking her for information that might help him in defend the work.

"Did we ever know the real name of the mother of the bad line in the Kallikak story?" Goddard asked. "The one that I called the nameless girl. One or two people, including Porteus, who are opposed to the idea of the heredity of feeblemindedness, have attempted to discredit the story of the Kallikak family,

---

[93] Myerson, 1922, p. 625.
[94] Myerson, 1925, pp. 78–79

among other things stating that it is absurd to attempt to declare that this girl was feebleminded when so little is known of her that we do not even know her name. I should like to turn the tables on them if possible by stating that we did know her name and that calling her 'The nameless feeble-minded girl' was in accordance with our policy of disguising names."[95]

Kite responded that she could not provide the name for Martin, Jr.'s, mother, although claimed to have interviewed a man who said that she was "not all there you know."[96]

"It is four years since Myerson wrote his stuff about the Kallikak Family," Goddard wrote in reply to Kite in 1929, "and I have paid no attention to it, but now Porteus comes out with a similar flare and Conklin, of Oregon, in his book on 'Abnormal Psychology' says that Myerson cast doubt upon the hereditary character of feeble-mindedness. It is very disturbing to find men who pretend to be scientists resorting to such 'babyish' tricks in order to maintain their position. Neither of them make any attempt to disprove the figures and statistics and logic of the complete study of the 300 feeble-minded children. I am going to take the matter up in a part of my paper at Battle Creek on Thursday, and can use to direct advantage some of the statements in your letter."[97]

Writing in 1933 in the *Journal of Educational Psychology*, psychologist Stuart Stoke did take aim at the "figures and statistics and logic" of, at least, the Kallikak study. Stoke, from the Department of Psychology and Education at Mount Holyoke College in South Hadley, Massachusetts, in an article titled *A Persistent Error in the Nature-Nurture Controversy*, noted there was "no statute of limitations on the life of an error in the scientific world," then proceeded to call several of the contemporary educational psychology textbooks to task for perpetuating "an error which was committed twenty years ago by one side of the [nature vs. nurture] controversy."[98] That error pertained to the methods in the Kallikak study.

First, Stoke quoted passages of *The Kallikak Family* in which Goddard made statements about diagnosing feeblemindedness by visual inspection, "such methods of character and mind reading have long been discarded by scientific psychologists. No reputable psychologist presumes to make a diagnosis of feeblemindedness 'at a glance' or to infer criminalistic tendencies in an embryo from 'appearance.'"[99]

Second, Stoke criticized Goddard's use of extant records. "Another of Goddard's methods which was used in the cases of the deceased was to make

---

[95] Goddard, 1928.

[96] Kite, 1928.

[97] Goddard, 1929.

[98] Stoke, 1933, p. 663.

[99] Stoke, 1933, p. 666.

recourse to original documents whenever these were available. Such documents, he admits, were few. However, this scarcity was considered almost as damaging evidence as the presence of such documents. 'For instance the absence of a record of marriage is often quite as significant as its presence' [Stokes quotes Goddard stating in *The Kallikak Family*]. Just how the absence of a marriage record can be used as a substitute for an intelligence test is a bit beyond this critic, so further comment will be withheld."[100]

Finally, Stoke criticized the use of hearsay and gossip by Goddard and Kite. "The talk of village gossips is seldom of such a nature as to give an unbiased picture which a dispassionate scientist might use."[101]

In 1942, after Amram Scheinfeld's *You and Heredity* (1939), Ernest Bayles and R. W. Burnett's *Biology for Better Living* (1941), and a critical article by Knight Dunlap in *Scientific Monthly* (1940) had appeared, all repeating and expanding Myerson's original charges, Goddard, four years since retired,[102] felt compelled to defend his work.

"For a decade the data were accepted apparently without questions" Goddard wrote in the journal *Science*. "But, as time went on, the inevitable happened and writers appeared who did not know, who obviously had not read the originals, and who therefore thought they detected certain flaws in the techniques which did not exist."[103]

Goddard identified Myerson as the first to make such an egregious mistake, and linked others to Myerson's criticism. He then attempted to rebut Myerson's primary criticisms.

"It is well known," began Goddard with reference to concerns about the field-workers' methods, "that superintendents of such institutions quickly learn [how to observe all grades of defectives], and when a new arrival appears they not only know whether he is a fit subject for their institution or is normal and does not belong there, but they also know his *grade*. Even the attendants acquire this ability rather quickly."[104]

"But these are cases that were seen. How about cases in earlier generations, no longer living? The field worker does not make any 'surmises,' nor does she ask for anybody's 'opinion,'" Goddard argued. "She first asks the perspective informant: 'Do you (or did you) know such a person?' If the answer is yes, she proceeds to ask many questions as to how he behaved, what he did, how he managed his affairs."

"From this," Goddard continued, "she gets an accurate picture of the kind of person he was. But she does not stop there. This informant may be prejudiced.

---

[100] Stoke, 1933, p. 667.

[101] Stoke, 1933, p. 667.

[102] Trent, 2001, p. 33.

[103] Goddard, 1942, p. 574.

[104] Goddard, 1942, p. 574.

His account must be corroborated. She hunts up everybody who knew the case. Finally she knows whether he was feeble-minded or normal."[105]

Following these obviously limited, generally unsatisfactory, defenses of dubious veracity, Goddard compounded his problems. "He [Myerson] ridicules the idea that we could know that the mother of the Kallikaks was feeble-minded, when we 'did not even know her name,' but had to put her down as 'Nameless.' I did not realize that it might mislead. All names are fictitious, and it occurred to me that 'nameless' would identify her without any possibility of confusion. She is nameless to the reader only. We had her name; and not only her name but her history. We were fortunate enough to find an intelligent lady of advanced age, *who knew personally the 'Nameless one.'*"[106]

This was, of course, simply not true. Kite had informed Goddard in response to his 1928 query that they did not have the "nameless one's" name or history. In a footnote in *The Inheritance of Mental Diseases*, Myerson added an aside to the Kallikak study that Goddard did not respond to in his rebuttal about the "nameless one." "Curiously enough," noted Myerson, "it was a very unsophisticated-looking girl student who suggested to me that it might well be that Martin Kallikak was not the father of his alleged sub rosa feeble-minded descendants, that no one knew who else might have mated with the 'nameless feebleminded girl.' As a bit of worldly wisdom this deserves the attention of Dr. Goddard and his field workers."[107]

In 1944, Scheinfeld published a rebuttal to Goddard's *Science* piece in the *Journal of Heredity*. "What motivates the present re-valuation of the study is, first the fact that Dr. Goddard himself virtually demanded it in a rather surprising communication published in *Science* about two years ago. Breaking a long silence, he attacked all those who had criticized his work and accused them of not having read carefully, or of having willfully misinterpreted what he had reported."[108]

Scheinfeld then systematically picked apart Goddard's defense and the study. He was, however, more interested in the way the study had been used in the intervening years. "What should interest us now is why, in view of the easily apparent flaws in the Kallikak study, . . . it has continued to be given such strong credence and to find such warm support in many quarters?

"The answer is a simple one . . . there are persons everywhere who relish the thought that some groups, races, classes or strains are born to be superior and dominant, and that other groups are destined by nature to be inferior and subordinate."[109]

---

[105] Goddard, 1942, p. 575.

[106] Goddard, 1942, p. 575.

[107] Myerson, 1925, p. 77.

[108] Scheinfeld, 1944, p. 259.

[109] Scheinfeld, 1944, p. 260.

"Certainly, Dr. Goddard cannot be held responsible for the misuses of his study nor should this article be construed as in any sense directed against him personally. As an Emeritus Professor of Psychology, with a long and fruitful career to look back upon, he has earned the respect and esteem of present-day psychologists and psychiatrists for his brilliant pioneering work, and for his many contributions to the study of mental defectives."[110]

Scheinfeld concluded, "we may grant the possibility that a good many of the bad Kallikaks, like their counterparts everywhere, were and are genetically defective, and that the human stock could be improved by suppressing their breeding. But, Dr. Goddard's study gives us no acceptable evidence on this score. Perhaps some other investigators, equipped with more modern techniques and approaches, will find it of interest to take up where he left off, to dig further into these pedigrees and produce more scientifically valid proof. But until this happens, we will have to nurse the suspicion that if all the bad little Kallikaks had been brought up in exactly the same environment as was accorded to all the good little Kallikaks, the distinctions between these two groups might not have been so glaringly marked, and not nearly so many of the bad Kallikaks would have toppled from their places or fallen by the wayside. Nor, might the Kallikak study itself have fallen down so sorely had it given the bad Kallikaks a fairer break."[111]

Goddard never responded to Scheinfeld. There was, after all, nothing really to say. *The Kallikak Family* was no longer credible science. No credible scientist accepted it as science. In 1957, Goddard's colleague, Edgar Doll, made one last attempt to defend the integrity of the Kallikak study.

"Granting the difficulties inherent in such a study," Doll claimed, "and the historical, as well as other, limitations of its proof, it nevertheless seems to me grossly improper to laugh this epochal investigation out of court as unjustly and as disparagingly as later 'students' speciously did. It became fashionable to decry the methods, the data, the treatment of the data, and the inferences. Yet the late Elizabeth S. Kite, the field worker for this extraordinary study, was a historian of excellent repute, with acknowledge social savior-faire, well prepared in the family history investigation, a specialist in United State colonial history and the author of several standard historical books, well informed on social and mental evaluation techniques and with other merits. But the tide of revolt or even revulsion had set in, and not Goddard nor Miss Kite nor the loyal Vinelanders felt it seemly or politic to do more than let the disparagement run its ungenerous course."[112]

And yet, all who read Doll's response recognized that it was, in fact, simply the sentiments of a loyal Vinelander.

The Kallikak story lived on, however, as myth.

---

[110] Scheinfeld, 1944, p. 262.

[111] Scheinfeld, 1944, pp. 263–264.

[112] Doll, 1957, p. 344.

In response to Goddard's 1942 defense of the Kallikak study, Davenport wrote to his old friend and colleague to congratulate him. Davenport's response to the criticisms of Myerson, Scheinfeld, and others was characteristically bigoted and racist.

"I wonder," he wrote to Goddard in 1942, "why it is that people with such names as Abraham Myerson and Amram Scheinfeld should think it necessary to attack so much of the work on heredity?"[113]

From Thursday, September 3, to Saturday, September 5, 1931, the Vineland Training School hosted a gala reunion of the Feebleminded Club in celebration of the 25th Anniversary of the Research Laboratory at Vineland. Organized by the president of the Vineland Training School board of Trustees, Howard Branson, the gathering was an opportunity for old friends to gather within the protective womb of the Training School, away from, at least for three days, the criticism that had mounted outside Garrison Hall. Goddard was there. He was, in fact, the guest of honor. Twenty-five years to the date after he had walked the path to Maxham Hall, he returned to the site of his triumphant years. Johnstone, now in his 31st year as director, served as host. Johnstone's boyish features were still evident in his 60-year-old visage, although the snowy white hair and dark, horn-rimmed glasses diminished his elfish look and made him look slightly like his predecessor, the Rev. Olin Garrison, minus the walrus mustache. Arnold Gesell, now with his M.D. and serving as director of the Yale Child Development Center, which he had founded, came in from New Haven for the weekend. Earl Barnes, whose "garden where unfortunate children are cared for" speech to the Training School board of directors in 1903 had led to the creation of the laboratory, took the train down from Philadelphia. Edgar Doll, who had assumed the role of director of the Research Laboratory after Stanley Porteus left to take a professorship at the University of Hawaii, was there; as was Ted Nash, Alice's husband, who had been promoted to superintendent.

Others of the fraternity had passed on and still others were absent not in memory but simply physically.

"I have never in my life enjoyed anything more than the weeks I spent on your campus in the spring of 1917," wrote Lewis Terman in his regrets, referring to his time at Vineland as part of the army testing project, "and I have always wanted to go back."[114]

"I wish I could be present to pay my tribute," wrote Davenport, "not only to the outstanding work that the Vineland Laboratory has done, but to the extraordinary contributions made by Goddard to the appreciation, by the public, of the social significance of feeble-mindedness."

---

[113] Zenderland, 1998, p. 332.
[114] Doll, 1932, p. 26.

Also not in attendance that weekend was Samuel Fels. "There is nobody to whom I would rather do honor than Dr. Goddard. It would gratify and please me much to meet Dr. Goddard and all of you on such a happy occasion and once more revive the memories of the really great work that was and is being done at Vineland."[115]

Perhaps so, or perhaps it was easier to stay away and write about Goddard's great works than to attend and do so in person. It was water under the bridge by then. After the fiasco at the Ohio Juvenile Bureau, Goddard became a professor of psychology at the Ohio State University in 1921. While the criticism of the Kallikak study mounted, Goddard turned his scholarly attention to the topics of dual personality and gifted education, neither of which brought him the recognition that had his work at Vineland.

Further, Goddard's views about moronity, feeblemindedness, and eugenics had begun to change.[116] In 1927, he published an article in *Scientific Monthly* titled "Who is a Moron?" in which he attempted to dislodge his conceptualization of "moron" from the condition of feeblemindedness.

Zenderland explained, "Goddard's own ideas of who ought to be designated as 'feeble-minded' were changing. Although he still regarded the army tests as a remarkable scientific achievement, by the end of this decade [1920s] Goddard too saw that they had also proven something unexpected: the concept of 'mental age' no longer meant anything definitive."[117]

Goddard began his *Scientific Monthly* revisitation of the "moron" category with a summary of the genesis of the term; a summary that read rather like the gentle boasting of a proud parent. He then became entangled in trying to distinguish between people who were feebleminded and people who were morons, starting with the assumption that not all morons were feebleminded. He lamented the still-unscientific state of the definition of feeblemindedness, particularly focusing on a definitional criterion for feeblemindedness that included the person's incapacity to manage his or her own affairs.

"We are curing some feebleminded," Goddard stated, citing research by Fernald and at Vineland, "in all our well-managed institutions."[118]

This was, in essence, equivalent to Goddard refuting his hereditarian past.

Goddard observed, "first of all, some of my readers may have already raised the question as to the advisability of letting these people go out into the world, even though they cannot support themselves. Is there no danger that they will marry and bring into the world feebleminded children and so continue this defective race? Yes, there is considerable danger of that, *if it is a danger*. Just what

---

[115] Doll, 1932, p. 55.

[116] Zenderland, 1998, p. 324.

[117] Zenderland, 1998, pp. 324–325.

[118] Goddard, 1927, p. 44.

is the danger? First, that we are propagating the feebleminded. Yes, but we have learned how to 'cure' them and when cured (trained) they are very useful. They are happy in doing their kind of work that you and I do not want to do—positions that it is hard to get people to fill. In other words, *we need these people.*"[119]

"The problem of the moron is a problem of education," Goddard stated. There would be very few morons, if any, in our institutions for the feebleminded if we had not been mistaken in our theories of education."[120]

From menace to societal necessity. Goddard's beliefs had come full circle, as he had stated in 1907 that "the problem of the feeble-minded is a psychological and educational problem. We must devise educational methods based on sound psychology."[121]

Goddard was not the only person to recant his beliefs. In 1924, serving his second term as president of the American Association for the Study of the Feebleminded, a term he would not live to complete, Walter Fernald told those assembled to hear his presidential address that, perhaps, the previous decades' treatment of the feebleminded had been too harsh. In 1930, Carl Brigham published an article in *Psychological Review* titled "Intelligence Tests of Immigrant Groups" retracting his findings from his analysis of the army testing data.

Not everyone was recalcitrant, of course. In 1929, Davenport, along with Morris Steggerda, published *Race Crossing in Jamaica*, which, even by the standards set by his other work, was overtly racist and dogmatic. It was no longer 1919, however, and there were, by 1929, many scientists willing to publicly eviscerate Davenport and *Race Crossing*'s racist eugenic dogma.

But if Davenport had held tight the course, Goddard had not. Speaking before the American Association for the Study of the Feebleminded in 1928, Goddard told his colleagues that he thought he "had gone over to the enemy."[122]

It was too late for Deborah Kallikak, though, and it would be too late for thousands of people who, in the next decades, would be forcibly sterilized or murdered.

Pluralitas non est ponenda sine neccesitate.

—William of Ockham, 14th century

Ockham's Razor, which translated means "entities should not be multiplied unnecessarily," is a widely accepted, or at least widely quoted, principle in science

---

[119] Goddard, 1927, p. 44.

[120] Goddard, 1927, p. 45.

[121] Goddard, 1907a, pp. 22–23.

[122] Zenderland, 1998, p. 326.

suggesting that if two or more theories explain a phenomenon, all other things being equal, the simpler such explanation is preferred. Psychologists and other scientists know, however, that attributing causality to any single event, circumstance, or factor usually yields an overly simplistic answer to a complex question. It was Goddard's attribution of heredity as the primary, if not sole, determinant of intelligence that led to the eventual downfall of his theories and reputation. Yet, the same naive attribution of single-source causality has also been used to explain the field of psychology's disassociation from and disavowal of Goddard's research. In light of the atrocities of the Holocaust and Nazi Germany's strong association with eugenic dogma, it is hardly surprising that many scientists, particularly biologists and geneticists, sought to put as much distance between themselves and Goddard and other eugenicists as possible.

However, as is usually the case, this perspective is overly simplistic, just as explanations of human behavior as exclusively caused by nature or nurture are overly simplistic. Today, Goddard's work justifiably occupies what Kings College professor Walter Gratzer calls the undergrowth of science; not outright fraud but a general loosening of the restraints put on the scientific endeavor. But Goddard's work occurred in multiple contexts that must be considered if we are to appreciate the factors contributing to the misuses of science in the first genetic revolution. Among these contextual factors were the emergence of psychology as a discipline distinct from philosophy, the struggle of psychologists to be viewed as legitimate scientists and to wrest control over certain aspects of science from the medical profession and psychiatrists, and societal fears about and misunderstanding of immigrants and immigration. They also included cultural stereotypes and biases about women, people with disabilities, and the poor; the role of religion in understanding human behavior and responsibility; societal anxiety about the impending World War I, corporate imperialism, and the end of the industrial age; assumptions about the hereditary sources of criminal behavior; and, last but not least, Goddard's own personality.

Driven to succeed and intense, Goddard was also "a personable, kindly fellow and good social mixer" who "had a flair for popular presentations of scientific data."[123] He was neither saint nor extreme sinner with regard to his views of others, when compared with his contemporaries.

"He was a fine gentleman, a delightful companion," wrote two of his colleagues, who also noted that "he had a fervor which took him into such diverse causes as eugenics and euthanasia and made him sometimes uncritically earnest in his work."[124]

Uncritically earnest or manipulator? The truth lies somewhere in the recesses between here and there, most likely.

---

[123] Wallin, 1953, p. 39.
[124] Burtt and Pressey, 1957, p. 657.

CHAPTER 9

Sterilizing the Unfit, Breeding the Fit

In *The Great Gatsby*, F. Scott Fitzgerald's 1925 classic novel of the extravagancies of the Roaring Twenties, Tom, Daisy, and Nick have the following exchange:

"Civilization's going to pieces," broke out Tom violently.

"I've gotten to be a terrible pessimist about things. Have you read 'The Rise of the Colored Empires' by this man Goddard?" "Why, no," I answered, rather surprised by his tone.

"Well, it's a fine book, and everybody ought to read it. The idea is if we don't look out the white race will be—will be utterly submerged. It's all scientific stuff; it's been proved."

"Tom's getting very profound," said Daisy, with an expression of unthoughtful sadness. "He reads deep books with long words in them . . ."

"Well, these books are all scientific," insisted Tom, glancing at her impatiently.

"This fellow has worked out the whole thing. It's up to us, who are the dominant race, to watch out or these other races will have control of things."

It is, for the most part, irrelevant that the book to which Tom was referring was not written by Goddard and was actually *The Rising Tide of Color against White World Supremacy* by Harvard-trained historian Lothrop Stoddard. Stoddard, along with New York attorney Madison Grant's equally vitriolic *The Passing of the Great Race*, was largely responsible for the racist and classist propaganda that fed on the pseudoscientific rhetoric emanating from the American eugenics movement.[1] Such eugenic rhetoric focused on the so-called scientific study of hereditary improvement of the human race by controlled or selective breeding, and was expounded most stridently by American eugenicists such as Charles Davenport and Harry Hamilton Laughlin.

---

[1] Spiro, 2009.

❧ ❧ ❧

In a 1914 issue of the *Journal of Heredity*, members of the Eugenics Research Committee of the American Genetic Association, including Davenport and Goddard's neuroanatomy professor, Adolf Meyer, published a "state-of-the-field" paper pertaining to studies in human heredity.

"The amount of research in human genetics and eugenics, now being carried on in the United States, is probably realized by few persons," the report began. "In the following report the Eugenics Research Committee of this Association has brought together data about some of these lines of investigation."[2]

The article summarized research efforts underway across the country: Alexander Graham Bell's Hyde Family study, investigating the heritability of congenital deafness; a Galton-like study on the families of distinguished American men of science being conducted by mental tester and G. Stanley Hall student James McKeen Cattell at Columbia University; a study of the heritability of "harelip" (the now-pejorative term for a person with a cleft lip) in men and Boston Terriers by William Blades of the Eugenics Record Office (ERO); and a study at the Vineland Training School on "the Jackson Whites," a group in Northern New Jersey "formed by an amalgamation of the "white race" with "the negro" and the "American Indian" early in the last century."[3]

"Free Jacks" was a pejorative term used to refer to some freed black slaves, and the combined "jacks and whites" eventually merged into "Jackson Whites."[4] This group, referred to now as the Ramapo Mountain people because of their residence in the Ramapo Mountain range of northern New Jersey and southern New York, are a geographically isolated mix of people of Native and African American, Anglo, European, and Hessian descent who have developed their own dialect consisting of Dutch and English. In 1911, workers from the Training School collected data on the "Jackson Whites" to add to the eugenic family narratives, but Goddard, perhaps because the Kallikak story was proving so fruitful, never published his report on the group, although the inclusion of this study in the Eugenics Committee report suggests that, at some level, Goddard was still working on the study as late as 1914. "Detailed analysis of this unusual racial mixture will certainly prove of great interest to [geneticists]; but one fact which already stands out prominently seems to be the very limited effect of environment, in influencing this mixed heredity. The socially degenerate group has spread to many points in the East, including cities and small towns; but wherever its members appear, they carry with them the 'Jackson White' characteristics. It is clear, then, that their physical, mental and social condition can

---

[2] Woods, Meyer, and Davenport, 1914, p. 547.

[3] Woods et al., 1914, p. 551.

[4] Cohen, 1972, p. 264.

not be ascribed to any environmental factors, but that their deficiencies are to be explained, for the most part, by bad heredity.

"In regard to the inheritance of feeblemindedness," this section of the report concluded, "Dr. Goddard's data . . . convince him that it behaves as a Mendelian recessive."[5]

Although always a component of eugenic rhetoric, race identity became, increasingly, a focus of the American eugenics movement in the late 1910s and into the 1920s. Eugenic rhetoric had always presupposed the desirability of improving the white "race," even if that was not always articulated in clearly ethnic or racial terms.

Theodore Roosevelt's warnings of the threat of "race suicide" during his presidencies were vague with reference to exactly which "race" might eventually be exterminated, but given his own mixed—Dutch, Welsh, English, Irish, Scots, French, and German—heritage, his call for race solidarity was more along the lines of his call for Americanism. The threat was to Americans of all types; of course, what had come to define "American" was, primarily, white.

Others framed the preference as seeking out wholesome groups. Before the Farmers' National Congress in New Orleans in November of 1912, Willett Hays, Roosevelt's Secretary of Agriculture, spoke about the farm as the "home of the race." Because one of the major tenets of eugenics was the production of "relatively larger families by the socially and individually efficient, the open country and the farm home take on a new racial significance beyond anything heretofore considered."[6] Of course, the plurality, if not totality, of the farmers attending the national congress would have been white.

Bell, writing in 1914, addressed how to "improve the race," arguing, ostensibly, against the eugenic movement's growing focus on negative eugenics. Bell supported positive eugenics, and spoke in terms of improving the "normal class" and increasing "the potency of the desirable class to produce desirable children."[7] Descriptors such as *normal* and *desirable* certainly excluded people who were disabled, but who can doubt, given the tenor of the times, that normal and desirable also had a "racial" component and presumed "white"?

By 1915, though, the racial message of eugenicists became less vague with regard to exactly which "race" warranted saving, and the movement's racialist sector assumed greater visibility in and control over the American eugenic agenda. Laughlin took center stage via his anti-immigration and pro-white agenda. When, in 1913, eugenicist Paul Popenoe became the editor of the *Journal of Heredity*, it provided him an editorial platform that he used to its full capacity to promote eugenic and racial dogma. The First and Second National Conferences

---

[5] Woods et al., 1914, p. 551.

[6] Hays, 1913, p. 16.

[7] Bell, 1914, p. 6.

for Race Betterment, held in 1914 and 1915, honed the racial message. Grant's *Passing of the Great Race*, published in 1916, paved the way for Stoddard's *Rising Tide of Color* in 1920. In 1923, Bingham's study of American intelligence provided the veneer of scientific credibility to a rapidly expanding racist agenda.

These voices moved the American eugenic movement's focus from an ambiguous "race" betterment focus to a targeted message about the superiority of the Nordic or Aryan race, and created a vitriolic and acerbic racist movement. By the Second International Eugenics Congress, held in New York City in September 1921, the racialist wing of the American Eugenics movement had taken control: Stoddard was in charge of publicity, Grant was treasurer, Laughlin was in charge of exhibits, and Henry Fairfield Osborn was the congress president.

Thus, as the science of genetics was leaving eugenicists like Davenport behind, the eugenics movement in America took on a populist tone that was voiced by nonbiologists like Stoddard and Grant, and that focused its message, honed for popular consumption, on the need for immediate and drastic action to turn back the "rising tide" of immigrants and people of color as threats to the "great race."

ERO stalwart Arthur Estabrook was among those spreading racialist propaganda. In late 1911, a gift fell into his hands. While cleaning out the basement of the Prison Association of New York, the wife of the general secretary of that institution stumbled across what, in essence, was the key to the persons listed in Richard Dugdale's study of the Juke Family. This key eventually found its way to the ERO and Davenport contacted the prison association to request that they do a thorough search for the files. These were eventually found, with Davenport and Goddard being the first notified, and were sent to the ERO, where, beginning in early 1912, Estabrook commenced a three-year project to track down all the Juke clan members he could find and determine their current status.

Estabrook wrote in 1916, "in the present investigation, 2,820 people have been studied, inclusive of all considered by Dugdale; 2,094 were of the Juke blood and 726 of the "X" blood who married into the Juke family; of these 366 were paupers, while 171 were criminals; and 10 lives have been sacrificed by murder. In school work, 62 did well, 288 did fairly, while 458 were retarded two or more years. It is known that 166 never attended school; the school data for the rest of the family were unobtainable. There were 282 intemperate and 277 harlots. The total cost to the State has been estimated at $2,093,685."[8]

And so it began. What followed was page after laborious page documenting the outcome of Estabrook's examination of each of those 2,094 extant members of the Juke clan. The narrative is mind-numbing in its detail and doggedly depressing and overwhelming in its enumeration of people described as

---

[8] Estabrook, 1916, p. 62

ne'er-do-wells, scallywags, and social misfits. At the end of this enumeration of human disaster, Estabrook summarized his findings. "One half of the Jukes were and are feeble-minded, mentally incapable of responding normally to the expectations of society, brought up under faulty environmental conditions which they consider normal, satisfied with the fulfillment of natural passions and desires, and with no ambition or ideals in life.

"All the Juke criminals," he claimed, "were feeble-minded . . ."[9]

What to do?

Estabrook concluded, "two practical solutions of this problem are apparent. One of them is the permanent custodial care of the feeble-minded men and all feeble-minded women of child-bearing age. The other is the sterilization of those whose germ-plasm contains the defects which society wishes to eliminate."[10]

The eugenics movement's public relations machine went into high gear with the release of Estabrook's findings. Davenport wrote in the book's preface, "the most important conclusion that may be drawn from Dr. Estabrook's prolonged study of the Jukes forty years later is that not merely institutional care, nor better community environment, will cause good social reactions in persons who are feeble-minded and feebly inhibited. There is, indeed, no conflict between environment and heredity; each is a factor in all behavior. The great mistake that social agencies have made in the past is that they have overlooked the constitutional or hereditary factor of the reaction. The chief value of a detailed study of this sort lies in this: that it demonstrates again the importance of the factor of heredity."[11]

Popenoe's review of *The Jukes in 1915* appeared in Volume 7, 1916, of the *Journal of Heredity*. He used the bully pulpit of his editorship to sing the study's praises. "Huge and notorious clan brought to light by Dugdale is now in its ninth generation—members have moved to good environments but in many cases, no improvement in their character is visible—in other cases, by eugenic marriages, they have taken places in respectable society,"[12] read the subtitle of Popenoe's review.

Popenoe provided Estabrook with yet another opportunity to trumpet his update on the Jukes the next year when Estabrook responded to a claim by a local aid agency, the Children's Aid Society of New York, that one of the Jukes children could have been salvaged had the aid agency been able to retain him in their care. Dismissing this claim as another example of unrealistic environmental optimism, his response was, as it had been previously to that argument, that

---

[9] Estabrook, 1916, p. 84

[10] Estabrook, 1916, p. 85.

[11] Estabrook, 1916, p. iv.

[12] Popenoe, 1916, p. 469.

it was "an attempt to show that the Jukes might have been reclaimed if given a good environment—evidence alleged has no critical value."[13]

The increasingly strident eugenic stance for sterilization was nurtured and fed by Laughlin. Goddard, in general, expressed a preference for segregation and confinement as the means of choice for the social control of the feebleminded. When speaking at the gala on the 25th anniversary of the Vineland Research Laboratory in 1931, Goddard avowed that sterilization "never was a distinctively Vineland idea."

"Vineland never opposed, yet never ardently espoused, that cause," Goddard claimed in his keynote address.[14] His protestations, though, seem somewhat disingenuous when one reads some of his statements on the topic. For example, the codicil to his articulation of the three options for "preventing this stream of bad protoplasm" in the *Menace* article was that although "the ideal one [e.g., method] would be to place them all in colonies where they would be kept as long as they live . . . inasmuch as this cannot be done entirely and is too slow, we must, I believe, resort to some form of either castration or vasectomy and it must be practiced on the female as well as on the male."[15] Such statements are perhaps not an "ardent espousal" of sterilization, but they are not far from it. Still, Vineland was not at the epicenter of the forced-sterilization movement, and it was after Goddard's departure from the scene that sterilization moved to front and center of the eugenic agenda.

The U.S. experiment with forced, involuntary sterilization had begun toward the end of the 19th century. Among the pioneers in this morally offensive movement was Dr. F. Hoyt Pilcher, superintendent of the Kansas State Asylum for Idiotic and Imbecile Youth in Winfield, Kansas. In 1894, Pilcher began "asexualization operations" on inmates of the asylum. At the 34th Annual Meeting of the American Association for the Study of the Feebleminded held in 1910 in Lincoln, Illinois, Dr. F. C. Cave, by then superintendent of the same Kansas institution, reported on results of asexualization operations performed on 58 inmates of the institution under Pilcher's watch. "These operations prevent the begetting of defective offspring and also limit lewdness and vice," proclaimed Cave, closing his report by observing that "it is time some drastic action were taken to stem the ever increasing tide of weak-minded individuals who are demanding more and more room in our charitable institutions by their increase."[16]

---

[13] Estabrook, 1917, p. 41.
[14] Doll, 1932, p. 59.
[15] Goddard, 1911e, p. 8.
[16] Cave, 1910, pp. 124–125.

Pilcher's enthusiasm for sterilization, however, exceeded the appetites of the citizens of Winfield. Headlines in the September 1, 1894, edition of the *Topeka Lance* trumpeted "Mutilation by the Wholesale Practiced at the Asylum."[17] By 1899, Pilcher had been forced to resign his position as superintendent, although as much because of the governorship changing political parties as the furor his experimental methods created.

The movement he advocated, though, lasted much longer, gaining credibility through the Progressive Era as part of the eugenic agenda and through the active advocacy of institution superintendents.[18] In 1897, Martin Barr, that year's president of the Association of Medical Officers of American Institutions for Idiotic and Feeble-Minded Persons, addressed the membership at its 21st annual meeting in Ontario, Canada, and posed the question: "How best to render the imbecile harmless to himself and to the world?" In his speech, he noted the potential benefit of "asexualization" laws over laws governing marriage of people with epilepsy or who were feebleminded (which, in Barr's estimation, were ignored and only encouraged free love and prostitution), and cited the "example of Pilcher of Kansas who had the moral courage and scientific conviction to perform operations to 'unsex' 11 boys" despite the fact that "Pilcher was censured by the newspapers."[19]

The superintendents supported sterilization for a number of reasons. Most of them were medical doctors and they sought treatments for nonmedical, often behavioral, problems through medical means, sterilization among them. Because of their training as physicians, they viewed sterilization from a clinical perspective. Because of their societal status as physicians, they also viewed sterilization from the perspective of "experts" who were used to dictating treatment regimes. As medical leaders, they also supported the eugenic objectives of social control. Finally, the institutions they led were burgeoning, filled to the brim with inmates, and their state legislators were becoming increasingly reticent to part with state dollars. Like Goddard, they recognized that warehousing people was not economically viable and sought other remedies.[20]

Not all superintendents initially supported sterilization. Edward R. Johnstone's brother-in-law and mentor, Alexander Johnson, in his position as superintendent of the Indiana School for Feeble-Minded Youth and in his influential role within the National Conference of Charities and Corrections, led a 1903 movement to oppose sterilization. Johnstone himself showed ambivalence about sterilization in his 1904 presidential address to the Association of Medical Officers of American Institutions for Idiotic and Feeble-Minded Persons. "Our great

---

[17] Seaton, 2004–2005, p. 253.

[18] Bruinius, 2006.

[19] Barr, 1897, p. 4.

[20] Trent, 1994, p. 193.

aim is to eliminate this class, and in order to do this we must of necessity consider the elimination of the neurotic, blind, deaf, and consumptives, tramps, paupers, petty criminals, prostitutes, etc., as well as the hereditary insane, epileptics
and imbeciles. Many plans for elimination have been proposed. Unsexing has
been suggested and many strong arguments brought in its favor, but as yet the
public knows too little of advantages of the operation and of the social dangers
from this class, and so will not agree to the idea."[21]

That Johnstone's hesitancy seems to hedge on the social acceptance of sterilization instead of its moral acceptability explains in part why, by 1911, he and
most superintendents had abandoned their opposition to the procedures. If society was on board, as they were by the end of the Progressive Era, then they were
willing to serve as society's henchmen.

The Progressive Era emphasis on social control and social hygiene, the lais-
sez-faire attitude of progressives toward segregation and sterilization, the advocacy of superintendents, and the emerging societal acceptance of the "science" of
eugenics soon resulted in states sanctioning the practice of forced sterilization
for some of society's "unfit." Michigan considered the first compulsory sterilization law in 1897, but it was rejected by the state legislature. The first state sterilization law was actually passed by the Indiana legislature on March 9, 1907,
providing for the "prevention of the procreation of confirmed criminals, idiots,
imbeciles, and rapists,"[22] but even that law was post hoc because, as sterilization
proponent Popenoe proudly observed, "six or seven hundred males were sterilized in Indiana, for eugenic reasons, between 1899 and the adoption of the law
in 1907."[23] Indiana's enthusiasm for sterilization was, like Kansas, propelled by a
physician at a state institution, in this case Dr. H. C. Sharp, medical director at
the Indiana State Reformatory who is credited with devising the surgical procedure with males, known as a vasectomy, to block or sever the vas deferens duct.

Between 1907 and 1921, 18 states passed sexual sterilization statutes;[24] by
January 1, 1921, an estimated 3,233 people had already been forcibly sterilized.[25]
The majority of those sterilized during this period were people in institutions
for the insane, for the simple reason, observed medical historian Philip Reilly,
that they were more likely to be released from the institution than were people
who were feebleminded, and their release was made contingent on undergoing
sterilization. Reilly estimated that just over 400 people who were feebleminded
were forcibly sterilized during the years up to 1921.[26] By 1912, though, many

---

[21] Johnstone, 1904, p. 65.

[22] Landman, 1932, p. 55

[23] Gosney and Popenoe, 1929, p. 185.

[24] Landman, 1932, p. 291–292.

[25] Whitney, 1934, p. 302.

[26] Reilly, 1991, p. 48.

states began to declare these laws unconstitutional. Between 1912 and 1921, laws in seven of the 18 states were struck down.

New Jersey was the first state to do so. The New Jersey eugenic sterilization act had been coauthored by physician David Weeks: Davenport, Johnstone, and Goddard's coauthor on the second *Eugenics Record Office Bulletin* on methods of charting family data and J. E. Wallace Wallin's old nemesis. When the state board of examiners established by the law approved their first sterilization, an inmate of Weeks's institution for epileptics, the woman's court appointed attorney appealed the decision. An appellate court eventually overruled the law and the woman was spared.[27]

"During the year 1918, when most of the judicial opinions were handed down," observed Reilly, "the sterilization laws faded almost as quickly as they had appeared."[28]

Because of Laughlin and Popenoe, however, they were not to disappear for long. In February 1914, *Eugenics Record Office Bulletin* 10A and 10B were released, both titled "Report of the Committee to Study and to Report on the Best Practical Means to Cut off the Defective Germ-Plasm in the American Population," with 10A subtitled "The Scope of the Committee's Work" and 10B subtitled "The Legal, Legislative and Administrative Aspects of Sterilization." Both reports were authored by Laughlin and issued by a subcommittee of the American Breeders' Association's Eugenics Section established in May 1911 bearing the same long-winded name as the reports. Vineland donor and sterilization advocate Bleecker van Wagenen chaired the committee and Laughlin was secretary. Serving on the advisory panel for the committee were Alexis Carrel, a future Nobel Prize winner in medicine; Immigration Restriction League cofounder and Harvard professor Robert DeCourcy Ward; Irving Fisher from Yale,[29] and Goddard representing the field of psychology.[30]

It was the work of this committee on which Van Wagenen had presented at the First International Eugenics Congress in London in July of 1912 when he represented the Training School, on whose board of directors he served. Van Wagenen also published an article about the committee's work in a 1914 issue of the *Journal of Psycho-Asthenics*. The Laughlin-authored ERO bulletins were, however the primary vehicle through which the entirely predictable "findings" of the subcommittee would be disseminated.

Eugenics Record Office Bulletin 10A identified the committee members, the committee's mission—conveniently, for memory sake, identical to its name—a

---

[27] Reilly, 1991, pp. 52–53.
[28] Reilly, 1991, p. 55.
[29] Black, 2001, p. 57.
[30] Van Wagenen, 1914, p. 185.

Good Blood, Bad Blood

stock explanation of the "problem" in terms of unit-characters and human traits, and a classification of the "cacogenic varieties of the human race."

"Individual misfits in the social fabric," the report claimed, "are sometimes classified as 'the Defective, the Dependent, and the Delinquent,' using Hall's classification of the 'big three D's.' Sometimes this classification . . . is recast and increased to the five D's by adding the 'Deficient' and the 'Degenerate' classes."[31]

Under the classes of the first "D," defectives, the committee repeated the menace of the moron message. "It is the moron or the high-grade feeble-minded class of individuals that constitute the greatest cacogenic menace, for these individuals, with little or no protection by a kindly social order, are able to, and do, reproduce their unworthy kind."[32]

Eugenics Record Office Bulletin 10A concluded with suggested remedies, including life segregation or segregation during the reproductive period, sterilization, restrictive marriage laws, eugenical education, eugenical mating, environmental betterment, polygamy, euthanasia, and neo-Malthusianism.

Polygamy may appear to be an odd solution, but the committee was referring to the animal-breeding model in which an animal of high quality sires many offspring through multiple partners. The "polygamous" solution to the menace of the moron, then, would be to have "high quality human stock" reproduce madly through multiple partners.

Roosevelt liked the neo-Malthusian notion of improving the fecundity of the better types, if not necessarily through legalized polygamy, and wrote the committee in January of 1913 to express his opinion that "the improving [of the race] must be wrought mainly by favoring fecundity of the worthy type and frowning on the fecundity of the unworthy types."

"At present," growled Roosevelt, "we do just the reverse. There is no check to the fecundity of those who are subnormal, both intellectual and morally, while the provident and thrifty tend to develop a cold selfishness, which makes them refuse to breed at all."[33]

When the committee asked, rhetorically, which of the available remedies to apply, it is not difficult to determine its answer, given the topic of *Eugenics Record Office Bulletin* 10B. Segregation was identified as the preferred remedy, with sterilization "advocated only as supporting the more important feature of segregation when the latter agency fails to function eugenically."[34]

If this sounds like something less than a full endorsement of sterilization as the "preferred remedy," one must consider Laughlin's next statement. "The relation between these two [remedies] is automatic, for it is proposed to sterilize

---

[31] Laughlin, 1914a, p. 17.

[32] Laughlin, 1914a, p. 19.

[33] Laughlin, 1914a, p. 56.

[34] Laughlin, 1914b, p. 47.

only those individuals who, by due process of law, have been declared socially inadequate and have been committed to state custody, and are known to possess cacogenic potentialities."[35] In other words, to involuntarily sterilize anyone, they first had to be institutionalized.

Eugenics Record Office Bulletin 10B bore all the fingerprints of Laughlin's modus operandi. It began with a state-by-state analysis of the text and a legislative history of existing sterilization laws. Next was a summary of laws that had been vetoed, revoked by referendum, or introduced but not passed. The bulletin then described litigation and legal opinions about and criticisms of the existing laws. Finally, Laughlin, under the guise of the committee, provided the principles and details for a model sterilization law. The principles undergirding the proposed statute were straightforward:

> [That] inmates of all institutions for the insane, the feeble-minded, the epileptic, the inebriate and the pauper classes ... be made liable to examination into their personal and family histories with the view to determining whether such individuals are potential to producing offspring who would probably, because of inherited defects or anti-social traits, become social menaces or wards of the state; that such determination be made by a Eugenics Commission composed of persons possessing expert knowledge of biology, pathology, and psychology; that the responsible head of the institution, in whose custody the particular inmate subject to the provisions of this act may be, be required to furnish the Eugenics Commission with data on said inmate's mental and physical conditions, innate traits, personal record, family traits and history; that in case it is found for any given individual of the classes herein enumerated that he or she is the potential parent of defectives, the commission shall report its findings and recommendations to a state court; and that the state court ... examine the evidence ... whereupon, if the aforesaid court is satisfied that the individual in question is a person potential to producing offspring who would probably, because of inherited defective or anti-social traits, become a social menace or a ward of the state, such court shall order the responsible head of the institution ... to cause to be performed upon such person in a safe and human manner, a surgical operation of effective sterilization before his or her release or discharge.[36]

The proposed law essentially put into more formal language what was outlined in the principles. The eugenics commission was to be appointed by the governor or a state board of control; institution superintendents would be legally bound to turn over data about the "person nominated for the operation" to the commission; and

---

[35] Laughlin, 1914b, p. 47.
[36] Laughlin, 1914b, p. 53.

all records of investigations, examinations, reports, and family histories were to be "declared to be the property of the state, and shall not be opened to public inspection except upon an order made by a judge of a court of record; provided, however," Laughlin added, "that all such records may be used for scientific study."[37]

Not everyone was ecstatic with Laughlin's campaign to sterilize the unfit. For one, the leadership of the Carnegie Institute of Washington, Davenport's long-time funder, was, according to Elof Carlson, unhappy with the publicity the institute was receiving from Laughlin's campaign for sterilization laws and concerned that its status as a nonprofit would be jeopardized by Laughlin's lobbying efforts. In 1917, the Carnegie board of directors ordered Davenport to put a leash on Laughlin.[38]

Laughlin was not easily curtailed, apparently. Reilly noted that Laughlin's work for the *Committee to Study and Report on the Best Practical Means of Cutting off the Defective Germ Plasm* "stimulated him to amass reams of data about sterilization practices and policies in each of the states, material that he faithfully updated and published in exhaustive detail over the next fifteen years."[39]

Laughlin's compulsive collection of data about sterilization laws, statutes, and practices led to the publication of *Eugenical Sterilization in the United States* in 1922. Unlike *Eugenics Record Office Bulletins* 10A and 10B, which appeared, by and large, at a time when sterilization laws were proliferating and, as such, probably had minimal impact on the movement,[40] *Eugenical Sterilization in the United States* was published as state laws were being struck down and, expanding the model sterilization law originally proposed in *Eugenics Record Office Bulletin* 10B, had a catalytic effect on the sterilization movement.

One reason that *Eugenical Sterilization in the United States* was able to galvanize the passage of state laws was because it was published by the Municipal Court of Chicago. Judge Harry Olson was Chief Justice of the court and president of the Eugenics Research Association. Through Olson, Laughlin was able to secure an appointment as Eugenics Associate of the Psychopathic Laboratory of the Municipal Court, thus separating the work from the ERO and its skittish Carnegie funders and having *Eugenical Sterilization in the United States* published and distributed by an entity with legal credibility.[41]

The Eugenics Research Association, over which Judge Olson presided, was yet another eugenics organization founded by Davenport and Laughlin, this one in 1913. A smaller organization than the AES, it was composed primarily of scientists and true believers—Goddard, Grant, and Stoddard among them.

---

[37] Laughlin, 1914b, p. 55.

[38] Carlson, 2001, p. 243.

[39] Reilly, 1992, p. 60.

[40] Reilly, 1992, p. 60.

[41] Black, 2003, p. 113.

Laughlin leveraged connections with Olson and his sympathy to the cause, to publish *Eugenical Sterilization in the United States* and, concurrently, to give the book the aura of legitimacy within the legal community. Olson authored the preface to the book, and copies were distributed to courts and legal offices throughout the country.

Davenport never embraced sterilization, or at least never endorsed it the way Laughlin did. In fact, during the court proceedings challenging the New York sterilization law, Davenport's testimony was lukewarm in its support of the law and may have done more to harm the law's viability than to help it. His equanimity didn't stop Davenport, though, from spreading the word about sterilization to institution superintendents.

"Dear Professor Johnstone," Davenport wrote in a December 1923 letter. "Do you know of Laughlin's book on "Eugenical Sterilization in the United States"? This has a model law which should be of use to you. If you do not know of the book, I think you can get a copy from the Municipal Criminal Court of Chicago care Judge Harry Olsen. If he does not reply I can lend you a copy but, unfortunately, we have only one or two copies so that we could not part with ours."[42]

"My dear Dr. Davenport," Johnstone wrote in reply. "I have a copy of Laughlin's book . . . and am glad to have this model law which I hope to have considered at least by the New Jersey Legislature this session. I wondered if you had besides that for distribution, any literature on the subject of sterilization that I might be able to put into the hands of the Federation of Women's Clubs in our State."[43]

Laughlin updated *Eugenical Sterilization in the United States* in 1926, by which time, Reilly reported, 23 states had sterilization laws.

The Second International Eugenics Congress was held at Osborn's American Museum of Natural History in New York in late September of 1921. Its themes—eugenics in race, family, and the state—reflected American eugenicists' evolving focus on race betterment.

"I doubt if there has ever been a moment in the world's history," claimed Osborn in his welcoming address to the assembled delegates, "when an international conference on race character and betterment has been more important than the present."[44]

Osborn's welcoming address was followed by a keynote presentation by Major Leonard Darwin, Charles Darwin's son and president of the Eugenics Education Society in Britain. Among the more respected scientists who presented during the week were Herbert Spencer Jennings, a Johns Hopkins Zoologist who, despite his

---

[42] Davenport, 1923.

[43] Johnstone, 1923b.

[44] Davenport, Osborn, Wissler, and Laughlin, 1923a, p. 1.

tributary name and the fact that Davenport had taught him experimental biology at Harvard, was not heavily involved in the eugenics movement; Herman Joseph Muller, genetics professor at the University of Texas at Austin who, in 1946, won the Nobel Prize for Medicine for his work showing genetic mutations could be caused by X-rays striking genes and chromosomes; and Bird T. Baldwin, whose research in child development at the University of Iowa pioneered the importance of early experience, particularly environment, in development.

Representatives from nearly 20 different countries participated, making the congress still a truly international affair, although despite the fact that many American eugenicists maintained close relationships with German eugenicists throughout the 1920s, German and Russian scientists were not invited to the congress as an outcome of their roles in World War I. Also in attendance was future president Herbert Hoover, then–Secretary of Commerce for President Warren G. Harding, as well as the aging Bell, who was less than a year away from his death at 75 and had long since given up his battle to repel the onslaught of negative eugenics, versus his preferred positive eugenics. Bell was named honorary president of the congress. Not a bad lineup, certainly, but down a notch from the star power present at the First International Eugenics Congress a decade earlier in London.

More visible, at least numerically, were presentations from most of the usual suspects in the American eugenics movement. Davenport presented on research in eugenics; Estabrook presented his eugenic family data on the Tribe of Ishmael; a representative from Kellogg's Human Betterment Foundation presented on heritable factors in human fitness; racial anthropologist Ernest A. Hooton presented on race mixture; C. W. Saleeby on preventative eugenics; Popenoe on the unlikely topic of eugenics and Islam; and Laughlin presented on his dubious claim concerning the high percentage of foreign-born inmates of institutions for the feebleminded and insane.

Perhaps the bravest presenter at the congress was New York City medical examiner and author of *The Jews: A Study of Race and Environment*, Maurice Fishberg. Fishberg's presentation was on the intermarriage between Jews and people from other religious affiliations. "For those who look with apprehension at 'race mixture,'" Fishberg claimed, "it may be stated that the flow of Jewish blood into the veins of European and American peoples does not infuse any new racial elements . . . and it is well known that intermixture of the European ethnic elements has proved to be of immense advantage to the European Nations. Moreover, it appears that the offspring of mixed marriages . . . [was] apt to be superior."[45] Fishberg then listed people of mixed Jewish–Christian heritage who had distinguished themselves in fields ranging from art to politics to science.

"Is it not true that these were mostly halfbreeds, that is, they were descendants of Jews and non-Jews?" Davenport asked Fishberg after the latter's talk had concluded.

---

[45] Davenport, Osborn, Wissler, and Laughlin, 1923b, p. 132.

"As such I read them," responded Fishberg curtly.

"The statistics of the psychological examinations of the army men do not justify the hope that we're receiving from Europe the best of her Jewish population," protested Davenport, "because these statistics indicate that the largest proportion of the lowest grade persons measured in the psychological tests were from Poland, and I presume that it is fair to say that a large proportion of the Polish immigrants come from the Jewish race.

"Would not Dr. Fishberg agree that we are receiving in this country a vast number of undesirable people?" Davenport challenged.

"The Jews constitute about one-quarter of 1 per cent of the world's population . . . did you know that five or six Nobel prizes have been given to persons of Jewish descent?" responded Fishberg. "As regards ability otherwise, the Jews fill the colleges and universities, and if we take that as an index, Poland and Russia make a good showing."[46]

Davenport was not likely convinced.

As was increasingly the case, the eugenics movement made its most visible, and sometimes risible, case for its cause to the public not through the lectures and papers presented at congresses such as the Second International Eugenics Congress, which were not open to the public, but through the exhibits at events like this and, increasingly, at world fairs and exhibitions, which were open for examination by all.

The congress exhibits committee had been chaired by Laughlin, with funding provided by Mary Harriman, and exhibits were, appropriately, displayed in the alcoves in the Forestry and Darwin Halls on the Natural History Museum's first floor. The Darwin Hall of Invertebrate Zoology had been dedicated, along with a bust of the great man, in March 1909 on the 50th anniversary of the publication of *Origins of Species*. The hall was dismantled in 1940 and the bust put in storage. The half-century celebration of *Origins*, which coincided with the centennial of Darwin's birth, had spawned a number of tributes in addition to Darwin Hall, including a commemorative lecture series titled *Fifty Years of Darwinism*, organized by the American Association for the Advancement of Science and held in Baltimore. The degree to which American eugenics had "claimed" Darwinism, or perhaps the degree to which biology and eugenics were intertwined in 1909, was exemplified by the preponderance of the invited lecturers who were active eugenicists, including Stanford President David Starr Jordan, W. E. Castle, Osborn, Hall, and Davenport.[47]

Not surprisingly, the ERO was well represented in the congress exhibit hall. Up first for the ERO was a bed sheet–sized poster of the "Eugenical Classification of the Human Stock," with said human stock divided into two major groups: the

---

[46] Davenport et al., 1923b, p. 457.

[47] American Association for the Advancement of Science, 1909.

"eugenically fit from sterling inheritance," and the "eugenically unfit from defective inheritance." Making the preferred list were persons of genius, special skill, intelligence, courage, unselfishness, enterprise, or strength; as well as "persons constituting the great normal middle-class, e.g., 'The People.'" Making the less-desirable "unfit" list were the feebleminded, criminalistic, epileptic, insane, and deformed.

Another ERO exhibit proclaimed the approaching extinction of Mayflower descendents because of declining birth rates among those of such distinguished lineage. In addition, the ERO had exhibits on the growth of the U.S. population by immigration; the heredity of "harelip" and cleft palate; and Estabrook's posters about the Tribe of Ishmael, the Nam family, and the Jukes of 1915. Davenport displayed a letter from Francis Galton and another from Charles Darwin, and Davenport's daughter, Jane, made it a family affair by exhibiting a statuette of the "average American White soldier"; an oddly risqué statuette, given the context and her father's Puritanical temperament, of a nude male "having the average proportions of 100,000 white soldiers at demobilization as determined by the United States War Department."

Perhaps because he was busy as chair of the exhibits committee itself, Laughlin himself had only one exhibit, a rather amateurish-looking poster highlighting eugenical sterilizations by state. The Race Betterment Foundation was represented by a poster documenting marriage, fecundity, and immigration and their "significance for the nation." The Vineland Training School, sans Goddard by this time, had an exhibit on the measurement of mental traits, although noticeably the measure displayed was the Porteus Tests-Vineland Revisions, not the Binet-Simon Scale, as Stanley Porteus had assumed the directorship of the research laboratory at Vineland.

And, seated among the busts and posters and display charts lining Darwin Hall, was Stoddard. Stoddard's exhibit consisted of copies of his newly released, racially inflammatory book *The Rising Tide of Color against White World Supremacy*, and a series of maps showing supposed racial zones across the world that were pulled out from *Rising Tide of Color*.[48]

Stoddard was a disciple of Grant and, as author of 1920's *Rising Tide of Color*, surpassed even his mentor as the archetype for eugenic racism. Grant received a congratulatory letter from Hitler for his book—Stoddard was invited to visit the Führer as a result of his.

Grant wrote the introduction to *Rising Tide of Color*, which at 32 pages ended up being as much an essay as an introduction to the book. Grant's theme was, predictably, the threat to "Nordic blood" and he, essentially, restated his message from *The Passing of the Great Race*.

Stoddard was writing to a post-WWI audience, and his worldview was less a celebration of the Nordic race than a stunned sense of cataclysm experience

---

[48] Laughlin, 1923.

that pervaded the nations after the war-to-end-all-wars had ended. *Rising Tide of Color* was a diatribe about the threat posed to the "white world" from the "colored world," which essentially would have been more accurately cast as the "non-white world." World War I, Stoddard argued, divided the white world against itself and placed the Nordic/Aryan race on the brink of disaster.

"The heart of the white world was divided against itself, and on the fateful 1st of August 1914, the white race, forgetting ties of blood and culture, heedless of the growing pressure of the colored world without, locked in a battle to the death. An ominous cycle opened whose end no man can foresee. Armageddon engendered Versailles; earth's worst war closed with an unconstructive peace which left old sores unhealed and even dealt fresh wounds. The white world to-day lies debilitated and uncured; the colored world views conditions which are a standing incitement to rash dreams and violent action."[49]

Yellow Man's Land. Brown Man's Land. Black Man's Land. Red Man's Land. Stoddard's invidious, vituperative text then went on to disparage all nonwhite peoples, asserting the putative right of the whites to hold their traditional lands. "I ... showed that the white stocks together constitute the most numerous single branch of the human species, nearly one-third of all human souls on earth to-day being whites," Stoddard claimed. "I also showed that white men racially occupy four-tenths of the entire habitable land-area of the globe, while nearly nine-tenths of this area is under white political control."[50]

Stoddard then identified the seminal events that led to supposed white global presence, if not dominance, extolling the near-simultaneous voyages of Christopher Columbus and Vasco da Gama as opening up the world to white race exploitation. "The effects of these discoveries cannot be overestimated. Whole new worlds peopled by primitive races were unmasked, where the white man's weapons made victory certain, and whence he could draw stores of wealth to quicken his home life and initiate a progress that would soon place him immeasurably above his once-dreaded assailants. Thus began the swarming of the whites, like bees from the hive, to the uttermost ends of the Earth. And, in return, Europe was quickened to intenser vitality. Goods, tools, ideas, men: all were produced at an unprecedented rate."[51]

To Stoddard, the fact that Columbus and de Gama were Italian (or, perhaps Catalan) and Portuguese, respectively, and thus non-Nordic, was irrelevant. What mattered was that they were "white" and not "colored."

"1900 was, indeed, the high-water mark of the white tide which had been flooding for four hundred years," Stoddard concluded after a summary of the accomplishments of those 400 years. "At that moment, the white man stood on the

---

[49] Stoddard, 1920, p. 16.

[50] Stoddard, 1920, p. 17.

[51] Stoddard, 1920, p. 148.

pinnacle of his prestige and power. Pass four short years, and the flash of Japanese guns across the murky waters of Port Arthur harbor [opening battle of the Russo–Japanese war] revealed to a startled world—the beginning of the ebb."[52]

"Ours is solemn moment. We stand at a crisis—the supreme crisis of the ages. For unnumbered millenniums man has toiled upward from the dank jungles of savagery toward glorious heights which his mental and spiritual potentialities give promise that he shall attain.

"Out of the prehistoric shadows the white races pressed to the front and proved in a myriad ways their fitness for the hegemony of mankind. Gradually they forged a common civilization; then, when vouchsafed their unique opportunity of oceanic mastery four centuries ago, they spread over the earth, filling its empty spaces with their superior breeds and assuring to themselves an unparalleled paramountcy of numbers and dominion.

"Three centuries later the whites took a fresh leap forward. The nineteenth century was a new age of discovery—this time into the realms of science. The hidden powers of nature were unveiled, incalculable energies were tamed to human use, terrestrial distance was abridged, and at last, the planet was integrated under the hegemony of a single race with a common civilization."[53]

"The prospects were magnificent, the potentialities of progress apparently unlimited. Yet there were commensurate perils," Stoddard warned. "All of these marvelous achievements were due solely to superior heredity . . . it is merely an effect, whose cause is the creative urge of superior germ-plasm.

"But now we have transgressed; grievously transgressed—and we are suffering grievous penalties. But pain is really kind. Pain is the importunate tocsin which rouses to dangerous realities and spurs to the seeking of a cure."[54]

The cure? "Clean, virile, genius bearing blood, streaming down the ages through the unerring action of heredity."[55]

Good blood. Bad blood. Kallos. Kakos.

In a 1915 review of Goddard's magnum opus *Feeblemindedness: Its Causes and Consequences* in the *Journal of Heredity*, Popenoe used his access as editor to extol the necessity for compulsory sterilization as proved by the family studies presented in *Feeblemindedness*. Popenoe cherry-picked information from the 327 family studies Goddard reported, with the resultant four-page review becoming a primer for eugenic thought and action, and a call for mandatory sterilization.[56]

---

[52] Stoddard, 1920, p. 153.

[53] Stoddard, 1920, p. 298.

[54] Stoddard, 1920, p. 304.

[55] Stoddard, 1920, p. 305.

[56] Popenoe, 1915, p. 35.

Popenoe was, however, to play a much larger role than just essayist in the movement to sterilize unwilling Americans, becoming, as medical historian Alexandra Stern noted, "America's sterilization guru."[57] Through Popenoe's leadership, California led all states, even Virginia, with the frequency of involuntary sterilizations.

"In absolute terms," observed Stern, "California far outpaced the rest of the country, performing approximately 20,000 sterilizations . . . from 1909 to the 1960s. California stood at the vanguard of the national eugenics movement."[58]

The advance detail for the California vanguard included Popenoe, philanthropists Ezra Gosney and Charles M. Goethe, Jordan, and Jordan's fellow Stanford Cardinal, mental tester Lewis Terman.

In 1926, Popenoe, already networked within the labyrinthian structure of the myriad eugenics associations and well connected because of his role as editor of the *Journal of Heredity*, moved to Altadena, California, to become secretary of the Human Betterment Foundation, established by Gosney to, as Gosney expressed to Laughlin, contribute to "practical work in family-stock betterment."[59]

Gosney was a Missouri railroad attorney who moved to Arizona for dry air to aid his recovery from a bout of tuberculosis. There he became involved with livestock breeding as director of the Arizona Wool Growers' Association. He later moved to California where he hit pay dirt as a lemon tree plantation owner. Gosney read *Eugenical Sterilization in the United States* and immediately contacted Laughlin to find out how he could become a part of the movement.[60]

Laughlin drafted a "Plan for Practical Work in Family-Stock Betterment"[61] expressly in response to Gosney's inquiry. "This ambitious proposal," described Stern, "recommended that Gosney assemble a board of representatives from the fields of genetics, law, business, and education, and hire able researchers and a clerical staff. Laughlin told Gosney that the group would need to stay abreast of current research in eugenics, encourage legislation by drafting bills, and oversee the administration of existing laws."[62]

As a first step to carrying out Laughlin's aggressive plan, Gosney recruited Popenoe, who several years before had returned to California, where he had lived as a child and where, like Gosney, he was a land owner—although Popenoe raised date palm trees. Popenoe proposed the conduct of a large-scale study of sterilization in California to Gosney. Three years later, in 1929, Popenoe's survey results, titled *Sterilization for Human Betterment: A Summary of Results of 6,000*

---

[57] Stern, 2005, p. 107.

[58] Stern, 2005, p. 84.

[59] Stern, 2005, p. 104.

[60] Stern, 2005, p. 104.

[61] Stern, 2005, p. 104.

[62] Stern, 2005, p. 105.

Operations in California, 1909–1929, was published by the Human Betterment Foundation under the authorship of Gosney and Popenoe. It joined Laughlin's *Eugenical Sterilization in the United States* as the two most influential works of propaganda in the sterilization movement.

Sterilization for Human Betterment began with a recounting of the Kallikak story, taking precedence over even the Jukes, Nams, and Tribe of Ishmael stories in its importance as justification for the putative need for forced sterilization. Of the advertised 6,000 operations, which in reality involved 6,255 sterilizations, 1,488 were inmates of California's institutions for the feebleminded. As in Virginia, sterilization was a necessary prerequisite to being released from the institution.

Gosney and Popenoe attempted to justify the California sterilization "experiment," as many German scientists would in later years refer to the state's systematic sterilization efforts, with the expected eugenic reasons, but also for what they called "personal" reasons.

Intermingling discussions about voluntary and involuntary sterilization, Gosney and Popenoe attempted to associate the personal benefits of voluntary sterilization with the coerced operations on which they were reporting.

After acknowledging that any "personal reason" for sterilization applied strictly to voluntary sterilization, *Sterilization* tried to downplay the "dissatisfaction" of involuntarily sterilized inmates by reporting on the supposed satisfaction of people who were not institutionalized and who had undergone the surgery willingly. "Among those questioned in California who have submitted voluntarily to sterilization outside of the state institutions, we have found only two men . . . and not one woman dissatisfied," Gosney and Popenoe claimed. "Inevitably, there must often be a sentimental regret over the inability to have any more children, but in almost every case of this sort which we have studied the patients family was already as large as was wise, and the removal of the possibility of more children was a source of great relief."[63]

"Among those who have undergone compulsory sterilization in the state institutions, there is naturally not quite such a unanimity of feeling."

Well, yes, naturally. Particularly because many of them, especially men and women who were feebleminded, didn't even fully understand what had happened to them.

And yet, Gosney and Popenoe proposed to equate the "sentimental regret" felt by those who underwent voluntary sterilization with the feelings of the thousands of Californians who were sterilized against their will and often without their full knowledge. "We were able to get in touch with 173 patients who had been released from hospitals. . . . Six out of seven were either well pleased or not dissatisfied; the remainder were regretful."[64]

---

[63] Gosney and Popenoe, 1929, p. 30.

[64] Gosney and Popenoe, 1929, p. 31.

Perhaps the remaining 6,082 sterilized Californians had laid low for fear that something worse would happen to them had they responded to Popenoe's queries. Did the 173 respondents feel well pleased to be sterilized, or well pleased to be out of the warehouse in which they had been incarcerated?

"People sometimes assume," Gosney and Popenoe concluded, "that any one to whom sterilization is suggested resents the suggestion as much as they themselves would do. One of the most significant of all the facts brought out in the study of California sterilization is that this supposition is largely incorrect, and is becoming more and more so all the time."[65]

That these scant *facts* fail to support Gosney's and Popenoe's ludicrous contention that people who are involuntarily sterilized are generally "not dissatisfied," if not downright pleased, was borne out in later years by the testimony of people who had been sterilized against their will.

Nor did the *facts* portrayed in *Sterilization for Human Betterment* support Gosney and Popenoe's equally absurd pronouncement that, in fact, any need for a law legalizing involuntary sterilization was merely so the state could "protect itself in emergencies," because most victims saw the benefit to the surgery and submitted willingly.

Gosney established the Human Betterment Foundation as a charitable organization in California in 1928 on the basis of Laughlin's original plan, with some modifications by Popenoe. The foundation's charter stipulated a governing board of at least 25 members who, in turn, elected nine trustees to run the affairs of the foundation. "The purpose of this organization," stated an Appendix in *Sterilization for Human Betterment*, "is to take over and perpetuate the work summarized in this volume and similar constructive work indicated by the name of the Foundation."

Among the original trustees, in addition to Gosney, were attorney Henry M. Robinson, Chairman of the First National Bank of Los Angeles and a close friend and advisor to President Hoover; Pasadena physician George Dock, President of the Las Encinas Sanitarium in Pasadena and who would later become a professor in the school of medicine at Washington University in St. Louis; Goethe; Popenoe; Pasadena Attorney and eugenics advocate Otis H. Castle; and Jordan. Terman was a member of the full advisory council.

Goethe, who had turned his family wealth from real estate, agriculture, and banking into a fortune through the booming California real estate business,[66] spent his money and his time in two primary areas; conservation and eugenics. Goethe became one of the most visible environmentalists in the country, funding efforts to save the Redwoods, to establish sanctuaries in national parks like

[65] Gosney and Popenoe, 1929, p. 37.
[66] Stern, 2005, p. 136.

Yellowstone or Yosemite, and writing letters to the editor decrying the disappearance of bird or plant species because of habitat encroachment.

His anti-immigrant, racist rhetoric was particularly targeted at Mexican immigrants whom he saw as breeding at prodigious rates, polluting the germ-plasm, and stealing American jobs.[67]

With civic and eugenic leaders behind them, Gosney and Popenoe were able to turn the Human Betterment Foundation into a force for sterilization nationally and internationally. "It [the foundation] rivaled the Eugenics Record Office and the American Eugenics Society in terms of influence both in the United States and abroad," encyclopedist Ruth Engs noted, "particularly in Germany where its publications helped shape Nazi Germany's sterilization program in the 1930s."[68] Although the Human Betterment Foundation expired with the death of its founder, Gosney, in 1942, its impact was felt both at home in the Golden State, and around the world.

Reilly calculated that "throughout the 1930s California continued to have the nation's largest eugenic sterilization program. From 1923 through 1926, the annual number of sterilizations in California climbed from 190 to 541. During the next six years (1927–1932), a total of 3,327 operations were performed—about 550 per year. The numbers continued to climb: in 1935 alone there were 870 sterilizations. From 1930 to 1944, nearly 11,000 persons were sterilized in California institutions."[69]

A primary mission of the Human Betterment Foundation was to educate the public about the putative benefit of eugenic sterilization for the greater good. Like other topics important to eugenicists, it found its way to the masses. In 1928, E. Haldeman-Julius published *Little Blue Book No. 1318, The Case for and against Sexual Sterilization*. Among those arguing the pros were Laughlin and Wilfrid Chase, the latter introducing the scenario in which "cacogenic persons" would be offered $100 or $200 to "voluntarily" submit to be sterilized.

"Probably great numbers would gladly avail themselves of what seemed to them an opportunity," suggested Wilfrid Chase. "The expenditure would be an exceedingly wise one. Suppose the original Jukes couple had been paid one-million dollars and had remained childless. Would not the expenditures have been a very wise one indeed?"[70]

Arguing in opposition was the indefatigable Abraham Myerson. Pointing out that the heredity and transmission of mental diseases was still largely unexplored, or at least unexplained, country and that "the classical and royal families of feeble-mindedness, have genealogies and histories which are an inextricable

---

[67] Stern, 2005, p. 140.

[68] Eng, 2005, p. 112.

[69] Reilly, 1992, p. 100.

[70] Haldeman-Julius, 1928, p. 43.

mixture of fact and fable,"[71] Myerson rebuffed notions that there was any validity to the eugenicists' claims. "I am frank to say," an apparently exasperated Myerson stated, "with all the good will in the world toward eugenics, that propaganda rather than research has apparently been the watchword of the eugenists."[72]

And no one was more gifted at propaganda for eugenics' sake than Leon Whitney. From 1924 to 1934, the height of the American eugenics movement, Whitney was executive secretary of the movement's most visible organization, the American Eugenics Society. In 1934, Whitney published *The Case For Sterilization*. It's pithy, sarcastic style was clearly targeted for a lay audience. "Carrie, the feeble-minded girl around whom such protection had been thrown that before she could be sterilized her case went to the Supreme Court of the United States," Whitney wrote, misrepresenting the circumstances leading to Carrie Buck's sterilization. "Carrie, the ultimate decision in whose case paved the way for thousands of other unfortunates to be relieved of part of the burden of their infirmities—the birth of unwanted children whose coming, along with the inherited deficiency, is so great a handicap that hope for them is impossible. Carrie, poor unfortunate Carrie—little does she know how greatly, if unconsciously, she has served the world!"[73]

Whitney's opening page of *The Case For Sterilization* let readers know his ambitions. "Many far-sighted men and women in both England and America, however, have long been working earnestly toward something very like what Hitler has now made compulsory. Ridiculed, even vilified, they have fought courageously and steadily for the legalization of what they consider a constructive agency in the betterment of the race."[74]

And if Whitney's book or the "steady stream of propaganda"[75] published by prosterilization forces, including the AES and Human Betterment Foundation, didn't find their way into the average American's hands, Mr. or Mrs. Average American was bound to run across the topic in one of numerous popular media outlets. In the May 1938 issue of the ubiquitous *The Reader's Digest*, for example, the Mr. PRO and Mr. CON feature was whether or not to sterilize the feebleminded.

Mr. PRO began, "This pretty girl coming out of ether has just been sterilized by the surgeon of a state hospital. The job awaiting her after her convalescence was secured for her by the state institution which has been training her for adjustment to society. When the idea was explained, she was pitifully eager for sterilization.

---

[71] Haldeman-Julius, 1928, p. 43.

[72] Haldeman-Julius, 1928, p. 35.

[73] Whitney, 1934, p. 164.

[74] Whitney, 1934, p. 7.

[75] Reilly, 1992, p. 126.

"Almost always socially useless," Mr. PRO continued, after having trotted out the Kallikak, Jukes, Jackson Whites, Namms [*sic*], and Hilllfolk, "often socially dangerous, our millions of feeble-minded are a staggering expense."

Mr. CON, who was not identified but whose arguments and prose sounded much like Myerson, refuted the eugenic message, arguing that sterilization laws were derived from misinterpretations of science and that the "belief that rapidly breeding millions of the mentally unfit are swamping the nation with unfit offspring fails to stand up under analysis." Further, he attacked the notion of submission to sterilization as a prerequisite for release as in any way voluntary a "grim joke."

The Reader's Digest's anonymous Mr. CON may well have been Myerson, for in 1935, Myerson was the lead author on a report that was highly critical of eugenic sterilization. The report, from the American Neurological Association's Committee for the Investigation of Eugenical Sterilization, was published in book form as *Eugenical Sterilization: A Reorientation of the Problem* the following year. As medical historian Ian Dowbiggin noted, "the committee's report epitomized the complexities surrounding eugenics by the 1930s," as it was "supported by a grant from the Carnegie Institute, which at the same time was funding Harry Laughlin's pro-eugenic campaign."[76]

There was, however, nothing pro-eugenic about the Carnegie-funded Committee for the Investigation of Eugenical Sterilization report. The report first set up, like targets on a shooting range, the main arguments for sterilization—that degenerate conditions were on the increase, that the degenerate themselves reproduce at prodigious rates, that the hereditary nature of these proliferate degenerate conditions guaranteed a growing supply of said degenerates, and that environment has no meaningful impact on the social ills caused by these degenerates; and then proceeded to knock them off, one at a time with charts, tables, and data.

With regard to the fecundity of the unfit, the report took a swipe at Davenport's family records studies, noting that "if the birth rate, marriage rate and death rate are studied by isolated family reports, then alarm may be felt, but if the statistics as a whole are considered, a curious, not easily explained, complete contradiction to the statements usually made in the eugenic literature appears."[77]

Myerson and colleagues even used data from Popenoe and Gosney's own report to debunk the fecundity charge, followed by a study by Fernald showing low rates of reproduction among the feebleminded. After reviewing multiple studies refuting the notion of the hyperfecundity of the unfit, the committee, tongue firmly in cheek, concluded that "it is only when one considers as representative of the feebleminded such families as the Nams, the Kallikaks, the Jukes,

[76] Dowbiggin, 1997, p. 114.

[77] Myerson, Ayer, Putnam, Keeler, and Alexander, 1936, p. 41.

the Hill Folk, the Zero family and like social monstrosities that one reaches the opinion that there is a menace in the prolificity of the feebleminded."[78]

The report laid bare the simplistic genetic equations used by sterilization advocates, relying on Thomas Morgan's pioneering research to point out the complexity of the genetic makeup of even simple human traits and the role of environment in releasing or restraining genetic expression. After an extensive review of the growing literature on the inheritance of mental diseases, and its concomitant complexity, the committee stated its recommendations, starting with three overarching principles.

"First," the report stated, "our knowledge of human genetics has not the precision nor amplitude which would warrant the sterilization of people who themselves are normal in order to prevent the appearance, in their descendents, of manic-depressive psychosis, dementia praecox, feeblemindedness, epilepsy, criminal conduct or any of the conditions which we have had under consideration."[79]

"Second," the report continued, "there is at present no sound scientific basis for sterilization on account of immorality or character defect. Until and unless heredity can be shown to have an over-whelming importance in the causation of dangerous anti-social behavior, sterilization merely on the basis of conduct must continue to be regarded as a 'cruel and unusual punishment.

"Third. Nothing in the acceptance of heredity as a factor in the genesis of any condition considered by this report excludes the environmental agencies of life as equally potent and, in many instances, as even more effective."[80]

The recommendations themselves pertained to the application of any law concerning sterilization in the United States and recommended that all such laws be "voluntary and regulatory" and not compulsory; that they be applied equally to patients in and out of institutions, to lessen discriminatory use; and that the authority to approve such surgeries be primarily retained by physicians, parents or guardians, or the patients themselves.[81]

Even this clear denunciation of eugenic sterilization left the door open to sterilizing feebleminded people, however. In a postscript to the recommendations, the committee stated that it could recommend sterilization in certain diseases, with the consent of the patient or those responsible for the patient, and included feeblemindedness of a familial type on that short list.

Another source of opposition to the widespread adoption of eugenic sterilization came from the Catholic Church. Although the response by organized religion, in general, to eugenics was lukewarm and in some cases warm, the

---

[78] Myerson et al., 1936, p. 47.

[79] Myerson et al., 1936, p. 177.

[80] Myerson et al., 1936, p. 177–178.

[81] Myerson et al., 1936, p. 178–179.

Catholic Church, in particular, protested the widespread adoption of sterilization to achieve eugenic purposes.

Gosney and Popenoe were well aware of the Catholic resistance to sterilization. Appendix VIII to *Sterilization for Human Betterment* was titled "A Roman
Catholic View of Sterilization." Summarized by Popenoe from a book by Joseph
Meyer, a German Roman Catholic priest and professor at the University of
Freiburg, Popenoe attempted to argue that the Catholic stance is, at best uncer-
tain, and that sterilization might, in fact, be acceptable under certain circumstances. "It is a matter of no ordinary interest," explained Popenoe, "that the
author [J. Meyer] comes to the conclusion, after an exhaustive examination
of the facts and the opinion of the leading Roman Catholic theologians, that
eugenic sterilization is, in principle, to be approved in suitable cases."[82]

Although this may have been the case with the Catholic Church in Germany,
it was clearly not so with the rest of the Catholic world. The Catholic Church
had an uneasy relationship with eugenics. Christine Rosen noted that Catholic
leaders put up what limited resistance to eugenics was evident from the religious community, and as Laughlin's and Popenoe's brand of human betterment
through eugenic sterilization took hold, many more Catholic clergy expressed
their reservations.[83]

On Christmas Eve 1930, Pope Pius XI issued a papal encyclical titled *Casti
Connubi*, which stressed the sanctity of marriage and prohibited birth control
and abortion. The encyclical addressed, for the first time, eugenics, although
it stopped short of opposing it outright. "Although the encyclical thoroughly
rejected birth control," indicated Christine Rosen, author of *Preaching Eugenics*,
"its disapproval of eugenics suggested a rejection of the methods eugenicists
employed (such as sterilization and birth control), but not necessarily eugenic
aims,"[84] as evidenced by this section of the encyclical:

> Finally, that pernicious practice must be condemned which closely touches
> upon the natural right of man to enter matrimony but affects also in a real
> way the welfare of the offspring. For there are some who over solicitous for
> the cause of eugenics, not only give salutary counsel for more certainly pro-
> curing the strength and health of the future child—which, indeed, is not con-
> trary to right reason—but put eugenics before aims of a higher order, and by
> public authority wish to prevent from marrying all those whom, even though
> naturally fit for marriage, they consider, according to the norms and conjec-
> tures of their investigations, would, through hereditary transmission, bring
> forth defective offspring. And more, they wish to legislate to deprive these

---

[82] Gosney and Popenoe, 1929, p. 187.

[83] Rosen, 2004.

[84] Rosen, 2004, p. 53.

of that natural faculty by medical action despite their unwillingness; and this they do not propose as an infliction of grave punishment under the authority of the state for a crime committed, not to prevent future crimes by guilty persons, but against every right and good they wish the civil authority to arrogate to itself a power over a faculty which it never had and can never legitimately possess. Those who act in this way are at fault in losing sight of the fact that the family is more sacred than the State and that men are begotten not for the earth and for time, but for Heaven and eternity. Although often these individuals are to be dissuaded from entering into matrimony, certainly it is wrong to brand men with the stigma of crime because they contract marriage, on the ground that, despite the fact that they are in every respect capable of matrimony, they will give birth only to defective children, even though they use all care and diligence.

The papal encyclical's objections were echoed in *Eugenical Sterilization*, published in 1936 and authored by Antoine D'Eschambault, a parish priest in Manitoba, Ontario, Canada and a crusader against both eugenics and sterilization. "The State has no direct dominion over the bodies of its members. Sterilization cannot be justified on the ground of the common good. . . . No individual is free to destroy any of his faculties. We do not enjoy the absolute dominion over our bodies and our lives."[85]

It was, of course, absolute dominion over the bodies and lives of some, if not all, Americans that American eugenicists sought. In the end, Laughlin, Popenoe, Goethe, Jordan, and Davenport were able to do so at a tragic cost to thousands of our society's most vulnerable people. By the 1970s, when the last sterilization laws generated by Laughlin's advocacy and Popenoe's propaganda were removed from the books, an estimated 60,000–80,000 Americans had been forcibly, involuntarily sterilized. Between 40,000 and 50,000 of them were people, like Carrie and Doris Buck, who were labeled as feebleminded.

In 1928 and 1932, the Third Race Betterment Conference and the Third International Eugenics Congress, respectively, were held. They were, for all intent and purposes, family affairs. Davenport was chair of the Third International Eugenics Congress, hosted again in New York City; Popenoe, DeCourcy Ward, Terman, A. E. Wiggam, and Goddard constituted the remainder of the program committee. The Great Depression was in its third year, and although the assembled zealots attempted to lay the blame for the massive unemployment accompanying that catastrophe on the shoulders of immigrants and degenerates, few could have really believed their propaganda.

---

[85] D'Eschambault, 1936, pp. 101–102, 105.

Goddard must have been gratified to see that despite its rough treatment in the hands of the scientific community in the years leading up to the Third International Eugenics Congress, his Kallikak narrative was still venerated by the congress attendees, many of whom continued to cite the study as proof irrefutable of heredity's darker side.

Gosney crossed the continent to tout the sterilization solution, and found a rapt and receptive audience as, noted historian Allan Chase, "the compulsory sterilization of America's mounting millions of unemployed human beings, and their children, was the main theme of the Third International Eugenics Congress."[86]

Chase further observed, "the Third International Congress of Eugenics' crusade to sterilize the people the eugenicists declared to be 'social inadequates' collapsed almost as soon as it was launched. The Galtonian dream of gelding the poor was far from dead, but the golden era of the forced sterilization of the helpless was yet to come. The Great Depression itself had taken care of the demands of the eugenicists that all government agencies should cease appropriating tax dollars for health, education, and family welfare programs. All that remained for the eugenicists and their political allies to do for their cause was to make certain that the anti-Italian, anti-Semitic, and anti-Catholic immigration quotas they helped write into law were not tampered with."[87]

---

[86] Chase, 1975, p. 330.
[87] Chase, 1975, p. 330.

CHAPTER 10

The Kallikaks Revisited

On February 8, 2003, *New York Times* reporter Scott Christianson, in an article titled "Bad Seed or Bad Science," played out what, hopefully, was the last act in the saga of the Jukes Family. From 1877—when Richard Dugdale published the study and eugenicists immediately discarded his environmental explanations—through 1915—when Arthur Estabrook revived the legacy of degeneracy associated with the notorious family by his study of Juke descendents—the Jukes story has been used to justify repression, segregation, sterilization, and discrimination.

"For more than a century," Christianson noted, "the Jukes clan has been presented as America's most despised family. Social science researchers long believed they were a case study of dysfunction, a bunch of genetically linked paupers, criminals, harlots, epileptics and mental defectives, whose care had placed a huge financial burden on taxpayers. The family's pedigree was used for decades as a textbook example of how heredity shaped human behavior and helped lead to calls for compulsory sterilization, segregation, lobotomies and even euthanasia against the 'unfit.'"[1]

In 2001, the graveyard associated with a poorhouse in New Platz, New York, was discovered, having been buried under a fairground and swimming pool for decades. Among the graves of those who died and who were given a pauper's burial in the Ulster County poorhouse cemetery were members of the "Jukes" family, which of course was never one family, but many. Their names, among others, included "Sloughter, Plough, Miller, DuBois, Clearwater, Bank and Bush."[2]

The information from the poorhouse graveyard records combined with information from the Arthur Estabrook papers, held at the M. E. Grenander Department of Special Collections and Archives at the University at Albany–State University of New York, allowed historians, for the first time, to link real-life, flesh-and-blood people with the pseudonymous Juke names.

Arthur Estabrook did not, unsurprisingly, reveal the whole truth about the Jukes of 1915. "It turns out," summarized Christianson, "that many family

---

[1] Christianson, 2003, p. B9.
[2] Christianson, 2003, p. B9.

members were neither criminals nor misfits, and that quite a few were even prominent members of Ulster County society."[3]

The "Jukes Family" patriarch, Max, was really Max Keyser, Christianson revealed. His heritage was, it turned out, fairly distinguished. Max was a direct ancestor of Dirck Cornelissen Keyser, an early New York Dutch settler. He was, in other words, from "good stock" or "good blood."

Max's daughter, Margaret, nicknamed by Dugdale as "Margaret, the Mother of Criminals" was Margaret Robinson Sloughter. Not only was Margaret descended from "good stock," so apparently was her husband, who was descended from a former governor of the state.[4]

Estabrook had interpreted and communicated only the data that reinforced the story he wanted to tell. That story was that the Jukes were still degenerate, criminalistic, morons who were a threat to society.

In December 13, 1931, a Christmas card was sent to Estabrook (now also placed in the University at Albany-SUNY archives):

Dear Dr. Estabrook,

I am taking great pleasure in writing you these few lines and to also to say how glad I was to see you at frist I didn't remember you but then I thought a little to my self and it came to me I did remember your face but I was really glad to see you.

Well Miss Reeves and I are getting ready for Christmas we are not going to have any play but just a minstrell I am helping Miss Reeves with the Costumes and with the girls Christmas presents so you see we are quite busy. I am sorry you were not able to hear our band the day you were here but hope you can hear it the next time you come (to see me)

I want to tell you a bout the nice time I had Miss Reeves took me to Philadelphia Dec. 12 and I saw a exebation of Persians and how I did enjoy them and the stores were so pretty.

I am sending you a little supprise I hope you will like it.

Well I can't think of any more to say so I will bring my letter to a close my too little *Persians* are *fine*.

Yours affectioneed [*sic*]

Emma Wolverton

hope to hear from you soon.[5]

---

[3] Christianson, 2003, p. B9

[4] Christianson, 2003, p. B10.

[5] Wolverton, 1931.

By 1931, at 42 years of age, Emma Wolverton, whom the world had known only as Deborah Kallikak, had no family to write for Christmas. The surprise for Estabrook was a picture of Emma, seated, with a dachshund in her lap, grinning impishly at the camera.

Emma had long ago lost her real family. All that she could do was substitute the people she could find in the institution, and those who were interested in her as Deborah Kallikak, for the mother and siblings she had never really known. It was common that people who were institutionalized eventually lost all contact with their families. Sometimes this was because of the difficulties of travel and communication. Other times it was due to institution rules and restrictions on family visits. In still other cases, it was because the families lost interest or were relieved to be rid of the institutionalized member. This severance of family ties was so complete in many cases that there was no traceable family to contact at the time of death. This is also the reason that most institutions have their own cemeteries.

Emma's presence at the Training School was fundamental to Goddard's Kallikak family narrative—fundamental in the sense, of course, that she was the starting point for his odyssey back through the Kallikak generations to the point at which the bad line, the Kakos line, had split from the good line, the Kallos line. Emma's residence at Vineland and the diagnosis of her as feebleminded was basic to the argument of the "bad seed." To Goddard, she served as the central example of the continuing and inevitable influence of hereditary mental defects.

The starting point for the Kallikak story is Martin Kallikak, Sr. In *The Kallikak Family,* Goddard tells of Martin's downfall.[6] "When Martin Sr., of the good family, was a boy of fifteen, his father died, leaving him without parental care or oversight. Just before attaining his majority, the young man joined one of the numerous military companies that were formed to protect the country at the beginning of the Revolution. At one of the taverns frequented by the militia he met a feeble-minded girl by whom he became the father of a feeble-minded son."[7]

"Two years later [i.e., 1778], he was wounded in a way to disable him for further service, and he then returned to the home farm. During the summer of enforced idleness he wooed and won the heart of a young woman of a good Quaker family. Her shrewd old father, however, refused to give his consent. To his objections, based on the ground that Martin did not own enough of this world's goods, the young man is recorded as saying, 'Never mind. I will own more land than ever thou did, before I die,' which promise he made true. That

---

[6] In the early 1980s, J. David Smith returned to Vineland and sought out information about Emma's family. Her story, recounted in part here, was published in 1985 in *Minds Made Feeble: The Myth and Legacy of the Kallikaks.*

[7] Goddard, 1912, p. 18.

the parental objection was overruled is proved by the registry of marriage, which gives the date of Martin's union with the Quakeress as January, 1779."[8]

Martin Kallikak, Sr. was, in reality, John Woolverton, born in Hunterdon County, New Jersey.[9] John was the grandson of Charles Woolverton, who, according to Woolverton genealogists David Macdonald and Nancy McAdams, came to North America from England in 1682 via, probably, Long Island. By 1714, Charles lived in Hunterdon County, New Jersey.[10]

According to the Revolutionary War pension records housed in the National Archives, John Woolverton did in fact enlist in April of 1776. He joined the New Jersey militia as a private in the Second Hunterdon County Regiment under a Captain Ely. His service was, however, neither long nor far from home. He served monthly tours, every other month, over a period of 1.5 years. He was back living at home every second month. Even during his months of service he was never far away. His duty consisted of standing guard in Hunterdon County. John never saw combat during the revolution. The records indicated that he was injured in the right arm by the accidental discharge of a musket, shortly before the Battle of Monmouth.[11]

John Woolverton's wife—Goddard's Quakeress—was Rachel Quinby.[12] They were married in January 1779. In 1833, John Woolverton applied for and was granted a pension for his military service. He died in 1837 at the age of 83. Rachel continued to receive the pension until her death in 1842.

John accumulated a great deal of real estate during his life, and his holdings were passed down through the family. His children were indeed favored by the environment provided by their parents. Through the generations, they tended to be financially successful, well educated, and socially prominent. A genealogy of the Wolvertons, published in 1932 by one of John's great-granddaughters, Emma Ten Broeck Runk, portrayed them as a productive and respected line. The information included in that publication is alluded to by Goddard in the Kallikak study.[13]

"This lady is a person not only of refinement and culture," Goddard wrote about Wolverton biographer Runk, "but is the author of two scholarly genealogical works. She has, for years, been collecting material for a similar study of

---

[8] Goddard, 1912, pp. 99-100.

[9] Information on the Woolverton/Wolverton geneaology was derived from *Minds Made Feeble: The Myth and Legacy of the Kallikaks* (Smith, 1985); *The Woolvertons, Early Legal Records of the Family in New Jersey and the Descendants of Charles Woolverton to the Seventh Generation* (Runk, 1932); *The Woolverton Family: 1693–1850 and Beyond* (Macdonald and McAdams, 2001); and *The Kallikak Family: A Genealogical Examination of a "Classic in Psychology"* (Straney, 1994).

[10] Macdonald and McAdams, 2001, pp. 1, 3.

[11] Smith, 1985, p. 90.

[12] Macdonald and McAdams, 2001, p. 94.

[13] Smith, 1985, p. 90.

the Kallikak family. This material she generously submitted to the use of the field worker. In the end she spent an entire day in the completion and revision of the normal chart presented in this book. No praise can be too high for such disinterested self-forgetfulness in the face of an urgent public need."[14]

For those who have wondered over the years how Goddard collected information on the hundreds of people described in the Kallikak book in such a short time, here is at least part of the answer. The data that he presented on the favored side of the family was taken directly from the manuscript of the great-granddaughter of John Woolverton (Martin Kallikak, Sr.). Even the wording in certain sections of Goddard's book is identical to that used in the earlier manuscript.

It is, of course, Martin Kallikak, Jr., the great-great-grandfather of "Deborah," who is the fulcrum in *The Kallikak Family* narrative. Martin Jr. links the "Kallos" of the Kallikak family to the "Kakos" of the family. Goddard's description of Martin, Jr., is laden with those traits he felt characterized people he described as morons. "In 1803, Martin Kallikak Jr., otherwise known as the 'Old Horror,' married Rhoda Zabeth, a normal woman. They had ten children, of whom one died in infancy and another died at birth with the mother. [15]

"He was always unwashed and drunk. At election time, he never failed to appear in somebody's cast-off clothing, ready to vote, for the price of a drink, the donor's ticket." [16]

"Old Martin could never stop as long as he had a drop," Goddard quoted one informant as saying. "Many's the time he rolled off of Billy Parson's porch. Billy always had a barrel of cider handy. He'd just chuckle to see old Martin drink and drink until finally he'd lose his balance and over he'd go!" [17]

According to census data for Hunterdon County, Martin, Jr., also named John Wolverton, was born in 1776. The spelling of Woolverton alternates from generation to generation, sometimes Woolverton, other times Wolverton. The spelling "John Woolverton" hereafter refers to Martin, Sr.; the spelling John Wolverton hereafter refers to Martin, Jr. John Wolverton married Elizabeth Roads,[18] whom Goddard called Rhoda Zabeth, in October 1804. They remained together for the next 22 years, until her death. The *Hunterdon County Gazette* reported this in November of 1826: "Died in this Township on the night of the 8th instant, after a severe illness of a few days, Elizabeth Wolverton, wife of John Wolverton."[19]

---

[14] Smith, 1985, p. 90.

[15] Goddard, 1912, p. 19.

[16] Goddard, 1912, p. 80.

[17] Goddard, 1912, p. 84.

[18] Macdonald and McAdams, 2001, p. 216.

[19] Smith, 1985, p. 93.

Unlike Goddard's description of Martin, Jr., John Wolverton actually appears to have been fairly successful. He owned land throughout most of his adult life. County records indicated that he purchased two lots of land in 1809 for cash. Deed books for the county contain records of his transferring his property to his children and grandchildren later in his life. The 1850 census record shows that he was living with one of his daughters and several of his grandchildren at that time. That record also lists all of the adults in the household as being able to read. The 1860 census record lists his occupation as "laborer" and his property as valued at $100 (not a meager amount for the average person at that time). John Wolverton died in 1861.[20]

Goddard devoted considerable attention to three daughters of Martin, Jr., as examples of the inevitable degeneracy of the moron's bad seed.

"Martin Jr.'s fourth child, 'Old Sal' was feeble-minded and she married a feeble-minded man. Four of their children are undetermined, but one of these had at least one feeble-minded grandchild. The two other children of Old Sal were feeble-minded, married feeble minded wives, and had large families of defective children and grandchildren."[21] Thus, "Old Sal" Kallikak is presented as a moron and the mother of morons. Following Dugdale's tradition, Goddard might have named her "Sal, Mother of Morons."

"Old Sal" was Catherine Ann Wolverton, born December 1811. She was married, in her father's house, to Elias Rake in January 1834, and died in 1897 at the age of 85.[22] Goddard's pejorative nickname of "Old Sal" probably came, according to MacDonald and McAdams, from Goddard and Kite mistaking Catherine for her sister-in-law, Sarah.[23]

There is not much more known about Catherine from the records, although a family history relayed by some of Catherine's descendants reveals many contradictions to Goddard's portrayal. Two of her grandchildren were still living in 1985. A brother and sister, they were both retired schoolteachers living in Trenton, New Jersey. One grandson moved from New Jersey to Iowa, became treasurer of a bank, owned a lumberyard, and operated a creamery. Another grandson moved to Wisconsin. His son served as a pilot in the Army Air Corps in World War II. A great, great-grandson of Catherine was a teacher in Chicago. A great-grandson was a policeman in another city in Illinois.

A 1930 newspaper article reported that all of Catherine's sons had been soldiers in the Civil War. The article was written by a man who had known Catherine's boys while they were in school. In writing of a boy who had been in school with one of the sons, he noted that "he and Aaron Rake were great cro-

---

[20] Smith, 1985, p. 93.

[21] Goddard, 1912, pp. 21 ,79

[22] Macdonald and McAdams, 2001, p. 218.

[23] Macdonald and McAdams, 2001, p. 811.

nies, often associated in harmless escapades." He described him in these words: "Aaron Rake was a man of good mind and something of a student in his way. At one time he was very much interested in physiognomy, which was then a local fad. He reached what he thought sufficient skill for a venture into the lecture field. So he posted notices of 'A Lecture on Physiognomy by Prof. Aaron Rake.' Several of us went out to hear what the 'professor' had to say . . . Aaron looked the crowd over, seemed to consider for a short time, then rose and said in his stammering way: 'The lecture will not be given tonight. I want an appreciative audience.'"[24] Men of higher social and academic status had certainly succumbed to the lure of physiognomy than Aaron Rake.

Goddard's profiles of John Wolverton's (Martin Kallikak Jr.) other daughters were just as debasing as that of his description of "Old Sal." "The fifth child of Martin Jr. was Jemima, feeble-minded and sexually immoral. She lived with a feeble-minded man named Horser, to whom she was supposed to have been married. Of her five children, three are known to have been feeble-minded, two are undetermined."[25]

"The sixth child of Martin Jr., . . . known as 'Old Moll' was feeble-minded, alcoholic, and sexually immoral. She had three illegitimate children who were sent to the almshouse, and from there bound out to neighboring farmers.

"Old Moll, simple as she was, would do anything for a neighbor. She finally died—burned to death in the chimney corner. She had come in drunk and sat down there. Whether she fell over in a fit or her clothes caught fire, nobody knows. She was burned to a crisp when they found her."[26]

Jemima, who in reality was Jane Wolverton,[27] was born in Hunterdon County and was still there when she died at age 86 in December 1900. She was indeed married (not "supposedly" as Goddard asserts); according to a newspaper report, she was the widow of a well digger in the vicinity,[28] John Hinkley.[29] In 1900, she had come into the town of Flemington to visit her daughter when she became ill; she was thought to be "on the mend" when she died. The 1860 census record shows her living at that time with her husband John, who was 50.[30]

"Old Moll," or more charitably Mary Wolverton, was also married and was living with her husband during the 1850 census. The story of her being burned to death is true and was reported in the *Hunterdon Democrat* in 1853.[31]

---

[24] Smith, 1985, p. 95.

[25] Goddard, 1912, p. 21.

[26] Goddard, 1912, pp. 21-22.

[27] Macdonald and McAdams, 2001, p. 218.

[28] Smith, 1985, p. 97.

[29] Macdonald and McAdams, 2001, p. 218.

[30] Smith, 1985, p. 97.

[31] Smith, 1985, p. 97.

A further clue to how Goddard and Elizabeth Kite collected their information and how they arrived at characterizations like those of John Wolverton's daughters is contained in the correspondence of Hiram Deats, founder of the Hunterdon County Historical Society. Russell Bruce Rankin, editor of the *Genealogical Magazine of New Jersey*, wrote to Deats on March 5, 1941: "I once read the Kallikak Family, but never found anyone who knows what family it is supposed to represent. Neither could I figure out how anyone could write such a complete genealogy of such a peculiar outfit, particularly on the dark side of the picture."

"It is doubtful if anyone ever identified the real name of the original of the Kallikak family," Hiram Deats responded on March 8, 1941. "The descendants had a lot of names, and none of them that I knew was the original name. The genealogy of the good part of the family was published and you have seen it. Dr. Goddard insisted on protecting them, even after a century and a quarter, and more, so out of respect to him, I have never mentioned it to anyone. I was District Clerk at the time, of Raritan Township, and we had two of the family in one school, and one in another. I had appointed myself truant officer, and tried to get some regular attendance out of them, though they were hardly fit for the Feeble Minded Institution at Vineland. Then when Dr. Goddard's assistant came, wanting help, I felt it might result in getting them out of the township, so gladly helped."

Deats was a gentleman farmer who left the operation of his farm to hired workers, probably people like the Wolvertons, while he devoted his time primarily to genealogy and local history. He was obviously more interested in the possibility of ridding the county of what he considered "undesirables" than in finding the truth.

The line of descent from Martin, Jr. to Deborah was through the son Goddard called Millard. "Millard [was]," wrote Goddard, "the direct ancestor of our Deborah. He married Althea Haight and they had fifteen children. . . . Millard married Althea Haight about 1830 . . . the mother died in 1857 . . . This mother, Althea Haight, was feeble-minded. That she came from a feeble- minded family is evidenced by the fact that she had at least one feeble-minded brother, while of her mother it was said that the 'devil himself could not live with her. . . .' Millard Kallikak married for his second wife a normal woman, a sister of a man of prominence. She was, however, of marked peculiarity."[32]

Millard, in real life William Wolverton,[33] was a cooper (barrel maker). He died in 1893 at 90 years of age. He was John and Elizabeth's oldest son and the father of John Woolverton (e.g., Justin in Goddard's account), Emma's grandfather. William owned a 46-acre tract of land in Hillsborough Township,

---

[32] Goddard, 1912, p. 23.
[33] Macdonald and McAdams, 2001, p. 540.

Somerset County. He and his wife, Ann Hoagland,[34] (Goddard's Althea) had, as indicated, 15 children.[35] The 1850 census record shows him owning real estate valued at $250. By 1860, the census record lists him as owning real estate valued at $1,600. Ann Hoagland Wolverton died in 1858. The *Unionist-Gazette* of Somerville, New Jersey, reported William Wolverton's death in June 1893. "William Wolverton, in his ninety-second year, died on Wednesday last and was buried on Saturday. He was a good Christian and well thought of by all who knew him."[36]

Hardly the obituary of a moron, one would think.

Goddard then described the children of Millard and Althea Haight (William and Ann Wolverton) beginning with the expectations that his simplistic Mendelian formula would predict. "According to Mendelian expectation, all of the children of Millard Kallikak and Althea Haight should have been feeble-minded, because the parents were such. The facts, so far as known, confirm this expectation, with the exception of the fourth child, a daughter, who was taken into a good family and grew up apparently a normal woman.

"The third child of Millard was Justin, the grandfather of our Deborah . . . He was feeble-minded, alcoholic, and sexually immoral. He married Eunice Barrah, who belonged to a family of dull mentality."[37]

With Justin, whose real name was, again, John, although reverting back to the earlier spelling of the surname (Woolverton), the lives of Emma's ancestors took a dramatic turn. John and his family moved to an area just outside Trenton and became part of the internal immigration from rural to urban United States. Up to that point, John Wolverton (Martin Kallikak, Jr.) and his descendants had lived in the rural and small-town atmosphere of Hunterdon and Somerset counties. Although many of them had lived with limited resources and against considerable environmental odds, the records suggest that they were a cohesive family. The change to an urban environment—and also perhaps the changing times—imposed a stress on this tradition of cohesion and support. The existing records suggest that John Woolverton (Justin) was unable to hold his family together. Following the death of his wife, John's children were taken into other families or were left to manage on their own.

John Woolverton (Justin Kallikak) was born in 1834;[38] he married Emma Burroughs (Goddard's Eunice Barrah) in 1862.[39] The 1870 census records show them living in the rural environment where the family had lived for generations.

[34] Macdonald and McAdams, 2001, p. 540.
[35] Smith, 1985, p. 99.
[36] Smith, 1985, p. 100; Macdonald and McAdams, 2001, p. 542.
[37] Goddard, 1912, p. 24.
[38] Macdonald and McAdams, 2001, p. 759.
[39] Macdonald and McAdams, 2001, p. 759.

The entry indicated that they had four children living at home with them. By 1880, John and Emma had moved to the growing urban and industrial sprawl of Trenton. The census records for that year show that none of their children were living with them. John's occupation is given as "laborer." Emma and John eventually had 11 children, six of whom died in infancy. After Emma's death in 1884, John married a woman that a relative remembered as being named Mayme, although according to Macdonald and McAdams, her name was Mary F. Scullion, suggesting that Mayme was a nickname. They were wed in 1888 and had no children. "I remember Grandpop John and Grandmom Mayme," a granddaughter recalled. "She was Catholic . . . Grandpop lived in Pennington. I don't know what he did. Mom used to take us down and we stayed there while Mom went shopping. Grandmom Mayme would give us her big rosary beads with the cross to play with." John Woolverton, Emma's (Deborah) grandfather, died in 1906. His second wife, Mary, lived until 1929.[40]

From Deborah's grandparents, Goddard moved to describing Deborah's mother and her aunts and uncles. "The children of Deborah's grandparents, Justin and Eunice, were as follows: first, Martha, the mother of our Deborah, whose story has already been partly told. This woman is supposed to have had three illegitimate children before Deborah was born. They died in infancy. The next younger half sister of Deborah was placed out by a charitable organization when very young. From their records we learn that in five years she had been tried in thirteen different families and by all found impossible. In one of these she set the barn on fire. When found by our field worker, she had grown to be a girl of twenty, pretty, graceful, but of low mentality. She had already followed the instinct implanted in her by her mother, and was on the point of giving birth to an illegitimate child. She was sent to a hospital. The child died, and then the girl was placed permanently in a home for feeble-minded. An own brother of this girl was placed out in a private family. When a little under sixteen, his foster mother died and her husband married again. Thus the boy was turned adrift. Having been well trained, and being naturally of an agreeable disposition, he easily found employment. Bad company, however, soon led to his discharge. He has now drifted into one of our big cities. It requires no prophet to predict his future."[41]

"The last family of half brothers and sisters of Deborah are, at present, living with the mother and her second husband. The oldest three of these are distinctly feeble-minded. The little ones appear normal and test normal for their ages, but there is good reason to believe that they will develop the same defect as they grow older.

---

[40] Macdonald and McAdams, 2001, p. 760.

[41] Goddard, 1912, p. 27.

"Besides the mother of Deborah, Justin and Eunice had ten other children, of whom six died in infancy. One of the daughters, Margaret, was taken by a good family when a very small child. When she was about thirteen, she visited her parents for a few weeks. While her mother was away at work, her father, who was a drunken brute, committed incest with her. When the fact became known in her adopted home, she was placed in the almshouse. The child born there soon died, and she was again received into the family where she formerly lived. The care with which she was surrounded prevented her from becoming a vicious woman. Although of dull mentality, she was a good and cheerful worker. When about thirty-five, she married a respectable workingman but has had no children by him.

"Another daughter, Abigail, feeble-minded, married a feeble-minded man by whom she had two feeble-minded children, besides a third that died in infancy. She later married a normal man.

"The next child of Justin and Eunice was Beede, who is feeble-minded. He married a girl who left him before their child was born. He lives at present with a very low, immoral woman.

"The youngest child of Justin and Eunice was a son," Goddard concluded, "Gaston, feeble-minded and a horse thief; he removed to a distant town where he married. He has one child; mentality of both mother and child undetermined." [42]

It is interesting, however, to contrast Goddard's portrayal of Emma's maternal aunts and uncles with census and courthouse records and with the recollections of two of Emma's half-sisters.

Abigail, supposedly feebleminded and the mother of feebleminded children, was in actuality Ann Wolverton, John and Emma's oldest child, who was born February 26, 1863. She was listed in the 1870 census as living in her father's home. She married in 1896 to Richard Trelfall and is listed in the census of 1900 as living with her husband and their two children. [43] Her husband's occupation was listed as laborer, his birthplace was listed as England, [44] and he was renting a farm at that time.

A third child, a boy, little Dickie, died at the age of three months, recalled one of Emma's half-sisters. "Aunt Abigail's husband, Uncle Dick, died of rabies about November, 1904. She remarried to Uncle William around 1907." As per Macdonald and McAdams, Richard died at the state hospital in Trenton in late 1902. [45] Ann married William Wilson around 1907. [46] According to the 1910

---

[42] Goddard, 1912, p. 28-29.

[43] Macdonald and McAdams, 2001, p. 760.

[44] Macdonald and McAdams, 2001, p. 760.

[45] Macdonald and McAdams, 2001, p. 760.

[46] Macdonald and McAdams, 2001, p. 760.

census, William was a laborer, and he and Abigail were renting a house. There were no children by the second marriage.

Goddard remarked about another sibling, Gaston, that he was "feeble minded and a horse thief [and] he removed to a distant town where he married. He had one child.

"Mentality of both mother and child undetermined."[47]

Presumed, of course, to be feebleminded.

Gaston was George Woolverton, John and Emma's second child. He married Catharine Leader, worked as a farmhand, and died in 1936. According to his obituary, he was a member of the Salvation Army. "Uncle George," recalled George Woolverton's niece in 1984, "lived at Easton. He had a daughter Katherine and a boy Leroy and, I think, a girl Edna. When they came down from Easton for Aunt Ida's funeral I saw Edna and Leroy. They are my second cousins. We got to talking about Mom dying. She and Uncle George both died on April 7th." Records show that actually Katherine was George's only child and that Edna and Leroy were children were from his wife's first marriage.

The niece didn't have much recollection about Margaret, whose actual name was Mary Woolverton, the supposed victim of her father's (John a.k.a. Justin) incestuous impulses. "Aunt Mary," her niece recollected, "married a man named Cochran and lived at Mt. Airy. They never had any children."[48] According to Macdonald and McAdams, Mary was born in 1867 and did, in fact, give birth to a daughter at the age of 13. "The index to criminal records of Mercer County indicate that a prosecution for incest against John Woolverton was commenced on 13 June 1882."[49] As consistent with the later informant, Mary did marry Albert Cochran.[50]

Goddard made a brief reference to another son of John and Emma (Justin and Eunice) named Beede, "who is feeble-minded. He married a girl who left him before their child was born. He lives at present with a very low, immoral woman."[51] According to Emma's half-sisters, Beede, named John Burroughs Woolverton,[52] but who seems to have gone by the name Burroughs, was a more complete person than Goddard's description would suggest. "Yes, Burroughs was one of Mom's brothers . . . . Burroughs' wife Ida (nee Abel) died. They had a daughter . . . she lives in Trenton. Uncle Burroughs got a job in Lambertville and Aunt Ida wouldn't go there with him, so he went alone . . . . Pop got Ida and Uncle Burroughs back together. Uncle Burroughs and Ida were Millie's par-

---

[47] Goddard, 1912, p. 29

[48] Smith, 1985, p. 104

[49] Macdonald and McAdams, 2001, p. 761.

[50] Macdonald and McAdams, 2001, p. 761.

[51] Goddard, 1912, p. 29

[52] Macdonald and McAdams, 2001, p. 762.

ents. Millie married and had a girl, May, who looked like Mom." The 1930 city directory of Trenton lists Burroughs and Ida and indicated that he was a rubber worker. In 1935, he was listed as a millworker. Burroughs died in April 1953.

And then there was Martha, Deborah's mother in Goddard's tale. Malinda H. Woolverton was born in April 1868. According to census data, in 1870 she was living with her parents, John and Emma. Later she lived and served as a domestic and child care helper in the home of a neighbor. She is shown living in this home in the 1885 census records. Emma was born to Malinda out of wedlock in February 1889. Although Goddard indicates that Emma's mother had three illegitimate children who did not live past infancy before Emma was born in the almshouse, Macdonald and McAdams noted that records suggest Emma was Melinda's only illegitimate child.

Malinda married her first husband, Charles Edward Manion,[53] in November of 1889 and divorced him after the birth of two more children. She married her second husband, Lewis R. Danbury,[54] around November of 1897, just after Emma was admitted to the Vineland Training School, and had seven children by him. She died on April 7, 1932. Her second husband died in 1942 and is buried beside her. "I look like my mother, recalled one of Malinda's daughters by Lewis Danbury, "dark eyes and dark hair like Mom. Jenny and Ward look like my father's people. Ward's in Harrisburg. Jess died when she was 60 and Fred drowned when he was in his 40's. Ward didn't do anything. He was the baby. Ward was home and away and then back home again. He fooled around just like a big baby. Mom spoiled him to death—the youngest one. Fred got married. Tess went to stay with Aunt Jane and her husband. Aunt Jane was Pop's sister. Jess went to school there. They spoiled her. She was stubborn—Pop's family were all stubborn."[55]

In the Kallikak book, Goddard comments on Emma's half-brothers and -sisters by Malinda's second husband. Lewis: "The last family of half brothers and sisters of Deborah are, at present, living with the mother and her second husband. The oldest three of these are distinctly feeble minded. Between them and the two younger children there was a stillbirth and a miscarriage. The little ones appear normal and test normal for their ages, but there is good reason to believe that they will develop the same defect as they grow older."[56]

The oldest of these children, one that Goddard described "distinctly feeble-minded," made the following comments in an interview in May, 1984. "I went to Marshall's Corner school, so did Dot, Tess, and Fred. When trolley cars came along Mom was afraid we'd get run over by one. She told Pop she could just see

---

[53] Macdonald and McAdams, 2001, p. 762.

[54] Macdonald and McAdams, 2001, p. 762.

[55] Smith, 1985, p. 107.

[56] Goddard, 1912, p. 28.

us tangled up under one and couldn't we go to the mountain school. Pop went to see the trustees and since we lived near the line between the districts—about as far from one school as the other—we started going to the mountain school. I didn't go too far in school. Mom had to help Pop work in the fields and I had to take care of the kids when they came along. I only went to the fifth grade. . . . My teacher, Julia Holcombe, said it was a shame I couldn't come more often because I could have learned. But I did learn how to read and write and figure.

"My daughter Dot was born in March and I was 21 the next July. Eve was born 7 years later. My husband died when Eve was little. I was left with two kids. I could go home to Mom and Pop whenever I needed to. I did practical nursing when babies were born. I got $15 for two weeks and board for me and the girls. If I got a job where I couldn't take the girls, I left them with Mom. I got married again 21 years after my husband died. My second husband was Jewish, Al Katz. I thought we'd grow old together. We were married 20 years. We built this house and he died two years later. . . . My husband was in the Army 31 years so I go to Fort Dix for my doctoring. That's where I had my leg off two years ago. They said I recovered good. I always took care of myself—never smoked or drank."

At the time of the interview, Emma's half-sister was 86 years old, was about 5 feet 3 inches tall, and weighed about 120 pounds. Except for her amputated leg, she appeared to be in good health. She was lively, alert, and lucid. Her great grandson Ray was a golf professional in Florida. "Jenny [sister] and I go to Florida every year now. I've been going down there for 40 years now. We used to have to pay, but now we stay with Ray and his family."

Jenny was another of Emma's siblings that Goddard considered to be "distinctly feeble-minded." She married a farmer who had a daughter by a previous marriage. Together they had one son, Peter. He served in the Army for 20 years. After he retired, he operated an airport taxi service. He retired from that business and moved back close to the area where the Kallikak story originated. "Even though he is retired," said Jenny, "he spends his week doing lawns and flower beds. He's ambitious and likes to keep busy. We are going down to Peter's Thursday for ten days. His wife will come up and get us and we'll stay with them."

The half-brother Fred was the third of Emma's half-siblings from her mother's second marriage Goddard diagnosed as being defective. This man was married, had children, and was apparently a responsible worker all of his life. He served in World War I and is listed in the Pennington honor roll of veterans. "Fred had always wanted to be an automobile mechanic," reported his half-sister. "He ended up as boss mechanic at Bob Jones's garage on Main Street for a good many years." The 1930 Trenton city directory listed him as an auto mechanic. Fred is buried beside his mother and father.

In commenting on Emma's siblings from her mother's first marriage—one who Goddard indicated had been "placed out by a charitable organization when very young" and "had been tried in thirteen different families and by all found impossible"; the other who "has now drifted into one of our big cities" and was destined for degeneracy—one of Emma's living half-sisters recollected in 1984: "Mom had Emma first before she was married. She wasn't Mom's first husband's daughter. She was a mistake. Then Mom married and had Harry and Anna. I don t recall ever seeing either Emma or Anna. We lost track of them. Anna was pretty. Mom had a picture of Anna; she had dark eyes and dark hair. I think I have that around here somewhere."

The birth records of Mercer County, New Jersey, show that Harry was born in 1890. He died in 1920. According to his half-sister: "I only remember Harry— he looked like me. He was my half brother. He died in Donnelly Memorial Hospital in Trenton of TB. He was only in his thirties. He worked in the thread mill at Yardville and got what we called 'weaver's consumption.' He was in Glen Gardner Sanitarium for about two years and left there to come home. But the doctors wouldn't allow him to stay at home because of the children. So he went into the hospital and only lived about two months. His wife Ella had two children by her first marriage and she and Harry had one together."

Anna was born in 1892 in Mercer County and, according to census listings, lived with her mother and father through most of her early years. Consistent with Goddard's account that she was "placed out at an early age," is the sister's recollection that "Anna went to Nate Blackwell's, I think—I'm not sure. He was the undertaker in Pennington. All the family was buried from there. Mom worked for them too, when she was young."

The 1915 census of Landis Township, Cumberland County, New Jersey, listed the "inmates" of the New Jersey State Institution for the Feeble-Minded. Anna's name appears on the list. The census record indicated that Anna could read, write, and speak English. So when, in July 1914, Emma was transferred to the New Jersey State Institution for the Feeble-Minded, she joined her younger half-sister. Family was as near as the next cottage, and yet there is no evidence that Emma ever knew this.

And so we come back to Emma. The records of the almshouse, or what was then called a "poor farm," show that Malinda came to the farm in November of 1888. She was admitted by order of the overseers. She gave birth to an illegitimate female child in February of 1889. The child was given the name Emma. In June of that year the mother and infant left the farm. Emma lived with her mother until 1897 when she entered the Training School at Vineland.

The real story of the disfavored Kallikaks, the "other Wolvertons," is not free of troubles and human frailties. The family had its share of illegitimate children, drunkards, "ne'er-do-wells," and the other skeletons that have a way of jumping out of genealogical closets. But so do most families, particularly those who have been faced with poverty, lack of education, and scarce resources for dealing with social change. But the family also had its strengths and successes. The tragedy of the disfavored Kallikaks is that their story was distorted to fit an expectation. They were perceived in a way that allowed only their weaknesses and failures to emerge. Their story was first interpreted according to a powerful myth, and then used to further bolster that myth. The myth was that of eugenics. All the "bad" Kallikaks were bad, and that legacy would remain unchanged.

"This is the ghastly story of the descendants of Martin Kallikak Sr.," Goddard concluded at the end of his recitation of Deborah's mother and her siblings, "from the nameless feeble-minded girl."[57]

But, of course, it wasn't. It wasn't because it was Goddard's story, constructed by Goddard and Kite to fulfill the need for a eugenic narrative to fit their world-view. It was also a story that Henry Goddard believed the world needed to know. It was, perhaps, "Deborah Kallikak's" story, but it wasn't Emma Wolverton's story. Her story was the story of many American families; people living simply in a rural setting who, for whatever reason, were swept at the end of the 19th century and start of the 20th century into the urban United States and into a life that, like many immigrants, was beset by hardships and for which they weren't adequately prepared.

There is another reason that this was not Emma's story, however.

"I am certain," explained Wolverton genealogist David MacDonald in 1997, "that Dr. Goddard plugged the [Kakos] line into the wrong part of the Wolverton family. He obviously wanted for the [Kallos] branch a set of people as good and prominent as possible, and I think that he was not very scrupulous about how he found it. No one could have done much poking around in Hunterdon County without knowing of the John Woolverton, Sr. branch, and I suspect that in many instances he got out of his interviewees precisely what he had fed into them."

"The immigrant Charles Wolverton had seven sons," continued MacDonald, "and 'Martin Sr.' (John Woolverton) was a descendent of the oldest son, Charles. In working down from the immigrant, I could not avoid placing 'Martin, Jr.' (also John Wolverton) as the eldest son of a Gabriel Wolverton, who was a grandson of the immigrant's sixth son, Joel."[58]

In 2001, MacDonald and McAdams completed their 860-page magnum opus on the Wolverton Family. All of the Kalllikaks are to be found there, clearly and carefully documented. In an appendix devoted to the Kallikak study, David MacDonald and Nancy McAdams wrote: "There should be no doubt that John Wolverton [referring to the man whom Goddard referred to as Martin Kallikak, Jr.] was a son of Gabriel Wolverton and Catherine Murray. John's parentage would not merit further comment if he had not been described in *The Kallikak Family*, a book published in 1912 as an illegitimate son of John Woolverton and an unnamed feebleminded tavern girl, when in fact 6.4.1 John and 1.1.1

[57] Goddard, 1912, p. 29.

[58] Macdonald, 1997.

John were second cousins and both perfectly legitimate sons of their married parents."[59]

Martin Kallikak, Jr., was not the illegitimate son of Martin Kallikak, Sr. Whether the dalliance with a feebleminded barmaid was fiction or fable, Goddard's natural experiment never occurred.

There were no Kallos, no Kakos . . . and no Kallikaks.

It shouldn't make a difference. We should be deeply saddened by the way Emma's family was portrayed and used by American eugenicists, whether or not there were the infamous Kallos–Kakos branches. We should be saddened by the impact this mythology had on the lives of many of America's lesser capable citizens, immigrants, and others.

But, it does make a difference, somehow. There was no good blood, no bad blood. One line of Wolvertons had access to resources . . . wealth, education, health care. Another line of Wolvertons had none of those and were swept, along with millions of other Americans and aspiring American citizens, into the bowels of urban abandonment and into institutions they would never leave as intact people. They were forced into lives that were barely livable, and largely invisible to those who were more fortunate through chance and circumstance.

The fortunate Wolvertons led lives of privilege.

The unfortunate Wolvertons were made into degenerates and morons all.

"I know it's hard to believe," Vineland long-term employee Alice Morrison Nash once observed, "but at least 100 boys who were at one time or another pupils here, passed their draft board examinations and went into the service in World War II. One of them even became a Marine."[60]

No, it's not really that hard to believe.

In spring 1943, Goddard received an honorary Juris Doctorate from his employer, the Ohio State University. It was, however, one of a diminishing number of bright spots in his life. In October 1936, his beloved wife, also and ironically named Emma, passed away after a long illness. Two years later, he was forced to retire on reaching the mandatory retirement age of 72.[61] "This loss of work," observed Leila Zenderland, "mixed with the increasingly frequent and often mocking attacks on his past accomplishments, left him depressed and filled with self-doubt. To his Ohio contemporaries, Goddard now became

---

[59] Macdonald and McAdams, 2001, p. 807.

[60] Fleming, 1965, p. 100.

[61] Zenderland, 1998, p. 335.

a reclusive figure who lived alone in a deteriorating part of the city, befriended mainly by a few devoted graduate students."[62]

On Sunday, December 29, 1946, Goddard lost his mentor and his friend, Edward Ransom Johnstone, Director-Emeritus, who died at his home on the Vineland Training School campus. The Tributes for "Uncle Ed" were effusive. The flags of all the institutions in New Jersey flew at half mast that day. "Someone once said to me of him," eulogized longtime Vineland employee Helen Hill, [that] deeds of week day holiness fall from him, gentle as the snow nor has he ever chanced to know that naught was easier than to bless."

"He was never too busy to be deeply concerned for even the slightest wishes of any young child," recalled Edgar Doll, "the future career of either wayward or promising youth, the immediate welfare of men in their primes, and the consideration of folks in their later years."

How do we reconcile the fact that Johnstone was both a kind, gentle soul who dedicated his life to some of his generations most vulnerable, deprived children and, through at least part of his professional career, advocated involuntary sterilization and marriage restrictions? How does Johnstone's warm correspondence with Davenport about introducing legislation based on Laughlin's *Immigration Restriction* coexist with a man whose motto was "Happiness First, All Else Follows?"

How are we to come to grips with the *historical* Henry Herbert Goddard, and not the Goddard as interpreted only through our 21st-century lens? That lens, as Steven Gelb noted, has labeled Goddard as "the most notorious example of a respected scientist pushing shoddy research in the service of an oppressive social agenda."[63]

"A personable, kindly fellow and good social mixer, a productive worker with a flair for popular presentations of scientific data," J. E. Wallace Wallin described Goddard.[64]

"Generous without stint," wrote Edgar Doll, "he was regarded for his honesty, candor, humor, consideration, humility—and sensibility. Sought as a speaker, respected as a writer, revered as a teacher, he lived a full, good life."[65]

These men were clearly not Davenport and Laughlin. They were caring individuals, respected and liked by many.

"Viewed from our vantage point," suggested Holocaust survivor Henry Friedlander, "eugenic research during the first half of the twentieth century was seriously flawed. The data collected by the ERO was highly subjective. The methodology that governed psychological mass testing was still rudimentary. By

---

[62] Zenderland, 1998, p. 335.

[63] Gelb, 1999, p. 240.

[64] Wallin, 1953, p. 39.

[65] Doll, 1957, p. 344.

the scientific standards of the time, eugenic research was on the cutting edge of science. Their research tools were the most advanced available at the time and they prided themselves in applying them meticulously. Their failing was not methodological error but their inability to recognize the ways in which their own prejudices corrupted their premises and tainted their conclusions."[66]

Goddard was "rather a tragic figure," summarized Steven Gelb. "We cannot read his statements from the period of his great influence without revulsion. He arrogantly diagnosed individuals and entire family lives—at a mere glance or through uncorroborated secondary anecdote—as being hopelessly and incurably inferior."[67]

"This was by no means, however," Gelb argued, "the whole man nor the whole career . . . it is not appreciated that Goddard led a movement supported not just by eugenicists, but also by women's organizations, advocates of mental hygiene and social welfare, fiscal conservatives, and social progressives."[68]

Not to mention the era's most important politicians, men like Theodore Roosevelt, and, for a time at least, many of the nation's, indeed the world's, most important scientists. And a movement supported by and eventually nurtured by the American public itself.

"Perhaps," observed Zenderland, "Henry Herbert Goddard's legacies to psychology, to American society, and to the population he was attempting to serve can only be expressed within a history framed not in dichotomies, but in ironies. In America, intelligence testing was embedded within a broader pedagogical reform movement which inspired an entire generation of special educators while predicting that their efforts would have only limited success; which markedly expanded medical research while simultaneously suggesting the futility of such labors in the face of genetic determinants; which forced the state to assume more responsibility for caring for the physically and mentally handicapped, while also overseeing their segregation and exclusion from the rights of citizenship; which spoke frequently and ominously of the 'menace' of the feebleminded while still repeatedly warning, 'Inasmuch as ye have done it unto the least of these.'"[69]

Professor Johnstone's body laid in state in Garrison Hall at the Training School on the final day of 1946. The light snow drifted across Maxham lawn. The second version of Maxham Cottage, toward which Goddard had walked that morning in 1907, had burned to the ground in 1926. The third reincarnation of Maxham Cottage stood where the previous building had burned, a pale imitation of the grandeur that had been its twin-towered predecessor. At 10 A.M.,

---

[66] Friedlander, 1995, p. 7.

[67] Gelb, 1999, p. 240.

[68] Gelb, 1999, p. 240–241.

[69] Zenderland, 1998, p. 362.

the children to whom Johnstone had dedicated his life lined up and filed quietly past his body, a silent homage to his importance in their lives.

The next year, 1947, Goddard moved from Columbus, Ohio, to Santa Barbara, California, to live with his sister-in-law, Mabel Stuart Whiting, and her daughter, Alice Merriam Whiting, the latter who had maintained an ongoing correspondence with Emma Wolverton through the years. Goddard's health worsened and by the time his sister-in-law died, in 1955, he had developed Alzheimer's-like symptoms and had to be cared for by his niece, Alice. He passed away at her home in June 1957, the same year that the city of Vineland honored Johnstone's lifelong contributions when it opened the Edward R. Johnstone Elementary School.

Goddard's cremated remains were transported back to Vineland, New Jersey, where they were interred in Siloam Cemetery next to his beloved wife, Emma. The land for Vineland's oldest cemetery was donated to the city by its founder, Charles Landis. There, the dignitaries of Vineland have been laid to rest, including Landis himself and grape juice inventor Thomas Welch. There too, not far from the final resting places of Henry and Emma Goddard, is buried Edward Ransom Johnstone. Johnstone's headstone carries the eulogy provided by Helen Hill: "God Made Him So and Deeds of Week-day Holiness Fell from Him Gentle as the Snow."

CHAPTER 11

Emma's Real Story

Goddard titled chapter 1 of *The Kallikak Family* "Deborah's Story"; but it wasn't, of course, Emma Wolverton's story. Shortly after Emma's transfer to the New Jersey State Institute for Feeble-Minded Women in July 1914, the state of New Jersey changed the institution's name to the New Jersey State Institution for Feeble Minded. She arrived at the institution as a minor celebrity. Helen Reeves, executive social worker at the institution when Emma moved in reflected on first meeting Emma when she transferred from the Vineland Training School: "For our part we knew we had acquired distinction in acquiring Deborah Kallikak, for by this time the story of her pedigree was becoming well known. And such a capable, well-trained and good looking girl must be an asset."[1]

"Deborah, at this time," described Reeves, "was a handsome young woman, twenty-five years old, with many accomplishments, though her academic progress had remained stationary just beyond the second grade. She excelled in the manual arts of embroidery, wood-craft and basketry, played the cornet beautifully and took star roles in all entertainments as a matter of course. She was well trained in fine laundry work and dining room service, could use a power sewing machine and had given valuable assistance as a helper in cottages for low grade children. Her manner toward her superior officers was one of dignified courtesy."[2]

In other words, Emma was one of those institution inmates who became indispensable to superintendents as the institution population soared.

While at the Training School, Emma had served in a nanny–housemaid role in the Johnstone household, and this personal servitude continued at the new institution, where Emma assumed childcare responsibilities for the assistant superintendent of the facility. Children from both of these institutions continued to visit and correspond with Emma throughout her life. A woman in

---

[1] Reeves, 1938, p. 196.
[2] Reeves, 1938, p. 195.

one of the families acknowledged her affection and respect by naming her own daughter after Emma.[3]

For a number of years, Emma worked as a nurse's aide at the institution's on-grounds hospital. "In the early nineteen-twenties," recounted Reeves, "a mild epidemic broke out in the building for low grade patients. Isolation was arranged and the hospital being short-handed at the time, Deborah was glad to assist the special nurse. She immediately mastered the details of routine treatment and was devoted to her charges."[4]

In 1924, Harry Laughlin was approached with an opportunity to test the air-tightness of his model sterilization law. Laughlin had mailed a copy of *Eugenical Sterilization in the United States* to Albert Priddy, superintendent of the Virginia Colony for Epileptics and Feebleminded in Lynchburg.[5] Priddy, with others, used the model law to craft sterilization legislation for Virginia, which was passed in March 1924, for implementation in June.[6]

Priddy's beliefs were, essentially, exactly those that Goddard wanted people to have about his morons—particularly women. Priddy wrote in a 1922–1923 report "the admission of female morons to this institution has constituted for the most part of those who would formerly have found their way into the red-light district and become dangerous to society . . . These women are never reformed in heart and mind because they are defectives from the standpoint of intellect and moral conception and should always have the supervision by officers of the law and properly appointed custodians."[7]

Among the women admitted to Priddy's institution who, in his estimation, fell into this category of moronity and moral imbecility, was Carrie Buck. Buck was admitted to the Virginia Colony on June 4, 1924. Like Emma Wolverton, Carrie Buck's early years were less than ideal for optimal development. Her mother, Emma Buck, had herself been committed to the Virginia Colony in 1920 for prostitution and "moral delinquency." Carrie was raised in foster homes and it was her foster family, with whom she had lived since she was three, who petitioned to have Carrie incarcerated, alleging that she was feebleminded and epileptic. The 17-year-old Carrie was also pregnant.

Unlike Emma Wolverton, Carrie Buck attended school up through sixth grade, but like her New Jersey counterpart, she was reported to be unmanageable. At a hearing to determine her mental status, Carrie's foster parents

---

[3] Doll, 1983, p. 31.

[4] Reeves, 1938, p. 196.

[5] Black, 2001, p. 113.

[6] Black, 2001, p. 113.

[7] Smith and Nelson, 1989, p. 32.

described her as "a strange, ungovernable girl, subject to 'hallucinations and out-breaks of temper,' and born with a mental condition characterized by certain 'peculiar actions'... she was dishonest and morally delinquent."[8]

Emma Buck and Carrie Buck were, in December of 1927, joined at the Virginia Colony by the only remaining female member of their family, Carrie's half-sister Doris. The colony clearly had heard and responded to the lamentations of eugenicists, like Walter Fernald, who had proclaimed the danger to society of the moron class and the need to segregate females who were "morons."

Priddy also, however, shared Laughlin's perspective that segregation should lead inevitably to sterilization. With the newly minted Virginia sterilization law implemented in the same month that Carrie Buck was incarcerated at the Virginia Colony, and given her family history of apparent feeblemindedness, Carrie was, Priddy and others felt, the perfect case with which to test the strength of the new law.

In October 1924, Priddy sent Laughlin a letter in which he explained his careful adherence to the guidelines provided in *Eugenical Sterilization in the United States* when drafting the Virginia statute. He outlined how the law was needed to ease the burden on the state and his institution with regard to the number of morally and intellectually degenerate women in Virginia by sterilizing them so as to be able to discharge them from the colony. He then provided Laughlin a rough case history of Carrie's life.[9]

Carrie's biography in the hands of Priddy was, not surprisingly, unflattering. He alluded to the bad stock of Carrie's families, the Bucks and Harlows; to her mother's abandonment of all three of her children to foster care and subsequent diagnosis as feebleminded; and to the birth of Carrie's illegitimate child.

"She is well grown," Priddy wrote in reference to Carrie, "has rather badly formed face, of a sensual emotional nature with a mental age of nine years, is incapable of self-support and restraint except under strict supervision."[10]

Priddy closed his communication with Laughlin with the request for the Eugenics Records Office (ERO) eugenicist to provide a deposition for the trial, to begin later in the month. Laughlin had no hesitancy providing the requested deposition. From the evidence of the mental testing to the obvious stigmata of the feebleminded, Carrie, in Laughlin's worldview, was clearly feebleminded and a menace.

"Laughlin made two major points to the court," summarized Stephen J. Gould in a 1984 essay on the case. "First, that Carrie Buck and her mother, Emma Buck, were feeble-minded by the Stanford-Binet test of IQ, then in its

---

[8] Smith and Nelson, 1989, p. 18.

[9] Smith and Nelson, 1989, p. 58.

[10] Smith and Nelson, 1989, p. 58.

own infancy. Second, that most feeblemindedness is inherited, and Carrie Buck surely belonged with this majority."[11]

The deposed Laughlin reported, predictably, that "generally, feeble-mindedness is caused by the inheritance of degenerate qualities; but sometimes it might be caused by environmental factors which are not hereditary. In the case given, the evidence points strongly toward the feeble-mindedness and moral delinquency of Carrie Buck being due, primarily, to inheritance and not to environment."[12]

Laughlin and the ERO also dispatched Arthur Estabrook to Virginia to testify in Carrie's trial. Estabrook recounted his experiences collecting data on the second Jukes study, the Nam Family study, and the Tribe of Israel. Perhaps because of his presence in the state, Estabrook didn't bring up his soon-to-be-published *Mongrel Virginians* study.

Estabrook was then steered by the prosecuting attorney, Aubrey Strode, to describe the long-abandoned-by-scientists description of feeblemindedness as a single unit-character recessive trait. Strode guided Estabrook into a full description of the odds, according to the ERO at least, of feebleminded people breeding only feebleminded children and elicited from Estabrook the judgment that Carrie Buck was feebleminded. Estabrook then, in testimony inviting incredulity, stated that he'd tested Carrie's six-month-old daughter, Vivian, and determined that she was already below her mental age level. Before he left the stand, of course, Estabrook brought up the Kallikak saga as irrefutable proof of the heritability of intelligence.

Another witness for the prosecution was Joseph S. DeJarenette, superintendent of the Western State Hospital in Staunton, Virginia. Historian Paul Lombardo noted that DeJarenette was such an impassioned proponent of asexualization that he claimed the initial of his middle name, "S," stood for "Sterilization," and referred to himself as "Sterilization DeJarenette."[13] DeJarnette, like Estabrook, sung the virtues of the Kallikak story as proving the supremacy of nature over nurture.

Shortly after the trial ended, the judge for the Commonwealth of Virginia found in favor of the state. Carrie Buck was to be sterilized. The case was then appealed to the Virginia Court of Appeals, in close collusion between the prosecution and defense, where the verdict was upheld. In September of 1926, papers were filed to have the case considered by the U.S. Supreme Court. By then, Priddy had died and had been replaced by Dr. J. H. Bell, so that when the Supreme Court agreed to hear the case, in April 1927, it would be known as *Buck v. Bell*.

---

[11] Gould, 1985, p. 310.

[12] Gould, 1985, p. 311.

[13] Lombardo, 2003, p. 197.

The opinion of the Supreme Court was written and delivered by Justice Oliver Wendell Holmes, Jr., one of the most celebrated jurists in the history of that hallowed institution. The son of one of the most important 19th-century American poets, Holmes, Jr., was a thrice-wounded Civil War veteran who had been appointed to the court in 1902 by Theodore Roosevelt. Holmes was a towering intellectual, known for his pithy, eminently quotable opinions. Unfortunately for Carrie Buck and thousands of others after her, he was also a eugenicist and a Social Darwinist. "I believe that the wholesale regeneration which so many now seem to expect cannot be affected appreciably by tinkering with the institution of property, but only by taking in hand life and trying to build a race. That would be my starting point for an ideal for the law."[14]

Holmes, Jr., biographer Albert Alschuler observed "many of Holmes's statements on race engineering seem chilling, especially in light of later history. He wrote of 'substitut[ing]' artificial selection for natural selection by putting to death the inadequate' and of his 'contempt for 'socialisms not prepared . . . to kill everyone below standard.'"[15]

It should not be surprising then, that when he delivered his opinion for the majority of the court, upholding Carrie Buck's sterilization, it was with a sharp wit that cut deeply for many Americans like Carrie. "Carrie Buck is a feeble-minded white woman who was committed to the State Colony. She is the daughter of a feeble-minded mother in the same institution, and the mother of an illegitimate feeble-minded child. We have seen more than once that the public welfare may call upon the best citizens for their lives. It would be strange if it could not call upon those who already sap the strength of the state for these lesser sacrifices. It is better for all the world, if instead of waiting to execute degenerate offspring for crime, or to let them starve for their imbecility, society can prevent those who are manifestly unfit from continuing their kind. The principle that sustains compulsory vaccination is broad enough to cover cutting the Fallopian tubes.

"Three generations of imbeciles are enough."[16]

Carrie Buck was sterilized on the morning of October 19, 1927.[17]

Between Laughlin's model sterilization legislation and the U.S. Supreme Court's seal of approval, the number of forced sterilizations in the United States rose dramatically. Between 1907 and 1921, 3,233 institutionalized people had been forcibly sterilized. Just prior to *Buck v. Bell* in 1927, the count stood at 8,515. It took only five years after *Buck v. Bell* to double that mark, with 16,066 people forcibly sterilized by 1932. It climbed to 27,869 by 1927, and 38,087

---

[14] Alschuler, 2000, p. 27.

[15] Alschuler, 2000, p. 27.

[16] Gould, 1985, p. 311

[17] Smith and Nelson, 1989, pp. 179.

by 1941. It is significant that although males and females were sterilized at about equal proportions prior to *Buck v. Bell*, the ratio changed to almost 2 to 1, women to men, after the decision.

"Institutional reports," noted Reilly, "show that young women who were at most mildly retarded [e.g., Goddard's morons] were often admitted for the sole purpose of being sterilized. Officials then discharged them, confident that they could not become pregnant."[18] Virginia's sterilization enthusiasts, unsurprisingly, took full advantage of their newly granted privilege, and in the next decade sterilized 1,000 institutionalized Virginians against or in oblivion of their will.

Carrie Buck and her half-sister Doris were among those whose later testimonies shredded any legitimacy to the claims in *Sterilization for Human Betterment*, and rend any caring person's heart. Doris Buck, by then Mrs. Matthew Figgins, was interviewed in 1979 by K. Ray Nelson, who as the superintendent of the Central Virginia Training Center—which had formerly been the Virginia Colony where Emma Buck and her daughters, Carrie and Doris, had been incarcerated—had access to institutional records of interest to Doris. "While visiting with [Doris and Matthew Figgins], Nelson brought out copies of institutional records that Doris was interested in knowing about. He read to her some of the important dates from the files, including her birth date, which she had not known. When he read the date of her sterilization, he heard a cry. Looking up from the records he was reading, he saw Doris and Matthew sobbing."[19]

"They didn't know," Nelson realized, reporting in an article describing his interview, "she'd been sterilized."[20]

The Figgins' had tried for years to have children. The inability to do so had been a deep and long lasting hurt for Doris.

Carrie Buck eventually left the Virginia Colony and, like her sister, Doris, married and lived an ordinary life, although her life outside the institution did not begin with freedom. She, like other women sterilized in the Lynchburg institution, was sent, almost immediately after her surgery, to a home in which she was to serve as a domestic servant. In November 1927, less than 12 months after her sterilization surgery, Carrie was put aboard a train to East Radford, Virginia, for such a home. She lasted only a few months there before being returned to Lynchburg. In February, she was sent to another home, in Bland, Virginia—near the West Virginia border—to act as a domestic servant at the rate of $5.00 per week. After a rocky start, Carrie settled into her new life.

In May 1932, Carrie married William Eagle, a widower who had previously served as Bland County's Justice of the Peace and Deputy Sheriff, and after his marriage to Carrie Buck, held positions as constable, game warden,

---

[18] Reilly, 1992, pp. 98-99.
[19] Smith and Nelson, 1989, p. 216.
[20] Smith and Nelson, 1989, p. 216.

and town sergeant. William Eagle died in 1941, and Carrie moved to Front Royal, Virginia, where, over the years, she held odd jobs, including housekeeping and dishwashing. In April 1965, Carrie married Charles Detamore, with whom she lived until her death in 1983. Carrie and Charles had fallen on hard times toward the end of their lives. Prior to her death, she and Charlie were discovered to be living in poverty near Charlottesville and were moved to a nursing home in Waynesboro after having been treated for malnutrition and exposure.

Carrie's daughter, Vivian, had, at nine months of age, been tested by Estabrook and declared as "below her mental age," which was good enough for Holmes, Jr., to proclaim a third generation of imbecile. And yet, as Gould discovered in the early 1980s, Vivian had remained with the Dobbs foster family who had petitioned to have Carrie committed when she was 17 and expecting with Vivian. Vivian had begun public school in 1930 and, up until her death at the age of eight from a childhood disease, had performed typically, indeed even making the honor roll one semester. During an interview late in her life, Carrie revealed that she had become pregnant by a nephew of the Dobbs family, who had raped her.[21]

Carrie was buried in Charlottesville in the same cemetery as her daughter, Vivian. "Three generations of imbeciles are enough," Oliver Wendell Holmes, Jr., had arrogantly proclaimed to the nation and the world in his opinion for *Buck v. Bell*.

Three generations of injustice is enough.

In 1925, Emma Wolverton was, in essence, hired out as part of a domestic service for hire program, operating out of a colony program established in a suburb off of the institution grounds. After less than a year, however, she was returned to the institution, whereby she was placed in charge of the gymnasium and made costumes for the plays and entertainments that were part of life at the institution;[22] taking on, almost, the role of producer. She constructed, repaired, and stored sets and props; sewed, mended, and collected costumes; and fitted participants for their roles.

The plays and entertainments became an important part of her life, being both avocation and, if you will, vocation; but other amusements were also important to her. Emma had a love of nature and animals that she expressed in a number of ways.

"Her published photographs show her with stray animals she had befriended," Eugene Doll, Edgar's son who had grown up with Emma, observed, "unpublished ones show her peeking coyly through the apertures of a rose garden. In the spring she loved to walk among the daffodils and flowering shrubs. She

[21] Smith and Nelson, 1989, p. 218.

[22] Doll, 1983, p. 31.

had a child's appreciation for the daisies and the dandelions or a bouquet of colorful leaves."[23]

At one point, Emma tried to turn her love for her Persian cats into a business, but after the cats showed a Malthusian-like fecundity, she abandoned this enterprise, retaining only her favorite Persian, whom she'd named Henry after Dr. Goddard.

On some occasions, Emma accompanied the official families of the institution to the New Jersey shore for holidays. Her favorite vacations, however, seem to have been a series of annual outings she and Helen Reeves took together. On these excursions, Emma kept bits of toast from her breakfast in her handbag on the chance that they might encounter a bird or squirrel during the day. She loved visiting Central Park, the Museum of Natural History, and the Bronx and Philadelphia Zoos.

Emma must have been a passionate and committed letter writer as well. She wrote letters and sent photographs of herself to her friends up to the very end of her life. In fact, Mary Rockwood Robbins, Henry Goddard's mother-in-law, indicated that Emma Wolverton had maintained a correspondence with Alice Whiting, Emma Goddard's sister.[24]

As was the case with the descriptions of Emma Wolverton's childhood and adolescence in *The Kallikak Family*, hers is not a story without problems by any means. Emma was not an angel. She is described time and again as willful, overbearing, and possessing what could be an impressive temper.

"Deborah's greatest liability," wrote Reeves, "is shown by the ease with which she succumbs to every passing fancy in the affectional field. The succeeding objects of her regard are usually new employees who cannot understand why such a superior person should be in an institution. First they are flattered by Deborah's ingratiating manner, then they are bored and finally exasperated by her demands for attention, her offers of unwanted service and her crafty presumption of equality. Deborah, being spurned, has been known to give way to hysterical outbursts of jealous rage, so obscene and profane they seem psychotic while they last."[25]

Given Emma's life history, this attention-seeking and histrionic behavior would not seem unwarranted. People who are institutionalized soon learn that the rules inside differ from those outside. Being polite, waiting your turn, asking permission: these may regulate behavior in society, but in an institution, they just guarantee that someone else will get attention or get the extra helping of food. Helen Reeves, however, attributed Emma's explosive and manipulative behavior simply to her "mental level." Emma repeatedly performed poorly on intelligence tests, to which she was subjected with depressing regularity, throughout her life.

---

[23] Doll, 1983, pp. 31–32.

[24] Robbins, n.d.

[25] Reeves, 1938, p. 198.

Incongruously, though, Emma was literate and well read.

"Deborah knows how to read," explained Reeves, "and has ready access to books and current magazines. While enjoying pictures, especially those showing dramatic action, she seems to guard her reading ability as a gift too precious for ordinary use."[26]

Mother Can you Hear Me? by Elizabeth Cooper Allen is the compelling story of one woman's search for her birth mother. This journey led Allen to the discovery that she was the daughter of a woman—deaf and unable to speak—who, given the era (1929), was automatically labeled as feebleminded, institutionalized, and had her daughter, Elizabeth, taken from her at birth.

By the time she started the search for her mother, Allen had earned her doctorate in psychology, specializing in child development, and was working as a child psychologist. During her training, Elizabeth had served an internship at the New Jersey State Institution for Feeble Minded in 1957, and there got to know Emma, who would have been 68 years old by then. Even as a young and inexperienced psychologist, Allen recognized the absurdity of Emma's diagnosis as feebleminded. "Test results found her to be retarded, but I found her to be informative and interesting to talk with. She was considerate and personable and certainly not what I would think of as a retarded person. It was said that her judgment was not fully developed—understandable for someone practically raised in an institution."[27]

"Emma was tall and reticent in her manner," wrote Allen about her encounter with Emma in 1957. "She had reminded me of anyone's elderly aunt. Her job was to do some of the hand ironing, and she had been allowed to set up a small space like a tiny apartment for herself. She was very friendly toward me. From her I learned firsthand about the classic study of two branches of the Kallikak family, from which she was descended. As the literature tells it, one branch was of subnormal intelligence while the other was of superior intelligence, with several high-ranking state officials dotting the family tree. Emma was supposed to have descended from the subnormal line. She had been brought to the institution as a child and her development was followed throughout her life. She was devoted to the people who conducted the study, as though they were her family."[28]

Later, Allen would recall that Emma had a canary in a cage in her room, and that she loved to tell about the kittens she used to raise and sell for pocket money.

---

[26] Reeves, 1938, p. 198.

[27] Allen, 1983, p. 52.

[28] Allen, 1983, p. 52.

Emma used a wheelchair during the final years of her life. She was often in intense pain because of severe arthritis, and was unable to continue the crafts and other artistic activities that she had loved so much throughout her life. She did, however, try to keep up her faithful correspondences.

"As long as she was able," wrote Eugene Doll in 1983, "she sent her friends photographs and dictated letters, (she could no longer write) of the meaningful events of her life. Not only did she pride herself on her fame, she made a profound impression on all who knew her, and had a queen's knack for inspiring devotion."[29]

In her final years, Emma was offered the alternative of leaving the institution. It is, of course, a cruel irony that the offer of greater freedom in her life came when it was impossible for her to embrace it. How could she now live in a community from which she had been segregated for essentially all of her life? Emma declined the opportunity; she knew she needed constant medical attention.[30]

Surely the outside world must have appeared to Emma by then to be a very dangerous place to be for a person of her age and needs. Life in an institution was the only life she understood. It was the only place she could now trust. It was, in fact, the only place she knew. "I guess after all I'm where I belong," Emma had told her support person, Helen Reeves, once in 1938. "I don't like this feeble-minded part but anyhow I'm not i-idic like some of the poor things you see around here"[31]

Emma was hospitalized for the last year of her life, but "bore the frequent intense pain most bravely and without a great deal of complaint."[32]

Emma Wolverton died in 1978. She was 89 years old. She had lived in an institution 81 of those years.

---

[29] Doll, 1983, p. 32.

[30] Scheerenberger, 1983, p. 151.

[31] Reeves, 1938, p. 199.

[32] Doll, 1988, p. 32.

Epilogue

dignity: \Dig"ni*ty\, n. [fr. L. dignitas, from dignus worthy.]

1. The state of being worthy or honorable; elevation of mind or character; true worth; excellence. 2. Elevation; grandeur. 3. Elevated rank; honorable station; high office, political or ecclesiastical; degree of excellence; preferment; exaltation. 4. Quality suited to inspire respect or reverence; loftiness and grace; impressiveness; stateliness.

—Webster's Revised Unabridged Dictionary

To suggest that the supreme injustice perpetrated on people with intellectual and developmental disabilities has been the loss of their dignity would seem to be nonsensical. People with disabilities have not been exalted, elevated, or honored. How can one lose what one has never possessed?

Yet, we suggest, it was the dehumanization and devaluation of people with intellectual disability that was the most egregious offense of the American eugenics movement. Indignity is the state more closely associated with people who were called feebleminded, idiots, imbeciles, morons, and worse. For indignity is not merely the lack of an exalted position or status . . . a station in life pertaining to most of us. The Latin root of dignity, *dignus*, means worthy. Indignity refers to humiliation or affronts to our pride, our self-esteem, our sense of self-worth, and value.

The injustice committed against people with intellectual and developmental disabilities throughout time has been to deny them the dignity afforded to persons simply by their status as human beings. That just societies are founded on principles of compassion, equal justice, and respect for human dignity seems self-evident and axiomatic. Yet from antiquity forward, people with disabilities, and particularly, perhaps, people with intellectual disability, have been viewed through the lenses of religious traditions of sin and faithlessness, medical and biological formulations of disease, pathology, and medical dispassion; economic models emphasizing social blight and destruction, and so forth. Such perspectives continue. Australian bioethicist Peter Singer proposed, in *Practical Ethics*, that killing a disabled infant was not morally equivalent to killing a person and, in some cases, is not wrong at all.

The American eugenics movement did not create the circumstance in which people with disabilities were devalued. It did, however, take this to what is perhaps its zenith. Henry Herbert Goddard, his fellow psychologists, and institution superintendents, created a mythology about people who were feebleminded, a mythology that was fronted by half-truths cloaked in the garb of scientific respectability; a mythology that was churned and beaten into a frenzy by eugenicists, and consumed by an accepting public whose religious morays, bigotries, stereotypes, and fears led them to accept such propaganda as unquestioned fact.

It is my name. If somebody mispronounces it in some foolish way, I have the feeling that what's foolish is me. If somebody forgets it, I feel that it's I who am forgotten.

—Frederick Buechner, 1973

When we strip people of their names, we strip them of their dignity, their value, their selfhood. It allows us to then talk about "them" in anonymity, referring to our pejorative name for them or the number we've tattooed on them, as if they were not people, not human. *We* can refer to them as morons, criminal imbeciles, or degenerates as if they were not really sentient beings. *We* can lock them away for the rest of their lives or sterilize them without their knowledge. *We*—we humans—can march them into gas chambers by telling them that they are going to take a shower.

Her name was Emma, not Deborah.

Emma Wolverton.

We at least owe her the respect of calling her by her name.

Bibliography

Allen, Elizabeth Cooper. *Mother, Can You Hear Me?* New York: Dodd, Mead & Co. 1983.

Alschuler, Albert W. *Law Without Values: The Life, Work, and Legacy of Justice Holmes.* Chicago: University of Chicago Press. 2000

American Association for the Advancement of Science. *Fifty Years of Darwinism: Modern Aspects of Evolution.* New York: Henry Holt and Company. 1909.

Barnes, Earl. A Study on Children's Interests. *Pacific Educational Journal,* February. 1893.

Barnes, Earl. Theological Life of a California Child. *The Pedagogical Seminary, Vol. 2.* 1897.

Barr, Martin W. President's address. *Journal of Psycho-Asthenics,* 2(1), p. 4. 1897.

Barr, Martin W. *Mental Defectives.* Philadelphia: P. Blackiston's & Sons. 1904.

Bell, Alexander Graham. How to Improve the Race. *Journal of Heredity, Vol. 5,* pp. 1–7. 1914.

Benson, Jackson J. *The Short Novels of John Steinbeck: Critical Essays.* Durham, NC: Duke University Press. 1990.

Bjorkman, F.M. (1911). An experiment station in race improvement. The *American Review of Reviews, 44,* pp. 327–333.

Black, Edwin. *War Against the Weak: Eugenics and America's Campaign to Create a Master Race.* New York: Four Walls Eight Windows. 2003.

Boas, Franz. Eugenics. *Scientific Monthly, Vol. 3,* pp. 471–479. 1916

Brigham, Carl C. *A Study of American Intelligence.* Princeton, NJ: Princeton University Press. 1922.

Bruinius, Harry. *Better for All the World: The Secret History of Forced Sterilization and America's Quest for Racial Purity.* 2006.

Buck, Pearl. *The Child Who Never Grew.* New York: The John Day Company. 1950.

Burtt, Harold E. and Pressey, Stanley L. Henry Herbert Goddard: 1866–1957. *American Journal of Psychology, Vol. 70,* pp. 656–657. 1957.

Carlson, Elof Axel. *The Unfit: A History of a Bad Idea.* Cold Spring Harbor, NY: Cold Spring Harbor Laboratory Press. 2001.

Castle, William E. *Genetics and Eugenics.* Cambridge, MA: Harvard University Press. 1916.

Cave, F.C. Report of sterilization in the Kansas State Home for Feeble-Minded. *Journal of Psych-Asthenics, 15*, pp. 123–125. 1910.

Chase, Allen. *The Legacy of Malthus: The Social Costs of the New Scientific Racism.* New York: Alfred A. Knopf. 1977.

Chesterton, Gilbert Keith. *Eugenics and Other Evils.* London: Cassell and Company. 1922.

Christianson, Scott. Bad Seed or Bad Science? *New York Times,* February 8, 2003, B9–B10.

Clarke, Arthur C. *2001: A Space Odyssey.* New York: New American Library. 1968.

Cohen, David Steven. The Origin of the "Jackson Whites:" History and Legend Among the Ramapo Mountain People. *The Journal of American Folklore, Vol. 85*, pp. 260–266. 1972.

Conn, Herbert William. *Social Heredity and Social Evolution: The Other Side of Eugenics.* New York: The Abingdon Press. 1914.

Cravens, Hamilton. *The Triumph of Evolution: American Scientists and the Heredity-Environment Controversy 1900–1941.* Philadelphia, PA: University of Pennsylvania Press. 1978.

D'Eschambault, Antoine. *Eugenical Sterilization.* Winnipeg, Canada: Canadian Publisher Limited. 1936.

Darwin, Charles. The Death of Charles Waring Darwin. In F. Burkhardt & S. Smith (Eds.), *The correspondence of Charles Darwin* (Vol. 7). New York: Cambridge University Press. 1858

Davenport, Charles B. [Letter]. Davenport to Johnstone, March 9, 1909. Davenport Papers, *American Philosophical Library*, accessed April 17, 2002. 1909a

Davenport, Charles B. *Eugenics: The Science of Human Improvement by Better Breeding.* New York: Henry Holt and Company. 1910b.

Davenport, Charles B. Feeble Inhibitionedness. *Journal of Psycho-asthenics, Vol. 18(3)*, pp. 147–149. 1914.

Davenport, Charles B. [Letter]. Davenport to Johnstone, December 14, 1923. Davenport Papers, *American Philosophical Library*, accessed April 17, 2002. 1923.

Davenport, Charles B., Laughlin, Harry H., Weeks, David F., Johnstone, Edward R., and Goddard, Henry H. *The Study of Human Heredity: Methods of Collecting, Charting and Analyzing Data.* Eugenics Record Office Bulletin No. 2, Cold Spring Harbor, NY. 1911.

Davenport, Charles B., Osborn, Henry Fairfield, Wissler, Clark, and Laughlin, Harry H. *Eugenics, Genetics, and the Family: Volume I: Scientific Papers of the Second International Congress of Eugenics.* Baltimore: Williams and Wilkins Company. 1923a.

Davenport, Charles B., Osborn, Henry Fairfield, Wissler, Clark, and Laughlin, Harry H. *Eugenics in Race and State: Volume II: Scientific Papers of the Second*

International Congress of Eugenics. Baltimore: Williams and Wilkins Company. 1923b.

Dickens, Charles. *A Christmas Carol.* London: Chapman and Hall. 1843.

Doll, Edgar A. *Anthropometry as an Aid to Mental Diagnosis: A Simple Method for the Examination of Sub-Normals.* Vineland, New Jersey: Publications of the Training School at Vinelend, Research Department, No. 8. February 1916.

Doll, Edgar A. *Twenty-Five Years: A Memorial Volume in Commemoration of the Twenty-Fifth Anniversary of the Vineland Laboratory, 1906–1931.* Vineland, NJ: Training School at Vineland Research Department. 1932.

Doll, Edgar A. What is a Moron? *Journal of Abnormal and Social Psychology, Vol. 43*, pp. 495–501. 1948.

Doll, Edgar A. H. H. Goddard and the Hereditary Moron. *Science, Vol. 126*, pp. 343–344. 1957.

Doll, Eugene E. Deborah Kallikak: 1889–1978, a memorial. *Mental Retardation, Vol. 21*, pp. 30–32. 1983

Doll, Eugene E. Before the Big Time: Early History of the Training School at Vineland, 1888 to 1949. *American Journal on Mental Retardation, Vol. 93*, pp. 1–15. 1988.

Donovan, Brian. *White Slave Crusades: Race, Gender, and Anti-vice Activism, 1887–1917.* Chicago: University of Illinois Press. 2006.

Dowbiggin, Ian Robert. *Keeping America Sane: Psyciatry and Eugenics in the United States and Canada 1880–1940.* Ithaca, NY: Cornell University Press. 1997.

Dubreucq, Francine. Jean-Ovide Decroly. *Prospects: The Quarterly Journal of Comparative Education, 23*, 249–275. 2001.

East, Edward M. *Heredity and Human Affairs.* New York: Macmillan. 1927.

Elks, Martin A. Visual Indictment: A Contextual Analysis of the Kallikak Family Photgraphs. *Mental Retardation, 43*(4), pp. 268–280. 2005.

Estabrook, Arthur H. *The Jukes in 1915.* Washington: Carnegie Institution of Washington. 1916.

Estabrook, Arthur H. Heredity vs. Environment. *Journal of Heredity, Vol. 8*, pp. 41–42. 1917.

Fancher, Raymond E. *The Intelligence Men: Makers of the IQ Controversy.* New York: W.W. Norton. 1985.

Fernald, Walter E. The Imbecile with Criminal Instincts. *Journal of Psycho-Asthenics, Vol. 14*(1), pp. 16–38. 1909.

Fernald, Walter E. *Report of the Committee on Classification of the Feeble-Minded.* Washington, D.C.: American Association for the Study of the Feeble-Minded. 1911.

Fernald, Walter E. The Burden of Feeble-Mindedness. *Journal of Psycho-Asthenics, Vol. 17*(3), pp. 85–111. 1912.

Fernald, Walter E., Birthwell, Charles W., Jaquith, Lucia L., and Mulready, Edwin. *Report of the Commission for the Investigation of the White Slave*

Traffice, So Called. Boston: Wright & Potter Printing Co., State Printers. 1914.

Fleming, A. *Great women teachers.* Philadelphia: J.B. Lippincott Company. 1965.

Freeberg, Ernest. *The Education of Laura Bridgman: First Deaf and Blind Person to Learn Language.* Cambridge, MA: Harvard University Press. 2001.

Friedlander, Henry. *The Origins of Nazi Genocide: From Euthanasia to the Final Solution.* Chapel Hill, NC: The University of North Carolina Press. 1995.

Galton, Francis. *Inquiries into Human Faculty and its Development.* London: Macmillan. 1883.

Garrison, S. Olin. *Report of the Principal. Ninth Annual Report of the New Jersey Training School for Feebleminded Children.* Vineland Training School Press. 1897.

Gelb, Steven A. Henry H. Goddard and the immigrants, 1910–1917: The studies and their social context. *Journal of the History of the Behavioral Sciences, 22,* pp. 324–332. 1986.

Gelb, Steven A. "Not simply Bad and Incorrigible": Science, morality, and intellectual deficiency. *History of Education Quarterly, Vol. 29*(3), pp. 359–379. 1989.

Gelb, Steven A. The Beast in Man: Degenerationism and Mental Retardation, 1900–1920. *Mental Retardation, Vol. 33,* pp. 1–9. 1995.

Gelb, Steven A. Spilled Religion: The Tragedy of Henry H. Goddard. *Mental Retardation, Vol. 37,* pp. 240–243. 1999.

Gibson, Mary. *Born to Crime: Cesare Lombroso and the Origins of Biological Criminology.* Westport, CT: Praeger. 2002.

Gitter, Elisabeth. *The Imprisoned Guest. Samuel Howe and Laura Bridgman, the Original Deaf-Blind Girl.* New York: Farrar, Straus and Giroux. 2001.

Goddard, Henry Herbert. Psychological Work Among the Feeble-Minded. *Journal of Psycho-Asthenics, 12,* pp. 18–30. 1907a.

Goddard, Henry Herbert. The Research Work. *The Training School Bulletin, 46,* pp. 1–9. 1907b.

Goddard, Henry Herbert. Heredity of feeble-mindedness. *American Breeders Magazine, Vol 1*(2), pp. 165–178. 1910b.

Goddard, Henry Herbert. [Letter]. Goddard to Davenport, April 13, 1910, Davenport Papers, *American Philosophical Library,* accessed April 17, 2002. 1910c.

Goddard, Henry Herbert. [Letter]. Goddard to Davenport, March 15, 1910. Davenport Papers, *American Philosophical Library,* accessed April 17, 2002. 1910d.

Goddard, Henry Herbert. [Letter]. Goddard to Davenport, June 17, 1910. Davenport Papers, *American Philosophical Library,* accessed April 17, 2002. 1910e.

Goddard, Henry Herbert. [Letter]. Goddard to Davenport, July 4, 1910. Davenport Papers, *American Philosophical Library,* accessed April 17, 2002. 1910f.

Goddard, Henry Herbert. Four Hundred Feeble-Minded Children Classified by the Binet Method. *Journal of Psycho-Asthenics, 15*, pp. 17–30. 1911a.

Goddard, Henry Herbert. Two Thousand Children Tested by the Binet Scale. Journal of *Proceedings and Addresses of the Forty-Ninth Annual Meeting of the NEA*, San Francisco, CA, July 8–14, pp. 870–878. 1911b.

Goddard, Henry Herbert. Review of Punnett's Mendelism. *Training School Bulletin*, Vol. 8. 1911c.

Goddard, Henry Herbert. *Heredity of Feeble-Mindedness*. Eugenics Record Office Bulletin No. 1, Cold Spring Harbor, NY. 1911d.

Goddard, Henry Herbert. The Menace of the Feeble Minded. *Pediatrics, Vol. 23*(6), pp. 1–8. 1911e.

Goddard, Henry Herbert. The Treatment of the Mental Defective Who is also Defective. In Johnson, Alexander (Ed.), *Proceedings of the National Conference of Charities and Corrections at the Thirty-Eighth Annual Session, Held in Boston, Mass. June 7–14, 1911*, pp. 64–65. 1911f.

Goddard, Henry Herbert. *The Kallikak Family*. New York: MacMillan and Company. 1912.

Goddard, Henry Herbert. The Binet Tests in Relation to Immigration. *Journal of Psycho-Asthenics, Vol. 18*(2), pp. 105–110. 1913b.

Goddard, Henry Herbert. *Feeble-Mindedness: Its Causes and Consequences*. New York: MacMillan and Company. 1914a.

Goddard, Henry Herbert. *School Training of Defective Children*. Yonkers-on-Hudson, NY: World Book Company. 1914b.

Goddard, Henry Herbert. A Brief Report on Two Cases of Criminal Imbecility. *Journal of Psycho-Asthenics, Vol. 19*(1), pp. 31–34. 1914c.

Goddard, Henry Herbert. *The Criminal Imbecile: An Analysis of Three Remarkable Murder Cases*. New York: MacMillan Company. 1915.

Goddard, Henry Herbert. Mental Tests and the Immigrant. *The Journal of Delinquency, Vol. 2*(5). September, 1917.

Goddard, Henry Herbert. [Letter] Goddard to Fels. *Fels papers* (Box 2, Folder 3, Correspondence). Philadelphia: Historical Society of Pennsylvania. 1918a.

Goddard, Henry Herbert. [Letter]. Goddard to Davenport, March 25, 1918. Davenport Papers, *American Philosophical Library*, accessed April 17, 2002. 1918b.

Goddard, Henry Herbert. *Human Efficiency and Levels of Intelligence*. Princeton, NJ: Princeton University Press. 1920.

Goddard, Henry Herbert. Who is a Moron? *Scientific Monthly, 24*, pp. 41–46. 1927.

Goddard, Henry Herbert. [Letter]. *Goddard papers* (Box 35.1, Correspondence). Akron, OH: University of Akron, Bierce Library, Archives of the History of Psychology. 1928.

Goddard, Henry Herbert. [Letter]. *Goddard papers* (Box 35.1, Correspondence). Akron, OH: University of Akron, Bierce Library, Archives of the History of Psychology. 1929.

Goddard, Henry Herbert. In defense of the Kallikak study. *Science, Vol. 95*, pp. 574–576. 1942

Gosney, Ezra.S., & Popenoe, Paul Bowman. *Sterilization for human betterment: A summary of results of 6,000 operations in California, 1909–1929*. Pasadena, CA: Human Betterment Foundation. 1929.

Gould, Stephen Jay. *The Mismeasure of Man*. New York: W. W. Norton and Company. 1981.

Gould, Stephen Jay. Carrie Buck's Daughter. In *The Flamingo's Smile* (pp. 307–313). New York: W. W. Norton & Company. 1985.

Greenman, Milton. [Letter] *Fels papers* (Box 2, Folder 3, Correspondence). Philadelphia: Historical Society of Pennsylvania. 1918.

Guzda, Henry P. Ellis Island a welcome site? Only after years of reform. Monthly Labor Review; 7/1/1986. Retrieved online July 8, 2006 at http://www.highbeam.com/library/docFree.asp?DOCID=1G1:4325593. 1986.

Haldeman-Julius, E. *The Case For and Against Sexual Sterilization, Robert C. Dexter, and Others.. Little Blue Book No. 1318*. Girard, Kansas: Haldeman-Julius Publications. 1928.

Hall, Granville Stanley. [Letter]. Hall to Davenport, June 12, 1909. Davenport Papers, *American Philosophical Library*, accessed April 17, 2002. 1909a.

Hall, Granville Stanley. [Letter]. Hall to Davenport, August 23, 1909. Davenport Papers, *American Philosophical Library*, accessed April 17, 2002. 1909b.

Hall, Granville Stanley. *Proceedings of the Child Conference for Research and Welfare*. New York: G.E. Stechert & Co. 1910.

Haller, Mark. *Eugenics: Hereditarian Attitudes in American Thought*. New Brunswick, New Jersey: Rutgers University Press. 1963.

Hays, Willet M. The Farm, the Home of the Race. *American Breeders Magazine, Vol. IV, no. 1*, pp. 11–21. 1913.

Hollingworth, Leta S. *The Psychology of Subnormal Children*. New York: The MacMillan Company. 1920.

Horn, David G. *The Criminal Body: Lombroso and the Anatomy of Deviance*. New York: Routledge. 2003.

Howe, Samuel Gridley. *On the Causes of Idiocy: being a supplement to a report by Dr S.G. Howe and the other commissioners appointed by the Governor of Massachusetts to inquire into the condition of the idiots of the Commonwealth, dated February 26, 1848 with An Appendix*. Edinburgh, Scotland: MacLachlan and Steward. 1858.

Hunt, Morton. *The Story of Psychology*. New York: Anchor Books. 1994.

Johnstone, Edward Ransom. President's Address. *Journal of Psycho-Asthenics, Vol. 8*, pp. 63–68. 1904.

Johnstone, Edward Ransom. *The Welfare of Feeble-Minded Children*. Proceedings of the Child Conference for Research and Welfare. New York: G.E. Stechert & Co. 1909.

Johnstone, Edward Ransom. [Letter]. *Fels papers* (Box 1, Folder 1, Correspondence). Philadelphia: Historical Society of Pennsylvania. 1912.

Johnstone, Edward Ransom. [Letter] *Fels papers* (Box 2, Folder 1, Correspondence). Philadelphia: Historical Society of Pennsylvania. 1917a.

Johnstone, Edward Ransom. [Letter] *Fels papers* (Box 2, Folder 2, Correspondence). Philadelphia: Historical Society of Pennsylvania. 1917b.

Johnstone, Edward Ransom. [Letter] *Fels papers* (Box 2, Folder 2, Correspondence). Philadelphia: Historical Society of Pennsylvania. 1917c.

Johnstone, Edward Ransom. *Dear Robinson: Some Letters on Getting Along with Folks.* Vineland, NJ: Smith Printing House. 1923a.

Johnstone, Edward Ransom. [Letter]. Johnstone to Davenport, December 31, 1923. Davenport Papers, *American Philosophical Library*, accessed April 17, 2002. 1923b.

Kandel, Eric R. Thomas Hunt Morgan at Columbia University: Genes, Chromosomes, and the Origins of Modern Biology. *Columbia Alumni Magazine, Living Legends Series*, Accessed online at http://www.columbia.edu/cu/alumni/Magazine/Legacies/Morgan/index.html on August 6, 2006. 1999.

Kellicott, William E. *The Social Direction of Human Evolution.* New York: Appleton and Company. 1911.

Kerlin, Isaac N. Moral imbecility. *Proceedings of the Association of Medical Officers of American Institutions for Idiotic and Feebleminded Persons*, pp. 32–37. 1887.

Kevles, Daniel J. *In the Name of Eugenics: Genetics and the Uses of Human Heredity.* New York: Alfred A. Knopf. 1985.

King, Desmond. *Making Americans: Immigration, Race, and the Origins of the Diverse Democracy.* Cambridge, MA: Harvard University Press. 2000.

Kirkbride, Thomas Story. On the Construction, organization, and general arrangements of Hospitals for the Insane. Philadelphia: J.B. Lippincott, 1880.

Kite, Elizabeth S. Mental Defect as Found by the Field Worker. *Journal of Psycho-Asthenics, Vol. 17*(4), pp. 145–154. 1913.

Kite, Elizabeth S. [Letter]. Goddard papers (Box 35.1, Correspondence). Akron, OH: University of Akron, Bierce Library, Archives of the History of American Psychology. 1928.

Klein, Ann G. *A Forgotten Voice: A Biography of Leta Setter Hollingworth.* Scottsdale, AZ: Great Potential Books. 2002.

Knox, Howard A. Tests for Mental Defects. *Journal of Heredity, Vol. 5*, pp. 122–130. 1914.

Kode, Kimberly. *Elizabeth Farrell and the History of Special Education.* Arlington, VA: Council for Exceptional Children. 2002.

Kohs, Samuel C. New Light on Eugenics. *Journal of Heredity, Vol. 6,* pp. 446–452. 1915.

Kuhl, Stefan. *The Nazi Connection: Eugenics, American Racism, and German National Socialism.* Oxford: Oxford University Press. 1994.

Kuhlmann, Frederick. Binet and Simon's System for Measuring the Intelligence of Children. *Journal of Psycho-Asthenics, Vol. 15*, Nos. 3–4, pp. 76–92. 1911.

Landman, J.H. *Human sterilization: The history of the sexual sterilization movement.* New York: The MacMillan Company. 1932.

Laughlin, Harry H. *Report of the Committee to Study and to Report on the Best Practical Means to Cut off the Defective Germ-Plasm in the American Population: The Scope of the Committee's Work.* Eugenics Record Office Bulletin No. 10A, Cold Spring Harbor, NY. 1914a.

Laughlin, Harry H. *Report of the Committee to Study and to Report on the Best Practical Means to Cut off the Defective Germ-Plasm in the American Population: The Legal, Legislative and Administrative Aspects of Sterilization.* Eugenics Record Office Bulletin No. 10A, Cold Spring Harbor, NY. 1914b.

Laughlin, Harry H. *The Second International Exhibition of Eugenics.* Baltimore: Williams and Wilkins Company. 1923.

Lindsey, Arthur Wood. *Textbook of Evolution and Genetics.* New York: Macmillan Company. 1929.

Lippmann, Walter. The Mental Age of Americans. *The New Republic, Vol. 32*, No. 412 (October 25), pp. 213–215. Retrieved from http://historymatters. gmu.edu/d/5172/ August 13, 2006. 1922a.

Lippmann, Walter. The Mental Age of Americans. *The New Republic, Vol. 32*, No. 415 (November 15), pp. 297–298. Retrieved from http:// historymatters.gmu.edu/d/5172/ August 13, 2006. 1922d.

Lippmann, Walter. The Mental Age of Americans. *The New Republic, Vol. 32*, No. 416 (November 22), pp. 328–330. Retrieved from http://historymatters. gmu.edu/d/5172/ August 13, 2006. 1922e.

Lippmann, Walter. The Mental Age of Americans. *The New Republic, Vol. 32*, No. 414 (November 29), pp. 9–11. Retrieved from http://historymatters. gmu.edu/d/5172/ August 13, 2006. 1922f.

Litchfield, Henrietta. *Emma Darwin: A Century of Family Letters.* New York, Littleton. 1915.

Lombardo, Paul A. Taking Eugenics Seriously: Three Generations of ??? Are Enough? *Florida State University Law Review, Vol. 30*, pp. 191–218. 2003.

Lombardo, Paul A. *Three Generations, No Imbeciles: Eugenics, the Supreme Court, and Buck v. Bell.* Baltimore, MD: The Johns Hopkins University Press. 2008.

Lombroso, Cesare and Ferrero, Guglielmo. *Criminal Women, the Prostitute, and the Normal Woman.* Translated and with a new introduction by Nicole Hahn Rafter and Mary Gibson. Durham, NC: Duke University Press. 1893 (2004).

Lombroso, Cesare. *Crime: Its causes and Remedies.* Translated by Henry P. Horton. Boston: Little, Brown, and Company. [1899] 1911.

Lustig, Abigail. Introduction: Biologists on Crusade. In Abigail Lustig, Robert J. Richards, and Michael Ruse (Eds.), *Darwinian Heresies* (pp. 1–13).

Cambridge, England: Cambridge University Press. 2004. Macdonald, David A.). [Letter to J. David Smith]. Personal correspondence, p. 1. 1997

Macdonald, David A. and McAdams, Nancy N. *The Woolverton Family 1693 – 1850 and Beyond: Woolverton and Wolverton Descendants of Charles Woolverton, New Jersey Immigrant*. Rockport, ME: Penobscot Press. 2001.

McCaffrey, Katherine Regan. *Founders of the Training School at Vineland, New Jersey: S. Olin Garrison, Alexander Johnson, Edward R. Johnstone*. New York: Columbia University. 1965.

Moon, Truman J., Mann, Paul B., and Otto, James H. *Modern Biology*. New York: Henry Hold and Company. 1951.

Moreno, Barry. *Encyclopedia of Ellis Island*. Westport, CT: Greenwood Press. 2004.

Myerson, Abraham. Psychiatric Family Studies I. *American Journal of Insanity, Vol. 73*, pp. 355–486. 1917.

Myerson, Abraham. Review of Samuel J. Holmes'The Trend of the Race. *Mental Hygiene, Vol. 6*, pp. 624–628. 1922.

Myerson, Abraham. *The Inheritance of Mental Diseases*. Baltimore: Williams and Wilkins Co. 1925.

Myerson, Abraham, Ayer, James B., Putnam, Tracy J.., Keeler, Clyde E., and Alexander, Leo. *Eugenical Sterilization: A Reorientation of the Problem*. New York: The MacMillan Company. 1936.

Partridge, G. E. *Genetic Philosophy of Education: An Epitome of the Published Educational Writings of President G. Stanley Hall of Clark University*. New York: Sturgis and Walton Company. 1912.

Popenoe, Paul. Feeblemindedness: A Review. *Journal of Heredity, Vol. 6*, pp. 32–36. 1915.

Popenoe, Paul. The Jukes in 1915: A Review. *Journal of Heredity, Vol. 7*, pp. 469–475. 1916.

Popenoe, Paul and Johnson, Roswell Hill. *Applied Eugenics*. New York: The Macmillan Company. 1918.

Porteus, Stanley David. *A Psychologist of Sorts: The Autobiography and Publications of the Inventor of the Porteus Maze Test*. Palo Alto, CA: Pacific Books. 1969.

Pulliam, John D. and Van Patten, James. *History of Education in America* (6th Ed.). Englewood Cliffs, NJ: Merrill/Prentice Hall. 1995.

Punnett, Reginald Crundall. Eliminating Feeblemindedness. *Journal of Heredity, Vol. 8*, pp. 464–465. 1917.

Rafter, Nicole Hahn. *White Trash: The Eugenic Family Studies, 1877–1919*. Boston: Northeastern University Press. 1988.

Rafter, Nicole Hahn. *Creating Born Criminals*. Chicago: University of Illinois Press. 1997.

Rafter, Nicole Hahn and Gibson, Mary. Introduction to Criminal Woman, the Prostitute, and the Normal Woman by Cesare Lombroso and Guglielmo Ferrero. Durham, NC: Duke University Press. 2004.

Reeves, Helen T. The Later Years of a Noted Mental Defective. *American Journal on Mental Deficiency, Vol. 43*, pp. 194–200. 1938.

Reilly, Philip R. *The Surgical Solution: A History of Involuntary Sterilization in the United States*. Baltimore; The Johns Hopkins University Press. 1991.

Renehan, Jr., Edward J. *The Secret Six: The True Tale of the Men Who Conspired with John Brown*. Columbia, SC: University of South Carolina Press. 1997.

Roback, A. A. *History of American Psychology*. New York: Library Publishers. 1952.

Robbins, Mary Rockwood. Accessed at http://endtimes.com/ewbc/maryauto. html on August 6, 2006.

Rogers, A.C. Editorial: The New Classification (Tentative) of the Feeble-Minded. *Journal of Psycho-Asthenics, Vol. 15*(2), pp. 68 – 71. 1910.

Rosen, Christine. *Preaching Eugenics: Religious Leaders and the American Eugenics Movement*. Oxford: Oxford University Press. 2004.

Rosen, Evelyn Bodek. *The Philadelphia Fels, 1880–1920: A Social Portrait*. London: Associated University Presses. 2000.

Rosenzweig, Saul. *Freud, Jung, and Hall the King-Maker: The Historic Expedition to America (1909)*. Seattle, WA: Hogrefe and Huber Publishers. 1992.

Runk, Emma Ten Broeck. *The Woolvertons, Early Legal Records of the Family in New Jersey and the Descendants of Charles Woolverton to the Seventh Generation*. Philadelphia: Harris & Partridge Press. 1932.

Scheerenberger, Robert C. *A History of Mental Retardation*. Baltimore: Paul H. Brookes. 1983.

Scheinfeld, Amram. The Kallikaks after thirty years. *Journal of Heredity, 35*, pp. 259–264. 1944

Seaton, Frederick D. The Long Road Toward "The Right Thing to Do": The troubled history of the Winfield State Hospital. *Kansas History, Vol. 27*, pp. 250–263. 2004–2005.

Selden, Steven. *Inheriting Shame: The Story of Eugenics and Racism in America*. New York: Teachers College Press. 1999.

Simpson, J.A., and Weiner, E.S.C. *The Oxford English Dictionary (2nd Edition), Vol. IX*, page 1090. Oxford: Clarendon Press. 1989.

Sloss, Robert. The State and the Fool. *Harper's Weekly, Vol. 56*(2876), February 3, 1912. 1912.

Smith, J. David. *Minds Made Feeble: The Myth and Legacy of the Kallikaks*. Rockville, Maryland: Aspen Systems Corporation. 1985.

Smith, J. David and Nelson, K. Ray. *The Sterilization of Carrie Buck: Was She Feebleminded or Society's Pawn?* Far Hills, NJ: New Horizon Press. 1989.

Sofair, Andre N., and Kaldjian, Lauris C. Eugenic Sterilization and a Qualified Nazi Analogy: The United States and Germany, 1930–1945. *Annals of Internal Medicine, Vol. 132*(4), pp. 312–319. 2000.

Spiro, Jonathan Peter. *Defending the Master Race: Conservation, Eugenics, and the Legacy of Madison Grant.* Burlington, Vermont: University of Vermont Press. 2009.

Stern, Alexandra Minna. *Eugenic Nation: Faults and Frontiers of Better Breeding in Modern America.* Berkeley, CA: University of California Press. 2005.

Stern, William. *The Psychological Methods of Intelligence Testing.* Baltimore: Warwick and York. 1914.

Stoddard, Lothrop. *The Rising Tide of Color Against White World Supremacy.* New York: Charles Scribner's Sons. 1920.

Stoke, Stuart M. A Persistent Error in the Nature-Nurture Controversy. *Journal of Educational Psychology, Vol. 24,* pp. 663–673. 1933.

Straney, Shirley Garton. The Kallikak Family: A Genealogical Examination of a 'Classic in Psychology,' *The American Genealogist, Vol. 69,* pp. 65–80. 1994.

Terman, Lewis Madison. The Significance of Intelligence Tests for Mental Hygiene. *Journal of Psyco-Asthenics, Vol. 18*(3), pp. 119–127. 1914b.

Terman, Louis Madison. *The Measurement of Intelligence.* Boston: Houghton Mifflin Company. 1916.

Trent, James W. *Inventing the Feeble Mind: A History of Mental Retardation in the United States.* Berkely, CA: University of California Press. 1994.

Trent, James W. 'Who shall say who is a useful person?': Abraham Myerson's opposition to the eugenics movement. *History of Psychiatry, Vol. 12,* pp. 33–57. 2001.

United States Treasury Department, Public Health Services. *Manual of the Mental Examination of Aliens.* Washington, DC: U.S. Government Printing Office. 1918.

Van Wagenen, Bleecker. Surgical Sterilization as a Eugenic Measure. Journal of Psycho-Asthenics, Vol. 18(4), pp. 185–196. 1914.

Wallin, John Edward Wallace. Who is Feeble-Minded? *Journal of the American Institute of Criminal Law and Criminology, Vol. 6*(5), pp. 706–716. 1916.

Wallin, John Edward Wallace. *The Education of Mentally Handicapped Children.* Boston: Houghton Mifflin. 1924.

Wallin, John Edward Wallace. Vagrant Reminiscences of an Oligoprenist. *American Journal on Mental Deficiency,* July, 1953.

Wallin, John Edward Wallace. *The Odyssey of a Psychologist: Pioneering Experiences in Special Education, Clinical Psychology, and Mental Hygiene with a Comprehensive Bibliography of the Author's Publications.* Wilmington, DE: Author. 1955.

Watson, R.I. *The Great Psychologists* (4th edition). New York: J.B. Lippincott Co. 1978.

Weikart, Richard. *From Darwin to Hitler: Evoluntionary Ethics, Eugenics, and Racism in Germany.* New York: Palgrave Macmillan. 2004.

Whitney, Leon F. *The Case for Sterilization.* New York: Frederick A. Stokes Co. 1934.

Wolf, Theta H. *Alfred Binet*. Chicago: University of Chicago Press. 1973.

Wolfensberger, Wolf. *Changing Patterns in Residential Services for the Mentally Retarded*. Washington, D.C.: President's Committee on Mental Retardation. 1975.

Wolverton, Emma. [Letter to A. Estabrook.] Arthur Estabrook Collection, Series 1, Box 1, SUNY Buffalo. 1931.

Woods, Frederick Adams, Meyer, Adolf, and Davenport, Charles B. Studies in Human Heredity. *Journal of Heredity, Vol. 5*, pp. 547–555. 1914.

Zenderland, Leila. On Interpreting Photographs, Faces, and the Past. *American Psychologist, Vol. 43*(9), pp. 743–744. 1988.

Zenderland, Leila. *Measuring Minds: Henry Herbert Goddard and the Origins of American Intelligence Testing*. Cambridge, England: Cambridge University Press. 1998.

Index

1907 Immigration Act, 71
2001: A Space Odyssey (Clarke), 17

A

ABCs of defectology, 52
Abel, Ida, 196
Abnormal Psychology (Conklin), 149
abortion, 104
adolescence (Hall), 10
adultery, 104
adults, Nazi murders of disabled, xi–xiii
Agassiz, Louis, 28
agricultural colonies, 99
alcoholism, 86, 104
Allen, Elizabeth Cooper, 213
almshouses, 1, 30, 31, 35, 48
Alschuler, Albert, 209
Alzheimer's disease, 84
amentia, 79
American Academy of Medicine, 53
American Anthropological Association
      (AAA), 139
American Association for the Advancement
      of Science, 171
American Association for the Study of the
      Feeble-Minded
Cave at, 162
   family charting at, 52
   Fernald at, 86, 155
   Goddard at, 27, 32, 52, 62, 77, 107, 129
   moron terminology at, 83
   presidents of, 122, 129
   at Vineland Training School, 32
American Breeders Association, 49, 50, 52, 54,
      58, 165
American Breeders Magazine, ix, 51, 71
American eugenics movement
   decreasing support of, 136–39, 215
   definition of, 11
   genetics versus, 133–35

Hall on, 12
immigration restrictions and, 5, 26, 74
Jordan and, 19
Kallikak family as myth in, vi, vii, xiii–xiv,
      151, 152, 199–201, 216
Malthus and, 17
mental hygiene and, 76
platforms of, 14, 15, 103, 105
Plato's writings and, 12
social Darwinism and, 18
see also Nazi eugenics movement
American Eugenics Society, 179
American Genetic Association, 158
Americanism, 159
American Journal of Insanity, 146
American Journal of Psychiatry, 146
American Journal of Psychology, 10, 11, 90
American Medico-Psychological Association,
      101
American Neurological Association, 180
American Psychiatric Association, 39
American Psychological Association, 10, 72,
      114, 117
American Society of Microbiology, 136
Anderson, Meta, 129
animal atavism, 104
anthropology, 139
anthropometric data, 26, 28, 59, 62
Applied Eugenics (Popenoe and Johnson),
      136
Army recruits. *see* U.S. Army Alpha and Army
      Beta intelligence testing programs
Aryan race, 160, 173
asexualization operations, 163
   see also sterilization
Association of Medical Officers of American
      Institutions for Idiotic and Feeble-
      Minded Persons, 101, 163
Association of the Vineland Training School,
      3, 23

asylums, insane, 145
  see also institutionalization
atavism, 97, 98, 100
  see also animal atavism
attractiveness, feeblemindedness and, 88
automatographs, 26, 27
autopsies, 95

B

Baldwin, Bird T., 170
Ballou, Frank W., 66
Barnes, Earl
  Fels and, 123
  Goddard's resignation and, 127
  overview of, 19–21, 22, 23
  Vineland Training School and, 5, 153
Barr, Martin, 40, 41, 101, 103, 163
Barrah, Eunice, 193
Bateson, William, 48, 58
Baur, Erwin, viii
Bayles, Ernest, 150
Beecher, Lida, 107, 108, 109, 111, 112
Bell, Alexander Graham, 57, 138, 158, 159,
  170
Bell, Catherine, 69, 70
Bell, J. H., 208
bell curve, 64
Bernburg, xii
"The Beverly Hillbillies", 6
biases. *see* cultural biases; gender bias
Binet, Alfred, 21, 35, 59
Binet-Simon Scale
  Army intelligence testing and, 118
  criminology and, 106, 107
  Goddard's revision to, 65
  as history, 115
  New York City School Survey and, 65, 66,
    68
  overview of, 59–63
  Terman's criticism and revision of, 74–75
  at Vineland Training School, 62–64, 77, 78
  Wallin's criticism of, 72, 114–15
  see also immigration restriction movement;
    Stanford-Binet Intelligence Scale
biogenic theory, 85, 97
Biology for Better Living (Bayles and Burnett),
  150
birth control, 16, 17
  see also sterilization
Bjorkman, Frances, 39, 43, 44

Black, Edwin, 136
Blades, William, 158
Boas, Franz, 10, 139
Bobbitt, John Franklin, 49
born criminals. *see* criminal imbeciles
Bowlby, John, 19
Brandenburg, xii
Branson, Howard, 153
Brave New World (Huxley), 133
breeding, 138, 152, 157, 166
Bridges, Calvin, 133
Bridgman, Laura, 11, 13
Brigham, Carl
  Army intelligence testing and, 117, 118,
    120, 155
  racial dogma of, 73, 121–22, 160
British Eugenics Society, 57
Buck, Carol, 4, 46
Buck, Carrie, 179, 183, 206–8, 209, 210–11
Buck, Doris, 183, 207, 210
Buck, Emma, 206, 207
Buck, Pearl, 4, 46
Buck, Vivian, 208, 211
Buck v. Bell, 34, 208–9
Burnett, David, 57
Burnett, R. W., 150
Burroughs, Emma, 193–94
Burt, Cyril, 58
Burtt, Harold, 81
Byers, Joseph, 118

C

cacogenic potential, 165, 166, 167, 178
California sterilization movement, ix, 175–77,
  178
Carlson, Elof Axel, 17, 168
Carnegie Bureau of Evolution, 49
Carnegie Institute, 168, 180
Carrel, Alexis, 165
Carr-Sanden, A. M., 147
The Case for Sterilization (Whitney), ix, 179
Casti Connubi, 182–83
Castle, Otis H., 177
Castle, William E., 57, 135, 171
castration, 83, 162
  see also sterilization
Catholic Church, 181–83
Cattell, James McKeen, 11, 21, 143, 158
causality, single-source, 156
  see also heredity

Cave, F. C., 162
cemeteries, 204
    see also graveyards
Central Virginia Training Center, 210
    see also Virginia Colony for Epileptics and
        Feebleminded
Charity and Correction in New Jersey (Leiby),
    Fig. 27
charting process, for genealogies, Fig. 24,
    51–52
Chase, Allen, 121, 184
Chase, Wilfrid, 178
Chesterton, G. K., 139–40
Chicago Tribune, 91
children, xi, 59–68, 74–75, 78, 98
    see also pregnancies, out-of-wedlock
Children's Aid Society of New York, 161
child-study movement, 19–21
    see also experimental pedagogy
Christianson, Scott, 185
A Christmas Carol (Dickens), 96
chronological ages, 63–64, 75
chronoscopes, 26
Churchill, Winston, 57
A Civic Biology Presented in Problems (Hunter),
    34
Clarke, Arthur C., 17
Clark University, 8, 9, 10, 11
classification of mental capacity, 78, 79–80, 81
clergy, killing center suspicions from, xiii
    see also Catholic Church
clinics, Nazi murders and, xi
Cochran, Albert, 196
colonization. *see* institutionalization;
    segregation
Commission for the Investigation of the
    White Slave Traffic, So Called, 105
Committee for the Investigation of Eugenical
    Sterilization, 180
Committee on Classification of the Feeble-
    Minded, 78
Committee on Provisions, 118
Committee on School Inquiry, 65
Committee on the Psychological Examining
    of Recruits, 118
Committee to Study and Report on the Best
    Practical Means of Cutting off the
    Defective Germ Plasm in the American
    Population, 54–55, 58, 168
Commonwealth of Virginia, 208

Conklin, Edmund S., 149
Conn, Herbert W., 133, 136–38
*The Contents of Children's Minds on Entering
    School* (Hall), 19
Cornell, Walter, 77
cottage system, 3, 38–39, 40
Courtis, Stuart A., 66
Courtis Tests in Arithmetic (Courtis), 66
Cravens, Hamilton, 133, 134
crematoriums, xiii
cretinism, 79, 84, 146
Crime: Its Causes and Remedies (Lombroso),
    100
The Criminal (Ellis), 100
criminal asylums, 99
    see also institutionalization
The Criminal Imbecile (Goddard), 107, 113
criminal imbeciles, 95–116
Criminal Man (Lombroso), 95, 98
criminals
    degenerates as, 1, 29, 55, 56
    hereditary traits of, 110, 111, 112
    insanity versus, 146–47
    moral imbeciles as, 86–87
    morons as, 82, 83–84
    sterilization and, 26, 181
    see also female criminals
Criminal Woman (Lombroso), 95, 104
Crisco, 119
cultural biases, 70, 119–20, 121, 156
    see also immigration restriction movement

D

Dacks, 29
Danbury, Lewis R., 197
Darwin, Charles, 11, 15, 17, 18–19, 21
Darwin, Charles Waring, 18, 19
Darwin, Leonard, 19, 57, 58, 169
Darwin, William, 21, 58
Darwinism, 171
data collection methods
    for anthropometric data, 26
    for determining cause of feeblemindedness,
        35
    reliability and, 47, 48, 50–51
    sample population and, 64
    subject cooperation and, 26–27
    teachers' role in, 19, 20, 21
    see also Binet-Simon Scale; surveys, post-
        admission

Davenport, Charles B.
    American Breeders Association and, 49
    on criminal hereditary traits, 110, 111, 112
    on Estabrook's study, 161
    Eugenics Record Office (ERO) and, 51
    Eugenics Research Association and, 168
    Fishberg and, 170–71
    German eugenicists and, viii
    Goddard and, 30, 48, 51, 52, 53–55, 128
    Hall and, 49
    heredity studies and, 47, 53, 158, 200
    International Congress on Eugenics and,
        57, 58, 170, 171, 172, 183
    Laughlin and, 168
    negative eugenics of, 73, 138, 155
    photo of, Fig. 31
    on Research Laboratory tribute, 153
    selective breeding and sterilization and, 53,
        157, 169
Davenport, Jane, 172
death penalty, 99
Deats, Hiram, 192
A Decade of Progress in Eugenics (Perkins),
    Fig. 31
Decroly, Ovide, 59
defectives, xi, 69, 85
    see also feeblemindedness
degeneracy
    criminals and, 1, 29, 55, 56
    as defined by society, 29, 37, 56
    as determined by intelligence testing, 65
    genealogical surprises within, 36
    Goddard on, viii
    physical stigmata of, 97, 101, 104–5
    polymorphism of insanity and, 146
degenerare, defined, 29
degeneration theory, 84, 86, 95, 102–3
DeJarenette, Joseph S., 208
delinquents, as mentally defective, 106
dementia praecox, 84, 146, 181
democracy, mental levels and, 132–33
denunciations, defined, x
D'Eschambault, Antoine, 183
Detamore, Charles, 211
developmental psychology, 21
devil. see religion
Dewey, John, 11, 52
Diagnostic and Statistical Manual, 9
Dial, 90
Dickens, Charles, 96

Dick Tracy, 91
disabilities, 13–14, 15
diseases, Kirkbride plan and, 40
"disinfected", Nazi murders and, xiii
Dock, George, 177
doctors. see physicians; U.S. Public Health
        Services (PHS)
doctrine of polymorphism of insanity, 146
Doll, Edgar A., 81, 129, 152, 153, 202
Doll, Eugene, 41, 211, 214
Donaldson, H. H., 10, 49
Dowbiggin, Ian, 180
Down, J. Langdon, 57
Down syndrome, 19, 57
    see also mongolism
Dugdale, Richard L., 29, 55, 56, 160
Dunlap, Knight, 150
dynamometers, 26

E

Eagle, William, 210–11
East, E. M., 91–92
Ebsen, Bonnie, 6
Ebsen, Buddy, 6
economics. see poverty
economy of hypotheses, 155–56
education, 27, 65, 131, 155
educational pedagogy, 59
Edward R. Johnstone Elementary School, 3,
    204
The Effects of Mind on Body as Evidenced by
        Faith Cures (Goddard), 11
elderly, criminal penalties for, 98
"elements of consciousness" experiment, 9
Eliot, Charles, 57
Elks, Martin, 89, 90
Elliott, Edward, 66
Ellis, Havelock, 57
Ellis Island, 5, 69–71
embryology, 85
Engs, Ruth, 178
environment
    feeblemindedness and, 55, 73, 89–90, 111
    genetic expression and, 181
    heredity as superior to, 161–62
    heredity versus, 88, 89, 133–34, 137, 138,
        144–45
    intelligence versus, 27, 76, 143
    moral idiots and, 102
    moral imbeciles and opportunistic, 86–87

as solution to degeneracy, 56
    see also institutionalization; slums
environmental betterment, 166
epilepsy, xii, 13, 98, 100, 146, 163, 181
ergographs, 26
Essay on the Principle of Population (Malthus),
    15, 16, 17
Estabrook, Arthur
    as author, 147
    Congress on Eugenics exhibits and, 172
    as expert witness, 208
    International Eugenic Congress and, 170
    Juke family and, 160–62, 185, 186
eugenical mating, 166
Eugenical Sterilization (D'Eschambault), 183
*Eugenical Sterilization: A Reorientation of the
    Problem* (Myerson), 180–81
Eugenical Sterilization in the United States
    (Laughlin), viii, 168–69, 175, 176
The Eugenic Prospect: National and Racial
    (Saleeby), 147
Eugenics (Carr-Sanden), 147
eugenics, defined, 34
Eugenics and Other Evils (Chesterton), 139,
    140
Eugenics Commission, 167
Eugenics Education Society, 57, 169
eugenics movement. *see* American eugenics
    movement; Nazi eugenics movement
Eugenics News, ix
Eugenics Record Office (ERO)
    Blades and, 158
    Bulletins, 51, 55, 58, 165–67
    Davenport and, 48, 51
    Goddard and, 54
    International Congress on Eugenics
        exhibits and, 171–72
    Juke family study and, 160
Eugenics Research Association, 168
Eugenics Research Committee, 158
*Eugenics: The Science of Human Improvement by
    Better Breeding* (Davenport), 53
euthanasia, 166
evolutionary theories, 15, 17–18, 28
examiner training, 62–63
exhibits (Congress on Eugenics), 49, 58, 171–72
experimental pedagogy, 23
    see also child-study movement
experimental psychology, 25–26
expert witnesses, 107, 112–13

F

faces, in intelligence testing, 60
faith. *see* religion
family charting, Fig. 24, 51–52
family involvement, Nazi murders and, xii
family size limitations, 16, 17
    see also sterilization
famines. *see* food shortages
Fancher, Raymond, 116
Farmers' National Congress, 159
Farrell, Elizabeth, 66, 68, 144
fecundity, 166, 180
    see also procreation fears
"Feeble Inhibitionedness" (Davenport), 112
Feeble-Minded Club, 153
feeblemindedness
    among immigrants, 72–73
    breeding choices and, 138
    Castle on, 135
    classification system of, 78, 80, 102, 103
    criminality and, 100–101
    Darwin on, 17
    as determined by intelligence testing, 64
    as determined by visual inspection, 66, 69,
        70–71
    environment and, 55
    family photos of, Fig. 17
    as generic and specific term, 79
    Goddard on, viii, 67, 82–83, 154–55
    heredity and, 15, 34, 37, 42, 111, 135, 208
    as ineducable, 32
    Knox on, 71
    parents, as informants about, 47–48, 50
    prevention of, 55, 82–83
    prostitution and, 105
    as result of sin, 14
    as social menace, 86–88
    sterilization and, x, 176, 181
    Whitney on, ix
    see also idiocy; imbecility; morons
Feeblemindedness: Its Causes and Consequences
    (Goddard), 52, 91, 174
Fels, Maurice, 22–23
Fels, Samuel, 34, 123–28, 129, 154
female criminals, 98, 103–7
    see also prostitution
The Female Delinquent (Lombroso), 100
The Female Offender (Lombroso), 103
fencing, of boundaries, 42

Ferdinand, Franz, 92
Fernald, Walter
    American Association for the Study of the
        Feeble-Minded and, 155
    on burdens imposed by the feebleminded,
        86–87
    on classification of mental capacity, 78, 79,
        80
    on criminal case studies, 101
    Goddard and, 49, 83
    Kite and, 33
    Mateer and, 129
    Virginia Colony for Epileptics and
        Feebleminded and, 207
    white slavery crusade and, 105
Ferrero, Guglielmo, 97
fieldworkers, 35, 50, 54, 69, 148, 150–51
    see also Kite, Elizabeth S.
Fifty Years of Darwinism, 171
Figgins, Doris. see Buck, Doris
Figgins, Matthew, 210
Fischer, Eugen, viii
Fishberg, Maurice, 170–71
Fisher, Irving, 165
Fitzgerald, F. Scott, 157
flu, 40
food shortages, 16, 17
Fourth International Congress of School
    Hygiene, 76
Free Jacks, 158
Freud, Sigmund, 8, 10
Friedlander, Henry, x, xi, xii, 202–3
Friedman, Max, 9
Friends meetings, 2, 7
fruit flies, 133, 135

G

Gall, Franz Joseph, 96
Galton, Francis, 11, 19, 34, 56, 57
Galton Society, 139
Garrison, Olin, 2–3, 13, Fig. 15, 24, 38, 93
Garrison Hall, Fig. 8, Fig. 13, 32, 203
gas chambers, xii, xiii
Gekrat, xii
Gelb, Steven, 71, 73, 101, 109, 202–3
gender bias, 126
    see also female criminals
Genealogical Magazine of New Jersey, 192
genealogies, pseudoscientific, 29, 51–52, 55–56
    see also Jackson Whites; Juke family; The
        Kallikak Family (Goddard)

gene theory, 134
genetic psychology, 21
    see also Hall, Granville Stanley
genetics, 133–35, 181
    see also unit-characters
Genetics and Eugenics (Castle), 135
Germany. see Nazi eugenics movement
germ plasm, 84, 88, 143, 161
    see also Committee to Study and Report
        on the Best Practical Means of Cutting
        off the Defective Germ Plasm in the
        American Population
Gesell, Arnold, 11, 153
Gesellschaft für Rassen Hygiene, 57
Gianini, Jean, 107–11, 112–13
Gibson, Mary, 98, 104
Goddard, Emma, 8, 49, 92, 126, 201
Goddard, Henry Clay, 7
Goddard, Henry Herbert
    accolades about, 201
    accollades about, 202
    American Association for the Study of the
        Feeble-Minded and, 27, 32, 52, 62, 77,
        107, 129
    American Breeders Association and, 49,
        50, 52, 55, 165
    child-study movement and, 19, 21
    classification of mental capacity and,
        64–65, 78, 79–80, 81, 103
    Committee on School Inquiry and, 68
    on criminality, 55, 100–101, 106–14
    criticisms of, 72
    on data collection and reliability, 47, 48,
        50–51, 63
    Davenport and, 30, 48, 51, 52, 53–55, 128
    death of, 204
    on dramatic properties of his book, 91
    Eugenics Record Office Bulletins and, 58
    Eugenics Research Association and, 168
    as expert witness, 107, 112–13
    family background and early life of, 7–8
    Feeble-Minded Club and, 22–23
    on feeblemindedness, 42, 82, 187, 216
    Fels and, 124
    genealogical surprises discovered by, 36,
        37–38
    on Gianini, 110–11
    in The Great Gatsby, 157
    Hall and, 10, 11
    immigrant inspections and data and, 69–73
    as intelligence tester, 59, 65, 76, 77, 115–16

International Congress on Eugenics and,
    58, 183–84
Juke versus Kallikak family and, 55–56
on *Mendelism* (Punnett), 48–49
Meyer and, 9–10
on "moron", 80, 81, 82, 87–88
National Education Association (NEA)
    and, 74
photo of, Fig. 29
Research Laboratory and, 23–28
rise and fall of, 117–56
Runk and, 188–89
on sterilization, 55, 83, 114, 162
ungraded class criticism by, 66–67
U.S. Public Health Services and, 74
Wallin on, 202
Wolverton family research and, 192
see also Binet-Simon Scale; *The Kallikak
    Family* (Goddard)
Goddard, Sarah Winslow, 7, 8
Goethe, Charles M., 147, 175, 177–78
Gosney, Ezra, ix, 175–77, 178, 182, 184
Gould, Chester, 91
Gould, Stephen J., xiii, 117, 120, 121, 207–8
Grafeneck, xii
Grant, Madison, 121, 135, 157, 160, 168, 172
Gratzer, Walter, 156
graveyards, 185
Great Depression, vii, 183, 184
The Great Gatsby (Fitzgerald), 157
The Great Psychologists (Watson), 10
Green, Robert S., 93
Greenman, Milton
    Fels and, 123
    Goddard and, 126, 127, 128
    Kallikak data validity and, 144, 148
    on research questions, 129
    Vineland Training School and, 118, 125
Grundlinien einer Rassenhygiene (Ploetz), 57
*Grundriss der menschlichen Erblichkeitslehre
    und Rassen-hygiene* (Baur, Lenz, and
    Fischer), viii
Grundzuge der Physiologischen Psychologie
    (Wundt), 9

H

Hadamar Institute, xii, Fig. 30
Haeckel, Ernst, 84–85
Haight, Althea, 192–93
Haines, Thomas, 118, 122
Haldeman-Julius, E., 178

Hall, Granville Stanley
    American Association for the
        Advancement of Science and, 171
    child-study movement and, 19, 21
    Conference on Research and Child
        Welfare and, 49
    Davenport and, 49
    immigration restrictions and, 73
    overview of, 8–12
Haller, Mark, 56
Hanus, Paul, 65–66
Happy Hickories, 29
Harding, Warren G., 170
harelip and cleft palate study, 158, 172
Harper's Weekly, 31, 32
Harriman, Mary, 53–54
Harris, Elisha, 55–56
Hartheim, xii
Hays, Willett, 159
Health and Medical Inspection of School Children
    (Cornell), Fig. 26
health care workers, denunciations by, x
Healy-Fernald form board, 74
hereditary diseases, viii, x
hereditary health courts, x
hereditary transmissions (Howe), 14, 15
heredity
    criminal behavior and (Lombroso), 100
    degeneration theory and, 84, 86
    environment as inferior to, 161–62
    environment versus, 88, 89, 133–34, 137,
        138, 144–45
    feeblemindedness and, 15, 34, 37, 42, 111,
        135, 208
    genetics and, 133–34
    Goddard's views on intelligence and, 131
    imbecility and, 53
    mental illnesses and, 145–46
    whites and superior, 173–74
    see also Mendel's laws of heredity
Hexter, Maurice, 147
high-grade feebleminded, 78
Hill, Helen, 202
Hinkley, John, 191
Hitler, Adolf, viii, ix, xi, xiii, 172, 179
Hitlerschnitte, x
Hollingsworth, Leta Stetter, 144
Holmes, Oliver Wendell, Jr., 209
Holmes, Samuel J., 147
Hooton, Ernest A., 170
Hoover, Herbert, 170

House Immigration Committee, 134
house-mothers, 39
housing conditions, 88, 89
hovels, 89–90
Howe, Samuel Gridley, 13–14, 47
Human Betterment Foundation, ix, 170, 175,
    177, 178
Human Efficiency and Levels of Intelligence
    (Goddard), 130
Hunt, Morton, 121
Hunter, George William, 34
Hunterdon County Gazette, 189
Hunterdon County Historical Society, 192
Hunterdon Democrat, 191
Hutchinson, Sam, 107–8
Huxley, Aldous, 133
Hyde family study, 158
hydrocephalus, xi, 79

I

idatas, defined, 12
idiocy
    as classification category, 12, 78, 80
    Howe on, 13–14, 15
    as inheritable degeneracy, 146
    Reich Ministry of Interior and, xi
    see also feeblemindedness
illegitimate children, 1, 30, 31, 37
    see also pregnancies, out-of-wedlock
imbecility, 53, 78, 80
immigrants, 122, 130, 147, 178
    see also Ellis Island
Immigration Restriction League, 165
immigration restriction movement, 5, 26,
    68–74
immorality, 86, 87, 181
    see also criminals
Indiana School for the Feeble-Minded Youth,
    4, 163
Indiana State Reformatory, 164
Industrial Revolution (England), 15–16
infanticide, 12, 85, 104
infants. *see* children
The Inheritance of Mental Diseases (Myerson),
    148, 151
inhibition, lack of, 112
insanity, transmission of, 145–46
inspection process, on Ellis Island, 69–71
institutionalization
    Goddard's recommendations for, 64, 106,
        162

loss of family ties and, 187
prevention of feeblemindedness through,
    55, 83
sterilization and, 163, 167, 176
trends in, 41–42
Institution for the Feeble-Minded, North
    Dakota, 79
intellectual disabilities, eugenics movement
    and, 215–16
    see also feeblemindedness; imbecility;
        morons
intelligence
    as determined by work capacity, 40
    environment versus, 27
    heredity and, 34, 131
    instinct versus (Conn), 137–38
    knowledge versus, 131
    measurement of, 21
    validity in determining, 32–33
intelligence quotient (IQ), 75, 116
intelligence testing
    cultural bias in, 70, 119–20, 121
    Gianini's conditions for, 109
    Lippman on, 140–42
    marriage record versus, 150
    overview of, 59–76
    Porteus Maze test, 144
    special educators and, 203
    see also Binet-Simon Scale; Stanford-Binet
        Intelligence Scale; U.S. Army Alpha
        and Army Beta intelligence testing
        programs
International Congress on Eugenics
    First, 57–58, 165
    Second, 134, 160, 169
    Third, 183–84
interpreters, for intelligence testing, 69, 70
interrater reliability, 63, 64
IQ. *see* intelligence quotient (IQ)
isolation, institutionalization and, 41–42

J

Jackson Whites, 158
James, William, 8, 9, 10
Janet, Pierre, 59
Jennings, Herbert Spencer, 169
The Jews: A Study of Race and Environment
    (Fishberg), 170
Johnson, Alexander, 4, 77, 118, 163
Johnson, Rosewell Hill, 136
Johnstone, Edward Ransom

American Association for the Study of the
  Feeble-Minded and, 52, 129
Army intelligence testing and, 118
Conference on Research and Child
  Welfare and, 49
Davenport and, 47, 169
death of, 202, 203–4
as dichotomy, 202
Eugenics Record Office Bulletins and, 58
Feeble-Minded Club and, 22–23
Fels and, 123–25
fieldworker training and, 54
Goddard and, 127
photo of, Fig. 15
Research Laboratory anniversary and, 153
sterilization and, 49, 163–64
as Vineland's superintendent and
  fundraiser, 3–4, 123–26
Vineland Summer School and, 27, 77
Wallin and, 43
Jordan, David Starr, 19–20, 57, 171, 175, 177
Journal of Delinquency, 72
Journal of Educational Psychology, 74, 149
Journal of Genetics, 48
Journal of Heredity
  feeblemindedness in, 71
  Goddard rebuttal in, 151
  heredity studies in, 158
  human traits in, 138
  Popenoe and, 159, 161, 174–75
  see also American Breeders Magazine
Journal of Psych-Asthenics, 80, 88, 115, 165
*Journal of the American Institute of Criminal
  Law and Criminology*, 115
judges, x, 168–69
Juke family
  Christianson on, 185–86
  degeneration and, 86
  Dugdale's study of, 55–56
  Estabrook's study of, 160–62
  as first eugenic family, 29, 32
  hovels and, 89
  as legitimizing sterilization, ix
  Lombroso on, 100
  in other textbooks, 136
  *The Jukes: A Study in Crime, Pauperism,
    Disease, and Heredity* (Dugdale), 55–56

K

Kaffir, 119
Kakos, xiv, 34

Kallikak, Deborah
  attention-seeking behavior of, 212
  intelligence testing of, 88–89
  Kite and, 33
  as moron, 83
  photos of, Fig. 3, Fig. 16, Fig. 19, Fig. 25–
    Fig. 28, 88, 89
  as poster child for society's fears, 6
  Reeves on, 205, 206
  strengths of, 42–43
  tasks and interests of, 41, 43, 44–46
  tasks and interests of (photos), Fig. 2, Fig.
    4–5, Fig. 7, Fig. 10, Fig. 20–22
  transfer to women's institution and, 93
  before and at Vineland admission, 1–2, 35
  see also Wolverton, Emma
Kallikak family
  Abigail, 195
  Beede, 195, 196
  Deats on, 192
  distorted perception of, 199–201
  Frederick, 36
  Gaston, 195, 196
  Jemima, 191
  Juke family versus, 83
  Justin, 193
  Margaret, 195, 196
  Martha, 30, 31, 194, 197
  Martin, Jr., 31, 37, 90, 145, 189–90
  Martin, Sr., xiii, 36–37, 38, 145, 187–88, 189
  Millard, 89, 192–93
  "Old Moll", 191
  "Old Sal", 190
  in other textbooks, 136
  see also Wolverton/Woolverton geneaology
The Kallikak Family (Goddard)
  confidentiality within, 34
  criminality causes in, 100–101, 111
  criticisms of, 143, 147–48, 152
  dedication of, 34, 123
  doubts on validity of, 143, 144, 149–51,
    152
  dramatic properties of, 91
  Eugenics Record Office (ERO) and, 51
  family charting in, 52
  Goddard's defense of, 150–51
  impact of, 29, 33, 34, 90
  as impetus for Nazi eugenics movement,
    ix, 34, 92
  as myth of American eugenics movement,
    151, 152, 199–201

as myth of eugenics movement, vii, viii,
    xiii–xiv, 1, 216
in other textbooks, 135–36
as part of expert testimony, 208
photos of and in, Fig. 16, Fig. 18, 89–90
reviews of, 88, 90
"The Kallikaks", 6
Kallos, xiv, 34
Kandel, Eric, 130, 133
Kansas State Asylum for Idiotic and Imbecile
    Youth, 162
Kauser, Alice, 91
Kellicott, William, 30
Kellogg, Vernon, 57, 58
Kelsey, Carl, 77
Kerlin, Isaac, 41, 42, 101–3
Kevles, Daniel, 139
Keyser, Dirck Cornelissen, 186
Keyser, Max, 186
killing centers, xii–xiii
Kirkbride, Thomas, 39
Kirkbride plan, 39–40, 145
Kite, Elizabeth S.
    at American Association for the Study of
        the Feebleminded, 32–33
    Fels and, 124
    as fieldworker, 30, 35, 36, 50, 69, 89
    Kallikak data validity and, 148–49, 151,
        152
    Stoke on, 150
    as translator, 35, 60
    Wolverton family research and, 192
knowledge, intelligence versus, 131
Knox, Howard A., 71
Kohs, Samuel, 72, 115, 138
Kraepelin, Emil, 84
Kraepelin-Morel disease, 84
Kuhl, Stefan, ix
Kuhlmann, Frederick, 115, 129

L

labeling. see classification of mental capacity
labor, compulsory, 40–41, 103
Lamarck, Jean-Baptiste, 15
Landis, Charles Kline, 2, 204
L'Anee Psychologique, 59
Laughlin, Harry Hamilton
    American Breeders Association and, 54
    Eugenics Record Office (ERO) and, 54,
        165

as expert witness, 134, 207
Gosney and, 175
honorary doctorate of, x
immigrants and, 68, 73, 159
International Congress on Eugenics and,
    58, 160, 170, 171, 172
Priddy and, 207
selective breeding and sterilization and,
    viii, 34, 157, 167–69, 178, 206
Law for Prevention of Offspring with
    Hereditary Defects Act, viii, ix, 34
    see also Nazi eugenics movement
Leader, Catharine, 196
Leiby, Jame, Fig. 27
Leland Stanford, Jr. University. see Stanford
    University
Lenz, Fritz, viii
Lindsey, Arthur Ward, 135
line inspections, 69
Linnean Society, 18
Lippman, Walter, 139, 140–44
Little Blue Book No. 1318 (Haldeman-Julius),
    178
Lombardo, Paul, 208
Lombroso, Cesare, 86, 95–100, 103–5, 111
Lord Bishop of Oxford, 57
low-grade feebleminded, 78

M

MacDonald, David. see Wolverton/
    Woolverton geneaology
Malthus, Thomas Robert, 15, 16, 17
Manion, Anna, 199
Manion, Charles Edward, 197
Mann, Friedrich, ix
Mann, Horace, 9
Mann, Paul, 136
Manual of the Mental Examination of Aliens
    (PHS), 74
Margaret, mother of criminals, 56, 186
Massachusetts School for Idiotic and Feeble-
    Minded Youth, 27, 78
Mateer, Florence, 69, 70, 124, 129
Mathewson, Christy, 119
Matteawan State Hospital for the Criminally
    Insane, 113
Maxham Cottage, 4, 5, 38, 45
Maxham Hall, Fig. 12–Fig. 13, Fig. 14
Maxwell, William, 65, 66

McAdams, Nancy. *see* Wolverton/Woolverton geneaology
McCaffery, Kathrine, 38
McDougall, William, 143
McDougle, Ivan, 147
McIntyre, John, 112
McMurry, Frank M., 66
measles, 40
The Measurement of Intelligence (Terman), 75, 115
The Mechanism of Mendelian Heredity (Morgan, Sturtevant, Muller, and Bridges), 133–34
medical field, psychology versus, 51, 81, 129
medical officers. *see* U.S. Public Health Services (PHS)
medical personnel. *see* physicians
Mein Kampf (Hitler), viii
Mendelism (Punnett), 48, 138
Mendel's laws of heredity, 29, 48–49, 54, 91–92, 193
mental ages
    of Army recruits, 120–21
    classification system of, 60–61, 62, 63–64, 75, 78, 80
    democracy and, 132–33
    IQ versus, 116
    Lippman on, 140–41
    lost meaning of (Goddard), 154
mental debility, 79
Mental Defectives (Barr), 41, 103
mental hygiene, 76
Mental Hygiene, 147
Mental Hygiene Committee, 122
mental illnesses, 145–46
Mental Levels and Democracy (Goddard), 132
Meumann, Ernest, 23, 25–26
Mexican immigrants, 147, 178
Meyer, Adolf, 9, 26, 57, 158–59
Meyer, Joseph, 182
Michigan Schoolmasters Club, 52
microcephaly, xi, 79
middle-grade feebleminded, 78
midwives, xi
Mind, 21
Minnesota Institution for Feeble-Minded, 80
Modern Biology (Moon, Mann, and Otto), 136
mongolism, xi, 79
Mongrel Virginians: The Win Tribe (Estabrook and McDougle), 147, 208

Monterey County School District, Calif., 20, 21
Moon, Truman, 136
moral idiots, 102
moral imbeciles, 79, 86, 87, 102, 103, 112
moral insanity, 103, 146–47
morally insane criminals, 98
Morel, Benedict Augustin, 84, 97
Morgan, Thomas, 133, 134, 135, 139, 181
morons
    army intelligence testing and, 120–21
    curing through education of, 155
    definitions of, 78, 80, 81, 83
    immigrants as, 122, 130
    see also moral idiots
Morrison, Alice, 23, 27
    see also Nash, Alice Morrison
Mother Can You Hear Me? (Allen), 213
Mr. PRO versus Mr. CON, 179–80
Muller, Herman Joseph, 133, 134, 170
Municipal Court of Chicago, 168, 169
Murdoch, J. M., 79
Murray, Catherine, 200
Myerson, Abraham, 145–48, 149, 150, 151, 178–81

N

Nam family, 29, 86
Nash, Alice Morrison, Fig. 25, 77, 153, 201
Nash, Ted, 153
National Conference of Charities and Corrections, 87–88, 106, 122, 163
National Conferences for Race Betterment, 159–60
National Education Association (NEA), 19, 65, 74
National Socialists, ix
natural selection, 12, 15, 18, 21
nature-nurture dichotomy, 68
Nazi eugenics movement, vii–xiii, 178
Nelson, K. Ray, 210
neo-Malthusianism, 166
The New Decalogue of Science (Wiggam), 147
New England Asylum for the Blind, 13
New Jersey Association for the Study of Childhood and Youth, 22
New Jersey Home for the Education and Care of Feeble-Minded Children, 2
    see also Vineland Training School, N. J.
New Jersey State Hospital for the Insane, 106

New Jersey State Institution for Feeble-
    Minded Women, Fig. 11, 93, 199, 205,
    213
New Jersey State Psychological Services, 24
"new orthodoxy", 9
The New Republic, 140
New York City School Survey of 1911-1912,
    65–68
New York Daily News, 91
New York Herald-Tribune, 140
New York Times, 185
nonwhite peoples, 173
    see also immigrants
Nordic race, 160, 172, 173
Norsworthy, Naomi, 144
nurses, Nazi murders and, xi, xiii

O

Oakland, Calif. schools, 20
Of Mice and Men (Steinbeck), vii
Ohio Bureau of Juvenile Research, 122, 128,
    129, 154
Olson, Harry, 168–69
On the Causes of Idiocy (Howe), 14, 15
*On the Construction, Organization and General
    Arrangements of Hospitals for the Insane*
    (Kirkbride), 39
ontogeny recapitulates phylogeny hypothesis,
    84, 85
The Origin of Species (Darwin), 15, 18, 56, 84,
    171
Osborn, Henry Fairfield, 134, 160, 169, 171
Otto, James, 136
overpopulation, 16
Oxford English Dictionary, 83

P

Padagogisches Magazin, ix
painkillers, Nazi murders and, xi
parental rights, Nazi murders and, xi
parents, as suppliers of data, 47–48, 50
The Passing of the Great Race (Grant), viii, 121,
    135, 157
Patterson, Joseph Medill, 91
Pediatrics, 82, 88
Pennington, Roland, 113
Pennsylvania Training School for Idiotic and
    Feeble-minded Children, 40, 41, 101
penury, 1
People of the State of New York v. Jean Gianini,
    107

Perils of the Mexican Invasion (Holmes), 147
Perkins Institute for the Blind, 13
Philosophie Zoologique (Lamarck), 15
phrenology, 95, 96
physical deformities, Nazi decrees regarding, xi
physicals, six-second, 69
physical stigmata, of criminals, 97, 101, 104–5
physicians, x–xiii, 24–25, 163, 164
    see also U.S. Public Health Services (PHS)
physiognomy, 95, 96, 191
physiology, 25, 26
Pilcher, F. Hoyt, 162–63
Pineys, 29
Pintner, Rudolf, 115
Plato, 12
Ploetz, Alfred, 57, 58
Plum Street Hall, 2, 5
police, compulsory sterilizations and, x
polygamy, 166
poorhouses, 56, 185
    see also almshouses
Popenoe, Paul
    as author, 136
    Goddard and, 71
    Human Betterment Foundation and, ix, 175
    International Congress on Eugenics and,
        170, 183
    on *The Jukes in 1915*, 161
    racist dogma and, 159
    sterilization and, 174–77, 178, 182
Pope Pius XI, 182
population control. *see* birth control;
        sterilization
Porteus, Stanley, 123, 128, 144, 148, 153, 172
Porteus Maze test, 144
positive checks, defined, 16
poverty, 16, 89, 102
Practical Ethics (Singer), 216
Practical Eugenics (Bobbitt), 49
"The Prayer of Agassiz" (Whittier), 28
Preaching Eugenics (Rosen), 182
pregnancies, out-of-wedlock, 31
    see also illegitimate children
Pressey, Stanley, 81
preventive checks, defined, 16
Prichard, James, 98
Priddy, Albert, 206, 207
Principles of Psychology (James), 9
Prison Association of New York, 55, 160
procreation fears, 42, 45, 93, 101, 154–55
    see also fecundity

Progress: It's Law and Cause (Spencer), 18
Progressive Era, 163, 164
Progressivism
    criminal imbeciles and, 103, 105, 106
    cultural bias and, 119
    institution superintendents and, 163
    morons and, 87
    in Vineland, New Jersey, 2, 5
    see also Ellis, Havelock; social Darwinism
prostitution
    as cultural prohibition, 104, 105–6
    heredity and feeblemindedness and, 100,
        111–12
    within Juke family, 56
    within Kallikak family, 86
    as reason for committment, 206
proximates, 79–80
psychiatry, 138, 145
psycho-asthenia, 79
Psycho-Educational Clinic, St. Louis, 114
The Psychological Clinic, 68
*Psychological Examining in the United States
    Army* (Yerkes), 120, 141
The Psychological Methods of Intelligence Testing
    (Stern), 75
psychological research laboratories, 1, 5, 9
    see also Research Laboratory (Vineland
        Training School)
Psychological Review, 11, 155
psychologists, army, 120
psychology
    medical field versus, 24–25, 51, 81, 129, 156
    mental ability measurement and, 21
    as needing the "defective", 26
    origins of modern, 9–10
    utility of, 19, 21, 27
    see also child-study movement; *specific type*
Psychology of Subnormal Children (Farrell), 144
psychoses, 145–46
public health officers. see U.S. Public Health
    Services (PHS)
public health services, Nazi eugenics
    movement and, x, xi, xiii
punishment, for criminals, 98–99
Punnett, Reginald Crundall, 48, 58, 138
Punnett Square, 48

Q

Quaker churches and schools, 2, 7, 8
Quaker influences, 28, 33, 101
Quinby, Rachel, 188

R

Race Betterment Conference, 183
Race Betterment Foundation, 172
Race Crossing in Jamaica (Davenport and
    Steggerda), 155
race engineering, 209
race identity, 159
race mixture, 170
    see also Jackson Whites
race suicide, 6, 17, 68, 159
racial hygiene, 1
racial superiority, 85, 117, 120–22, 139, 151,
    160
    see also white "race"
Rafter, Nicole Hahn, 86, 101, 104, 107
Rake, Aaron, 190–91
Rake, Elias, 190
Ramapo Mountain people, 158
Rankin, Russell Bruce, 192
The Reader's Digest, 179–80
recapitulation theory, 84, 86
Reeves, Helen, 186, 205, 206, 212, 214
Reich Committee for the Scientific
    Registration of Severe Hereditary
    Ailments, xi
Reichministerium des Innern, xi
Reich Ministry of Interior, xi, xii
Reid, Whitelaw, 57
Reilly, Philip, viii, 164–65, 168, 169, 178, 210
religion, 12–13
    see also Catholic Church
reproduction, imbecility and, 53
    see also procreation fears
The Republic (Plato), 12
research. *see* Binet-Simon Scale; child-study
    movement
research, social agenda versus shoddy, 202–3
    see also The Kallikak Family (Goddard);
        Dugdale, Richard L.
Research Laboratory (Vineland Training
    School), Fig. 1, 23–28, 118–19, 123,
    153
The Revolt Against Civilization (Stoddard), 140
Rhea County Central High School, Tenn., 34
*Riddle of the Universe at the Close of the
    Nineteenth Century* (Haeckel), 84–85
rigor, in intelligence testing, 62–63
*The Rising Tide of Color against White World
    Supremacy* (Stoddard), 157, 160, 172–74
Roads, Elizabeth, 189

Robbins, Emma Florence. see Goddard, Emma
Robbins, Mary Rockwood, 212
Robinson, Henry M., 177
Rogers, A. C.
    charting process and, 52
    classification system and, 80–81
    Committee on Eugenics and, 49
    on housing conditions, 88
    on intelligence tests, 32
    on moral imbeciles, 103
Roosevelt, Theodore, 119, 135, 159, 166
Rosen, Christine, 182
Runk, Emma Ten Broeck, 188–89

S

Saleeby, Caleb, 147, 170
savage peoples, 97–98, 99
Scarborough Mansion, 5
scarlet fever, 13, 18, 40
Scheinfeld, Amram, 150, 151–52, 153
schizophrenia, 84
School Efficiency Series, 66, 68
School Training of Defective Children (Goddard), 66
Science, 11, 150, 151
Scientific Monthly, 139, 150, 154
Scopes, John Thomas, 34
Scullion, Mary F., 194
sedatives, Nazi murders and, xi
The Seed, 91
segregation
    among inmates, 40, 42
    of born criminals, 99
    of feebleminded people, 82, 114, 166
    as preferred remedy, 166
    see also institutionalization
Seguin form board, 74
Selden, Steven, 144
Sharp, H. C., 164
Simon, Theodore, 59
sin, idiocy and, 13–14, 15
    see also religion
Singer, Peter, 216
six-second physicals, 69
Skillman Village for Epileptics, 10, 24, 77
Sloss, Robert, 31, 32
Sloughter, Margaret Robinson, 186
    see also Margaret, mother of criminals
slow learners, 67
slums, 35, 36, 136

smallpox, 40
Smoky Pilgrims, 29
social activism (Howe), 13, 17
social control, need for, 15, 16, 17
social Darwinism, vii, 17, 18, 85, 86
    see also American eugenics movement
The Social Direction of Human Evolution (Kellicott), 30–31
Social Heredity and Social Evolution (Conn), 136
socialism, 16, 132
Socialist Party, 91
social Spencerism, 18
social workers, 148
society
    degeneracy as defined by, 29, 37, 56
    feeblemindedness as menace to, 82, 86–88, 102, 110, 166
    intelligence level as place in, 130–31, 132
    isolation and, 42
Society of American Bacteriologists, 138
soldiers, 172, 201
    see also U.S. Army Alpha and Army Beta intelligence testing programs
Sonnenstein, xii
sophomore, defined, 81
special education, segregation of, 67, 68
special educators, 23, 27–28
Spencer, Herbert, 17–18
spirometers, 26
Spurzheim, Johann Gaspar, 96
Stanford-Binet Intelligence Scale, 72, 75, 76, 115–16, 141, 142
    see also Binet-Simon Scale
Stanford University, 5, 19–20, 72
starvation, Nazi murders and, xi
State Epileptic Colony of New Jersey, 58
    see also Skillman Village for Epileptics
state hospitals, Nazi murders and, xi
State Institution for the Care and Training of Feeble-Minded Women, 32
    see also New Jersey State Institution for Feeble-Minded Women
State Normal School, West Chester, Pa., 19, 21, 23, 27, 122
Steggerda, Morris, 155
Steinbeck, John, vii
sterilization
    of criminals, 26
    Davenport on, 53
    DeJarenette on, 208

Goddard on, 55, 83, 114
Johnstone on, 49
Nazi eugenics movement and, ix, x
overview of support and opposition to,
    157–84
statistics on, x, 164, 183, 209–10
see also California sterilization movement
Sterilization for Human Betterment (Gosney
    and Popenoe), ix, 175–77, 182
sterilization laws
    as anti-discriminatory, 181
    effect in numbers of, 183
    in Indiana, 26
    Laughlin and, 34, 167–69
    in Michigan, 164
    Nazi eugenics movement and, viii, ix
    as protection for the state, 177
    rescinding of, 164–65
    U.S. Supreme Court and, 34, 135, 179
    in Virginia, 206
    see also Buck v. Bell
Stern, Alexandra, 175
Stern, William, 75
St. Louis Board of Education, 114
stock
    breeding choices and, 152, 166
    degeneracy of, 36
    eugenical classification of, 11, 171–72
    Kallikak family as, 55
    race suicide and, 68
    rehabilitation of, 88
Stoddard, Lothrop, 140–43, 157, 160, 168,
    172, 173–74
Stoke, Stuart, 149–50
Strode, Aubrey, 208
A Study of American Intelligence (Brigham),
    117, 120, 147
Sturtevant, Alfred, 133
Sumner, William Graham, 18
superintendents, institution
    Nazi eugenics movement and, x
    observation skills of, 150
    platforms of, 103
    responsibilities of, 102
    sterilization and, 163, 164, 167
    see also *specific name*
surveys, post-admission, 48, 50
    see also New York City School Survey of
    1911-1912
survival of the fittest, 15, 17–18
Symposium (Plato), 12

T

Tarr and McMurry Common School Geographies
    (Tarr and McMurry), 66
Taunton State Hospital, 145, 146
Taylor, William, 108
teachers
    child-study movement and, 19, 20, 21
    Farrell's criticism of, 68
    physicians versus, 24
    Vineland Summer School and, 23, 27–28,
        77
Terman, Lewis
    Binet-Simon Scale and, 11, 74–75, 76, 109
    California sterilization movement, 175
    on Clark University, 10
    Hall and, 21
    heredity versus environment and, 143
    immigration restrictions and, 73
    as intelligence tester, 115–16, 118, 122,
        141
    International Eugenics Congress and, 183
    on *The Kallikak Family*, 90
    Kohs and, 115
    on Lippman, 143–44
    on Research Laboratory tribute, 153
    Stanford-Binet Intelligence Scale and, 72
Textbook of Evolution and Genetics (Lindsey),
    135
Thompson, Frank V., 66
Thorndike, Edward, 144
three big "d's", 12, 166
Tiergarten Strasse 4 (T4), xi–xii
Topeka Lance, 163
Tower, William, 57
Training School Bulletin, 48, 59, 62
*Traité des Dégénérescences Physiques,,
    Intellectuelles et Morales de l'espèce
    Humaine* (Morel), 84
traits
    degeneration of, 166
    eugenics movement and degeneration of,
        86, 95–96, 103, 104
    Gall and, 96
    heritability of criminal, 110–11
    Mendel and, 91
    Punnett Square and, 48
    see also unit-characters
Transeau, Gertrude, 129
Trelfall, Richard, 195
The Trend of the Race (Holmes), 147
Trent, James, 40, 102, 136

Tribe of Ishmael, 170, 172
Tronson, Fred, 113

U

"undesirables", 192
The Unfit: A History of a Bad Idea (Carlson), 18
ungraded classes, 66, 67
uniforms, 42, 45
Unionist-Gazette, 193
Union Theological Seminary, 9
unit-characters, 82, 133, 134, 146, 166, 208
U.S. Army Alpha and Army Beta intelligence
    testing programs, 117–22, 131–32,
    141–42
U.S. Immigration Offices, 26, 71
U.S. Public Health Services (PHS), 69, 70,
    71, 74
U.S. Supreme Court, 34, 135, 179, 208

V

Vagrant Reminiscences of an Oligophrenist
    (Wallin), 25
Vanuxem, Louis Clark, 130
Vanuxem Lecture, 130–33
Van Wagenen, Bleeker, 57, 58, 124, 165
vasectomy, 83, 162
    see also sterilization
Vineland, N. J., 2, 5
Vineland Training School, N. J.
    American Association for the Study of the
        Feeble-Minded meeting at, 32
    as anomaly, 23–24
    budget for, 124–25
    campus photos of, Fig. 2, Fig. 6, Fig. 8–Fig.
        9, Fig. 12–Fig. 13, Fig. 14
    Committee on Provisions, 118
    compulsory labor at, 40–41, 43
    Congress on Eugenics exhibits and, 172
    creed of, 38, 43
    donors to, 57
    entertainment and pastimes at, Fig. 4–Fig.
        8, Fig. 10, Fig.22–Fig. 23, Fig. 25,
        43–44
    Feeble-Minded Club and, 22–23
    field workers at, 35
    holidays at, 44
    iconic image of, 38
    intelligence testing at, 62–63
    Jackson Whites study at, 158
    overview of, 1, 2–5

research plans within, 125–27, 129
    reunion at, 153
    staff photos of, Fig. 15
    Summer School at, 27–28
    see also Research Laboratory (Vineland
        Training School)
Virginia Colony for Epileptics and
    Feebleminded, 206, 207
    see also Central Virginia Training Center
Virginia Court of Appeals, 208
viriculture, 11
Von Gruger, M., 57

W

Wallace, Alfred Russell, 15
Wallin, J. E. Wallace
    on Deborah Kallikak, 29–30, 42, 44
    on Goddard, 72, 81
    Hall and, 10
    heredity versus environment and, 144–45
    overview of, 24–25
    on psychological testing, 114–15
wanderlust, 110, 111
Ward, Julia, 13, 73
Ward, Robert DeCourcy, 165, 183
Watson, Robert, 10
Wechsler Scales of Intelligence, 115
Weeks, David, 24, 25, 52, 58, 77, 165
Weikart, Richard, 85
Weismann, August, 57
Welfare of the Feebleminded (Johnstone), 49
Western Pennsylvania Institution for the
    Feeble-Minded, 79
Western State Hospital, Staunton, Va., 208
Whipple, Guy, 118
white "race", 159, 173–74
    see also racial superiority
white slavery crusades, 105–6
Whiting, Alice Merriam, 204, 212
Whiting, Mabel Stuart, 204
Whitney, Leon, ix, 179
Whittier, John Greenleaf, 28
whooping cough, 40
Wiggam, Albert, 147, 183
Wilbur, Hervey B., 24, 42
Williams, William, 69
Willson, Marcius, 93
Wilmarth, Alfred, 42
Wilson, William, 195–96
Wilson, Woodrow, 77, 120, 140

Wisconsin Home for the Feeble-Minded, 42, 77, 78
Wistar Institute, 49, 123, 126, 128–29, 144
Wolf, Theta, 59, 60
Wolfensberger, Wolf, 41
Wolverton, Emma
    Allen and, 213
    Estabrook and, 186–87
    final years of, 214
    respect for, 216
    siblings of, 197–99
    tasks and interests of, 205–6, 211–12, 213
    Whiting and, 204
    see also Kallikak, Deborah
Wolverton/Woolverton geneaology, 188–200
    see also Kallikak family
women, 70, 87, 104, 210
    see also female criminals
Wood, Job, 20
work, inmate. see labor, compulsory
workhouses, 16, 98, 99
World War I, 92, 117, 173

Wundt, William, 9, 23, 25–26
Wylie, Arthur, 79, 83, 86

Y

Yale Institute for Child Development, 11, 153
Yale Laboratories of Primate Biology, 118
Yerkes, Robert, 73, 117–18, 120–21, 122
You and Heredity (Scheinfeld), 150

Z

Zabeth, Rhoda, 189
Zenderland, Leila
    on cultural bias in intelligence testing, 119
    on Goddard after Vineland, 122, 201–2, 203
    on Goddard and heredity, 49, 154
    on Goddard's computational skills, 63
    on Goddard's family, 7
    on Goddard's use of Binet's tests, 65
    on parents' understanding of child's impairment, 48
    on Transeau and Mateer's rivalry, 129

Acknowledgments

As with any book like *Good Blood, Bad Blood*, we are indebted to many people who supported and informed us as we wrote Emma's story. First, it is worth acknowledging that without Professor Leila Zenderland's comprehensive book about Henry Herbert Goddard, *Measuring Minds: Henry Herbert Goddard and the Origins of American Intelligence Testing*, it would have been difficult if not impossible to tell the full story of Emma's life. Zenderland's scholarship humanized Goddard and created a three-dimensional portrait when, up to that point, he had been seen through a single lens and, essentially, as an evil scientist purposefully doing harm. We hope we have adequately represented Goddard in ways that are consistent with Zenderland's portrait. On a more personal level, several of our colleagues have endured our lamentations and tirades about Emma's story for years and privileged us with their encouragement and support, so to Drs. Jim Patton, Ed Polloway, and Tom Smith, our gratitude. The number of colleagues that have informed our work over the course of our careers are too numerous to list, so we will just say thanks, you know who you are. We would like to especially acknowledge Elizabeth Black, whose thoughtful reading of an early draft of the manuscript gave us insights about how to tell this important story, and Doug Crandell, who read the full manuscript and provided needed encouragement that it was important to persist in finding an outlet for this story. We're also grateful to Neal Salkind for his due diligence in finding a home for the book. Importantly, we are grateful to Lisa Marie O'Hearn and Dr. Maggie Nygren at AAIDD for taking a chance with *Good Blood, Bad Blood*. They have gone above and beyond in responding to our requests that created a wonderful presentation of our work. Their personal commitment to the importance of telling Emma's story made the match between this book and AAIDD seem predestined! We'd also like to thank Dac Nelson for an exceptional job of polishing and editing. Our families have listened to us tell this story, read versions of the manuscript, and encouraged us to continue when the odds seemed against us that the story would see the light of day. Michael is grateful for the unwavering love and support from Kathy, Geoff and Graham. David, as always, treasures the love and support of Joyce, Lincoln, Allison and Sallie.

Finally, we are indebted to Emma Wolverton. Like Goddard's tale, our story begins with "Deborah." Unlike Goddard's story, ours ends with Emma ...